The Impact of European Communities' Policy on Quality Management in Construction
Construction Industry Research and Information Association
CIRIA Special Publication 89, 1993

Keywords:

Quality management, European Communities, technical harmonization, standards, public procurement, post-construction liability, attestation of conformity, Single Internal Market

Reader interest:

Construction and design services organizations of all types – architects, consulting engineers, quantity surveyors, design offices of contractors, commercial and industrial organizations, utilities and local authorities, construction materials and components producers, publically funded or controlled bodies, governmental bodies, lawyers specializing in construction law

ISBN 0 86017 354 2

CLASSIFICATION	
AVAILABILITY	Unrestricted
CONTENT	Advice/guidance
STATUS	Committee guided
USER	Construction, design services organizations

Published by CIRIA, 6 Storey's Gate, Westminster, London SW1P 3AU

Foreword

Many of the directives and related policy documents produced by the EC in preparation for the Single Internal Market have considerable implications for quality management in the construction industry. These include the directives produced under the New Approach to Technical Harmonization and Standards, such as the Construction Products Directive, which set minimum requirements that must be satisfied before products can be placed on the market. The requirements include both technical specifications and procedures for conformity assessment. Although their aim is to remove administrative and regulatory barriers to trade, they have important implications for quality management. The directives on public procurement seek to open up public purchasing of goods, services, and construction works to competition from firms throughout the EC but they also affect quality management. They require the use of European standards where possible and set out the technical references and questions on technical support that can be asked of potential contractors. The Mathurin Report on Responsibilities, Guarantees and Insurance in the Construction Industry revealed wide differences in post-construction liability. It has led to calls for the harmonization of guarantees and assurances in the interest of removing barriers to trade.

It has become apparent that the UK cannot pursue its own approach to quality management in isolation as its policies touch upon areas in which it has been agreed to surrender sovereignty to the EC. The policies emerging from Brussels do not appear to be well understood in the construction industry and many people find it difficult to comprehend how quality management in the industry will operate within the framework provided by EC legislation. For these reasons, therefore, CIRIA considered it timely and appropriate to review the impact of European Communities' legislation on quality management in construction, to outline the issues, and to provide information for all sectors of the construction industry.

The review was intended to analyse the effects which EC policies might have on :

- Quality management systems in the construction industry, in both design firms and contracting firms,
- The freedom of action of purchasing bodies,
- Testing and certification, both mandatory and voluntary, of construction products,
- Certification of quality management systems, certification of product conformity and product approval.

The review was to explain the institutional structure in each of these areas as well as the issues that arose from proposals, and to offer an interpretation as to their potential commercial consequences. It was to reflect the different views that had been put forward and to show an awareness of approaches in other Member States as well as the UK. This is the report of that review.

The report has substantially met these objectives but has also led to some unexpected results. The research uncovered considerably more written material than had been expected and revealed interfaces between policies that had not been suspected. The range of policies means that the UK construction industry must come to terms with a more rigorous regulatory regime than it has been used to hitherto. Comparisons with other Member States proved difficult to accomplish, as the UK has been a pioneer in bringing this legislation into force while some other countries have still to resolve the issues involved. The systems described in the report are not complete. Policy-makers have had to tackle unexpected problems and there have been delays in reaching satisfactory solutions in some cases. The various pieces do not always fit together very well and potential inconsistencies between related measures have had to be resolved. However, although the UK is having to adapt its quality management systems to meet the requirements of the EC, these systems have proved resilient and capable of responding to changed circumstances. Those in the construction industry who have adopted quality management are likely to find that they are well prepared for the requirements of EC policy.

Steering Group Members

Mr E L Morgan CEng, FIM, FIQA (Chairman)	UK Certification Authority for Reinforcing Steels
Mr R H Courtier MA, CEng, MASCE, MIEAust	W S Atkins and Partners
Mr P M Dawson LCG, LicIQA	GMW Partnership
Mr C J Fox BSc, MSc, MICE, MIHT	Department of Transport
Mr D I A Harrison BSc(Eng), FGS	Harrison and Company (Soils and Foundation Engineers) Ltd
Mr N I Kemp DipQS, ARICS	Dearle and Henderson
Mr K W Langley FRICS, FCIOB, ACIArb	Wm Bryen Langley and Company
Mr C B Richards MICT	Costain Dow Mac Cladding
Mr P Titman Bsc(Hons) MICE, MIHT, MIQA	Edmund Nuttall Ltd

The research contractor was the School of Estate Management at Oxford Brookes University. The authors were Richard Grover, Principal Lecturer in Economics (principally responsible for Sections 1–8) and Dr Anthony Lavers, Fishburn & Boxer Reader in Law (principally responsible for Sections 9–11). Catherine Jessop and Georgina Mason provided research assistance, Gwen Turner bibliographical assistance, and Chris Rush advice on presentation, while Anna Stolwood assisted with the preparation of the manuscript.

CIRIA's Research Manager was G B M Oliver, BSc CEng, MICE, MIQA, MAQMC.

Acknowledgements

The work was funded substantially by the Department of the Environment, in part by BSI Quality Assurance, the UK Certification Authority for Reinforcing Steels (CARES), and the Department of Education and Science, and in part by contributions from the following organizations which were surplus to expenditure on the work leading to CIRIA Special Publication 72 (of which, indeed, this review was originally a part):

Babtie Dobbie Ltd
Bickerdike Allen Partners
Binnie and Partners
British Airports Services Ltd
British Railways Board
British Waterways Board
Bucknall Austin plc
Building Design Partnership
Bunyan Meyer and Partners
CEGB (Procurement Department)
Charcon Tunnels Ltd
Brian Colquhoun and Partners
Conder Services Ltd
Costain Civil Engineers Ltd
Dames and Moore International
W A Dawson Ltd
Department of Trade and Industry
J F Donelon and Co. Ltd
R M Douglas Construction Ltd
Robert M Douglas Holdings plc
Fairclough Civil Engineering Ltd
Fitzpatrick and Son (Contractors) Ltd
Sir William Halcrow and Partners
Ham Gray Associates Ltd
Harrison and Company (Soils and Foundation Engineers) Ltd
Higgs and Hill plc
Hilti (Great Britain) Ltd
Kenchington Little and Partners
Knight Morrish and Partners
Lowry McKinney (Piling) Ltd
MMG Civil Engineering Systems Ltd
Milton Pipes Ltd
Mott MacDonald
Netlon Ltd
Pell Frischmann Consulting Engineers Ltd
Property Services Agency
John Pryke and Partners
Felix J Samuely and Partners
Travers Morgan Ltd
George Wimpey plc
Whitby and Bird
Wrekin Construction Co. Ltd

CIRIA and Oxford Brookes University would like to express their gratitude to the following individuals and organizations for supplying information:

Association of Metropolitan Authorities
British Board of Agrément
British Coal
British Gas
British Quality Association
British Standards Institution
British Standards Society Building Standards Group
Building Research Establishment
CEN
Commission of the European Communities
Department of Employment
Department of the Environment
Department of Trade and Industry
Department of Transport
Dun and Bradstreet
European Organization for Testing and Certification
Mr L W Floyd
Foreign and Commonwealth Office
Mr H Gudmundssen
Health and Safety Executive
Her Majesty's Stationery Office
HM Treasury
Home Office
Institute of Purchasing and Supply
KPMG European Business Centre
Mr C Mathurin
Midlands Electricity
Ministry of Defence
National Accreditation Council for Certification Bodies
National Audit Office
National Measurement Accreditation Service
NHS Procurement Directorate
National Power
Overseas Development Administration
Powergen
Property Services Agency
Reinforced Earth Company Ltd
Scottish Homes
Scottish Office
Severn Trent Water
UK CARES
WRC plc
Yorkshire Electricity

Mr John Barber, Department of the Environment, Department of Trade and Industry, Department of Transport, Health and Safety Executive, and Reinforced Earth Company Ltd kindly reviewed parts of the manuscript.

The Reinforced Earth Company Ltd kindly consented to use being made of an unpublished paper on procurement systems in the EC, and the Commission of the European Communities to quotation from and reproduction of EC documents.

Contents

Part C Public procurement

List of Figures

List of Tables

Glossary

Abbreviations: CPA Consumer Protection Act, 1987; CPD Construction Products Directive; CPR Construction Products Regulations, 1991; EMC Electromagnetic Compatibility Directive; GA Gas Appliances Directive; MY Machinery Directive; PPE Personal Protective Equipment Directive; PP Public Procurement directives (i.e., Public Works, Public Supplies, Public Services, Utilities).

Acknowledged rule of technology (CPD, CPR):	Defined by CPR as 'technical provision acknowledged by a majority of representative experts as reflecting the developed stage of technical capability . . . based on relevant consolidated findings of science, technology and experience'. Applies to minor part products.
Agreement groups:	Established by EOTC to design and maintain mutual recognition agreements. The groups can be product, service, or discipline orientated. They must meet certain criteria, such as participants coming from at least three EC or EFTA countries, participants satisfying the criteria of the relevant standard in the EN 45000 series, and the agreement being open to other EC or EFTA participants on the same conditions as existing participants. Agreement groups that are not part of EOTC also exist.
Annex IV machinery (MY):	Machinery that has particular hazards, which is subject to additional attestation of conformity requirements. Examples include machinery for working on wood, cold metal, and plastics, and machinery for underground working.
Apparatus (EMC):	A finished electrical or electronic item with an intrinsic function. Synonymous with the term equipment.
Approved body (CPD):	Bodies designated by Member States and notified to the Commission as being competent to act as testing, inspection, or certification bodies. For the directives adopted before 1992, the bodies must satisfy the five conditions first used in the Toy Safety Directive of having the means to carry out their task, having personnel with technical competence and professional integrity, being impartial, being able to maintain professional secrecy, and having civil liability insurance. Since 1992 directives have contained the seven conditions used in the Hot-water Boilers Directive. Alternative name for notified body.
Attestation of conformity:	Set of procedures by which manufacturers attest to their products meeting technical specifications.
Basic requirements (PPE):	Used instead of the term essential requirements to be found in other New Approach directives.
Bodies governed by public law (PP):	Bodies that have a legal personality, are established for the purpose of meeting needs in the general interest, and which either draw the majority of their finance from public sources, or have the majority of their board of management appointed by a public body, or are subject to management supervision by a contracting authority.
Candidate (PP):	Supplier who has sought an invitation to take part in restricted or negotiated procedures.
Category A standards (CPD):	Standards for the design and execution of construction works.

Category B standards (CPD): Standards relating to construction products including standards for basic materials used in the manufacture of products, standards for products with specific end uses, and test methods.

CE mark: Comprises the symbol 'CE'; signifies that a product has satisfied the requirements of all relevant directives. The requirements include technical specifications and attestation of conformity procedures. Usually referred to in UK legislation as the EC mark.

CEN: European Committee for Standardization; comprises the national standards bodies of the EC and EFTA. It drafts standards either because its members deem there to be a need for them or under mandate from the Commission. Three types of standard are produced: EN, European standards transposed into identically worded national standards; HD, harmonization documents that are transposed into national standards which have the same effect but are differently worded between countries; and ENV or European pre-standards used experimentally for up to three years. Weighted majority voting can be used.

CENELEC: European Committee for Electrotechnical Standardization. Electrotechnical counterpart of CEN.

Certificate of adequacy (MY): Issued by a notified body for an Annex IV machine's technical file to verify that the standards have been correctly applied.

Certification body (CPD): An approved body that carries out conformity certification.

Commission: The Commission comprises 17 members; two each from France, Germany, Italy, Spain, and the UK, and one each from the remaining Member States. Commissioners are appointed for four years by agreement between the governments, but must act only in the interests of the EC as a whole. They can be obliged to resign collectively by the European Parliament. The Commission is the only body that can propose measures to the Council. It implements EC policies and ensures that the Treaties and rules are followed.

Competent body: Bodies designated by Member States as being competent to carry out specified tests and certification. In directives adopted before 1992 they must satisfy five criteria for approved or notified bodies originally found in the Toy Safety Directive. Since 1992 they have had to satisfy the seven conditions laid down in the Hot-water Boilers Directive. Unlike approved or notified bodies, their identity does not have to be notified to the Commission.

Components (EMC): Electrical or electronic items that do not have an intrinsic function whose purpose is to be incorporated into apparatus.

Conformity to type: Module C of the modular approach to conformity attestation. Designed to be used in conjunction with Module B (EC type-examination). Manufacturer takes all measures necessary to ensure that production conforms to the EC type-examination certificate and draws up a declaration of conformity. As a supplement, a notified body may test or check the product.

Construction product (CPD): Any product produced for incorporation in a permanent manner in construction works.

Construction works (CPD):	Includes buildings and civil engineering works.
Contract award notice (PP):	Makes known the result of an award.
Contract notice (PP):	Used in open and restricted procedures and, in some circumstances, negotiated procedures. Makes known the nature of the contract the contracting authority proposes to award. Also known as tender notice.
Contracting authorities (PP):	The state, regional and local authorities, bodies governed by public law, and associations formed by one or more contracting authorities.
Contracting entities (PP):	Utilities bodies engaged in the purchase of goods, construction works, or services.
COREPER:	Committee of Permanent Representatives (i.e. ambassadors) of the Member States to the EC.
Council of Ministers:	This makes major policy decisions, where appropriate by qualified majority voting. Governments are represented in the Council by the appropriate departmental minister. The Presidency of the Council is held by each Member State for six months in turn.
Criteria for qualitative selection (PP):	The grounds on which a supplier may be excluded from participation in a contract and the information that may be sought on a contractor's financial and economic standing and technical knowledge.
Decisions:	Form of EC legislation that are binding on the governments, enterprises, or individuals to whom they are addressed.
Defect (CPA):	If the safety of the product is not such as persons generally are entitled to expect taking into account the manner of marketing, the use of any mark, instructions and warning, when the product was supplied, and what might reasonably be expected to be done with the product.
Derogation:	The allowing of discretion to a Member State as to whether to adopt or not certain parts of a directive.
Design contest (PP):	Procedures which aim at providing a contracting authority with a plan or design, mainly in the fields of area planning, town planning, architecture, civil engineering, or data processing, and which are selected by a jury on the basis of competition.
Design documentation (GA):	General description of appliance, designs standards applied, test reports, manuals for installation and use, and, where appropriate, attestation and certificates relating to components and manufacture.
Directive:	Form of EC legislation that is binding on Member States as to its objectives but leaves the method of achieving its objectives to the discretion of the Member States.
EC certificate of conformity:	Certificate drawn up by notified or approved body to show that the requirements of relevant directives have been satisfied.

EC declaration of conformity:	Declaration of conformity drawn up by the manufacturer that the requirements of relevant directives have been satisfied. In general, it comprises identification of the manufacturer, the technical specifications complied with, the identity of any notified body involved in attestation of conformity, and the identity of the signatory.
EC declaration of conformity to type (GA):	Manufacturer produces design documentation and takes steps to ensure homogeneity of production. Notified body tests prototype and carries out random on-site checks.
EC declaration of conformity to type [guarantee of product quality] (GA):	Manufacturer produces design documentation, installs and maintains quality system, and tests each appliance for conformity. Notified body tests prototype and evaluates and maintains surveillance of quality and testing systems. Quality systems that satisfy EN 29003 (BS 5750: Part 3) are deemed to satisfy quality system requirements.
EC declaration of conformity to type [guarantee of production quality] (GA):	Manufacturer produces design documentation and installs and maintains quality system. Notified body tests prototype and evaluates and maintains surveillance of quality system. Quality systems that satisfy EN 29002 (BS 5750: Part 2) are deemed to satisfy quality system requirements.
EC design examination certificate:	To be issued under Module H (full quality assurance) of the modular approach to conformity assessment by a notified body to confirm that the design of a product meets the requirements of a directive.
EC quality control system for final products (PPE):	A body chosen by the manufacturer carries out random checks on production at least once a year.
EC quality of production system (PPE):	Third-party approval of the quality control system by a body chosen by the manufacturer.
EC surveillance (GA):	Checking of a manufacturer's quality system by a notified body at intervals of not less than two years.
EC type-examination:	Module B of the modular approach to conformity assessment. The manufacturer produces technical documentation, which is presented to a notified body together with a specimen of the product. The notified body verifies that the type has been manufactured in conformity with the technical documentation and test that the specimen conforms to the relevant standards or essential requirements. It is to be used in conjunction with Modules C (conformity to type), D (production quality assurance), E (product quality assurance), or F (product verification). A procedure that is substantially similar to this and called by the same name is to be found in some of the New Approach directives that were adopted before 1990.
EC verification (GA):	Manufacturer produces design documentation and takes steps to ensure homogeneity of production. Notified body tests prototype and either sample batches of appliances or each appliance.
EC verification by unit (GA):	Intended where appliances are produced as single units or in small quantities. Manufacturer produces design documentation. Notified body tests each appliance.

Economic and Social Committee:	This comprises 189 members proposed by governments and appointed by the Council from employers, workers, and other interest groups. The opinion of the Committee must be sought on certain issues before a proposal can be adopted by the Council.
Economically reasonable working life (CPD):	Period of time during which the performance of construction works fulfils the essential requirements.
Efficiency requirements:	Used by the Hot-water Boilers Directive in the same sense that other New Approach directives use the term essential requirements.
Electromagnetic disturbance (EMC):	Any electromagnetic phenomenon that may degrade performance.
Equipment (EMC):	A finished electrical or electronic item with an intrinsic function. Synonymous with the term apparatus.
Essential requirements:	Used in New Approach directives to define the minimum specifications that a product must satisfy in order to be regarded as being safe.
Eurocodes:	Common design codes being prepared by CEN under mandate from the Commission.
European Atomic Energy Community (Euratom):	Established in 1957 for the development of nuclear energy for peaceful purposes. Has shared the Commission and Council with the EEC and European Steel and Coal Community since 1967.
European Court of Justice:	Reaches judgements on the interpretation of EC law and the legality of actions by EC institutions or Member States.
European Economic Community:	Established by the Treaty of Rome in 1957. It is a customs union with no tariff barriers or quotas between members and a common external tariff. The Treaty provides for free movement of people, services, and capital and for common policies, for example on agriculture and transport. Has shared the Commisison and the Council with the European Steel and Coal Community and Euratom since 1967.
European Organization for Technical Approvals (CPD):	Organization comprising all the European technical approvals bodies designated by Member States.
European Organization for Testing and Certification:	Set up in 1990 by the EC, EFTA, CEN, and CENELEC to coordinate mutual recognition of testing and certification, to disseminate information on mutual recognition, and to assist the Commission and European standardization bodies on conformity assessment.

European Parliament: Approves the EC budget, considers proposals for legislation, and debates the activities of the EC. It has no powers to initiate legislation but can dismiss the Commission. The Single European Act requires that the Parliament is involved in the adoption of qualified majority decisions to do with the Internal Market. The Council receives proposals from the Commission and obtains the opinion of the Parliament. It then adopts a common position, which is referred to the Parliament with three months in which to accept, reject, or amend it. The Commission has one month in which to decide to accept or reject any amendments proposed by the Parliament. The measure then proceeds to a second reading by the Council. If the Parliament rejects the common position, the Council is required to adopt the measure unanimously. If the Parliament has proposed amendments, the Council votes on them by qualified majority, where these are endorsed by the Commission, or unanimously if they are not. The measure fails if the Council does not reach a decision within three months.

European pre-standard (ENV): Draft used as prospective standards experimentally for an initial period of up to three years.

European specifications (PP): National standards implementing European standards, European technical approvals, or common technical specifications drawn up in accordance with procedures recognized by Member States, applied uniformly in all Member States, and which have been published in the *Official Journal*.

European Standard or EN: Standard produced by CEN or CENELEC that is transposed into identically worded national standard.

European Steel and Coal Community: Established by the Treaty of Paris in 1951 to pool the production and consumption of coal and steel. Has shared the Commission and the Council with the EEC and Euratom since 1967. Source of loans and grants for the regeneration of coal and steel producing areas.

European technical approval (CPD): Favourable technical assessment of the fitness for use of a product for an intended use based on fulfilment of the essential requirements for building works for which the product is used. Awarded by a European technical approval body designated for this purpose by a Member State.

European Union of Agrément (UEAtc): Comprises the agrément bodies of each of the EC countries, except Greece and Luxembourg, and Austria with Finland, Norway, and Sweden having observer status. The UK member is the British Board of Agrément. UEAtc drafts guides which serve as a common framework for the assessment of the fitness of a new product and confirms agrément documents for use in other countries.

Excluded sector (PP): Public procurement in the area of transport, water, energy, and telecommunications.

Factory production control (CPD): The permanent internal control of production exercised by the manufacturer. Must be documented in a systematic manner in the form of written policies and procedures. Must ensure a common understanding of quality assurance and enable the achievement of the required product characteristics and the effective operation of production control system to be checked. A system that meets the requirements of EN 29002 (BS 5750: Part 2) is deemed to satisfy these requirements.

Forfeiture order (CPA,CPR):	Order for the forfeiture of goods that contravene the legislation. The order may specify their destruction or their release to a specified person for scrap, repair, reconditioning.
Framework agreement (PP):	Agreement between a contracting authority and a supplier which establishes the terms for the supply of goods or services during a given period.
Full quality assurance:	Module H of the modular approach to conformity assessment. Manufacturer operates an approved quality system for design, manufacture, and final inspection and testing. A notified body carries out initial and periodic assessment of the quality system. As a supplement, it may also examine the design of the product and issue an EC design examination certificate. A quality system that meets the requirements of EN 29001 (BS 5750: Part 1) is presumed to satisfy this module.
Gas appliance (GA):	Appliances that burn gaseous fuels used for cooking, heating, hot water production, refrigeration, lighting, or washing and have a normal water temperature not exceeding 105°C.
Gas fitting (GA):	Safety devices, controlling devices, regulating devices, and subassemblies marketed for trade use and designed to be incorporated into an appliance.
Gaseous fuels (GA):	Fuels which are in a gaseous state at a temperature of 15°C under a pressure of 1 bar.
Harmonization document (HD):	Type of European standard which is transposed into national standards which are differently worded between countries but have a similar effect.
Harmonized European standard:	Standard drafted by one of the European standardization bodies under mandate from the Commission.
Information notice (PPE):	The basic requirements oblige the manufacturer to provide an information notice that shall include, for example, information on storage, use, maintenance, performance, obsolescence, and transportation.
Inspection body (CPD):	An approved body that is able to perform functions such as the assessment, recommending for acceptance, and audit of manufacturers' quality control operations and evaluation of products on site or in factories.
Installation (EMC):	Several combined items of apparatus or systems put together to fulfil a specific objective but not intended to be placed on the market as a single functional unit.
Internal production control:	Module A of the modular approach to attestation of conformity. Manufacturer establishes technical documentation, takes all necessary steps to ensure that production takes place in conformity with the technical documentation, and declares conformity with the essential requirements. As an option, a notified body may be involved in product testing.
Interpretative documents (CPD):	Series of six documents, one for each essential requirement, that give concrete form to the essential requirements and provide the legal basis for their interpretation.

Machinery (MY): Assemblies of linked parts or components joined together for a specific application, at least one of which moves.

Machinery capable of independent operation (MY): To be distinguished from component parts, which are not capable of functioning independently. Each is subject to different attestation of conformity requirements.

Member States: The founder states of the EC were Belgium, France, Federal Republic of Germany, Italy, Luxembourg, and the Netherlands. Denmark, Eire, and the UK joined in 1973, Greece in 1981, and Portugal and Spain in 1986. The former Democratic Republic of Germany joined as a result of reunification with the Federal Republic.

Methods of Assessment and Test (Moats): Technical guides serving as common frameworks for assessing fitness for purpose of products issued by the European Union of Agrément.

Minor part products (CPD): Products that play only a minor role with respect to health and safety, which may be placed on the market providing that the manufacturer declares that they comply with the acknowledged rule of technology. Such products do not bear the CE mark. Similar devices exist in certain other New Approach directives, such as the Simple Pressure Vessels Directive.

Modular approach to conformity assessment: A Council Decision in December 1990 adopted a modular approach to attestation of conformity that is to be used in the future for New Approach directives. Directives are to make use of eight modules rather than devise new attestation of conformity procedures.

Most economically advantageous tender (PP): Criteria that can be used to determine this include price, period for completion, running costs, profitability, and technical merit. The criteria to be used must be recorded in either the contract documentation or the contract notice.

National Accreditation Council for Certification Bodies (NACCB): Set up in 1984 to advise the DTI on the accreditation of certification bodies. There are four categories of accreditation: certification of quality management systems, product conformity assessment, product approval, and the certification of personnel engaged in quality system verification.

National Measurement Accreditation Service (NAMAS): Formed in 1985 as a result of the amalgamation of the National Laboratory Testing and Accreditation Service (NATLAS) and the British Calibration Service. Managed by the National Physical Laboratory on behalf of the DTI. Accredits laboratories for testing and calibration.

Negotiated procedures (PP): Procedures whereby contracting authorities negotiate terms with the suppliers of their choice.

New Approach directives: Technical harmonization directives produced under the New Approach to Technical Harmonization and Standards of 1985. They include the Construction Products, Gas Appliances, Machinery, Electromagnetic Compatibility, Personal Protective Equipment, Toy Safety, and Simple Pressure Vessels directives. They set out essential requirements that products must comply with, procedures by which technical specifications are drawn up from the essential requirements, and procedures by which manufacturers attest to the compliance of their products with the technical specifications.

Non-tariff barrier to trade:	Rules, regulations, administrative devices and the like that serve to limit the access of imports to a market either by raising their cost, in the manner of a tariff, or excluding them from entry, in the manner of a quota.
Normal maintenance (CPD):	Measures applied to construction works in order to enable them to fulfil the essential requirements during their working lives.
Normally used (GA):	When an appliance is correctly installed, regularly serviced, used with a normal variation in gas quality and supply pressure, and used in accordance with its intended purpose.
Notice on the existence of a qualification system (PP):	Notice published by a utility undertaking to identify the purpose of such a system, where the rules can be obtained, and the duration of the qualification system.
Notices to warn (CPA, CPR):	Notices requiring a person to publish at his own expense a warning as to the inadequacy of a product.
Notified body:	Body designated by a Member State to carry out specific conformity assessment tasks and whose identity is notified to the Commission. Described in the Construction Products Directive as an approved body. In directives adopted before 1992, they must satisfy the five conditions first used in the Toy Safety Directive of having the means to carry out their task, having personnel with technical competence and professional integrity, being impartial, being able to maintain professional secrecy, and having civil liability insurance. Since 1992 directives have contained seven conditions found in the Hot-water Boilers Directive.
Open procedures (PP):	Procedures whereby all interested suppliers may submit tenders.
Periodic indicative notice (PP):	Notice published by utility undertaking at least once a year to identify the total supply contracts in an area so as to alert potential suppliers.
Principles for safe operation of construction sites:	Set out in the proposed Temporary or Mobile Construction Sites Directive, they include keeping the site in good order, conditions for handling materials, and dealing with hazardous substances.
Prior indicative notice (PP):	Notice intended to alert suppliers to the intention of a contracting authority to award contracts in the future. Contains essential characteristics of contracts but not detailed documentation.
Prior notice:	Notice to be given by the client under the proposed Temporary or Mobile Construction Sites Directive to the authorities responsible for health and safety at work before the commencement of building work with a planned duration of at least 30 days.
Product quality assurance:	Module E of the modular approach to conformity assessment. Can stand on its own but is usually to be used in conjunction with Module B (EC type-examination). Manufacturer operates an approved quality system, which is subject to initial and periodic assessment by a notified body. A quality system that accords with EN 29003 (BS 5750: Part 3) is deemed to meet the requirements.

Product verification:	Module F of the modular approach to conformity assessment. Can stand on its own but is usually to be used in conjunction with Module B (EC type-examination). Manufacturer takes all measures necessary to ensure that manufacturing conforms to specifications. A notified body checks the conformity of the product with the requirements of a directive by sampling or individual examination of each item produced.
Production quality assurance:	Module D of the modular approach to conformity assessment. Can stand on its own but is usually to be used in conjunction with Module B (EC type-examination). Manufacturer operates an approved quality system for production, which is subject to initial and periodic assessment by a notified body. A quality system that accords with EN 29002 (BS 5750: Part 2) is deemed to meet the requirements.
Prohibition notice (CPA,CPR):	Notices prohibiting persons from supplying goods that contravene the legislation.
Project execution stage:	Used in the proposed Temporary or Mobile Construction Sites Directive for construction phase of building project.
Project preparation stage:	Used in the proposed Temporary or Mobile Construction Sites Directive for project planning and design phase of building project.
Project Supervisor:	Term used in the proposed Temporary or Mobile Construction Sites Directive to mean the natural or legal person responsible for design and/or execution of building projects acting on behalf of the client.
Protection requirements (EMC):	Term used in EMC to mean what other New Approach directives refer to as essential requirements.
Public procurement:	That part of public expenditure put out to contract.
Public services concessionaires (PP):	Those who provide services on behalf of a public body in return for the right to receive payments.
Public services contracts (PP):	Contracts for pecuniary interest, concluded in writing, between a contracting authority and a supplier of services.
Public supply contracts (PP):	Contracts for pecuniary interest, concluded in writing, between a contracting authority and a supplier of products.
Public works concessions (PP):	Public works contracts in which consideration consists wholly or in part of the right to exploit the works constructed.
Public works contracts (PP):	Contracts for pecuniary interest, concluded in writing, between a contractor and a contracting authority for building or civil engineering works.
Qualified majority voting:	The Council may act by qualified majority on proposals from the Commission for the approximation of laws, regulations, and administrative actions other than those concerned with fiscal matters, the free movement of persons, and the rights and interests of employed persons. There are 76 votes allocated to Member States and 54 in favour constitute a majority. France, Germany, Italy, and the UK have 10 votes each, Spain 8, Belgium, Greece, the Netherlands, and Portugal 5 each, Denmark and Eire 3 votes each, and Luxembourg 2 votes.

Regulation:	Form of EC legislation that is of general application. They are binding in their entirety and applicable in all Member States.
Restricted procedures (PP):	Procedures whereby only those suppliers invited by a contracting authority may submit tenders.
Resolution:	Declarations by the Council that are declarations of intent.
Safety regulations:	UK regulations made under Section 11 of the Consumer Protection Act 1987. They can encompass requirements with respect to the content, design, packaging, testing, approval, and supply of goods.
Simple design (PPE):	Equipment for which the user can assess the level of protection provided against minimal risks, e.g. waterproof gloves for washing up. The manufacturer merely has to draw up a declaration of conformity and affix the CE mark before the equipment is placed upon the market.
Single European Act, 1986:	Came into force on 1 July 1987. This amended the treaties establishing the European Communities. It laid down the objective of the creation of a Single Internal Market by the end of 1992 and a procedure for a qualified majority voting. Enacted into UK law by the European Communities (Amendment) Act 1986.
Special award procedure (PP):	Used for certain public housing contracts which, because of their size, duration and complexity, require the contractor to be a part of the team together with the contracting authority and its advisers. The procedure enables the contractor who is most suitable for integration into the team to be selected.
Standing Committees:	Set up under New Approach directives to advise the Commission on the implementation of a New Approach directive and to carry out specific tasks in relation to a directive. Generally, the standing committee is that set up under the Directive 83/189/EEC but the Construction Products, Machinery, and Personal Protective Equipment directives also make use of their own standing committees.
Suspension notice (CPA,CPR):	Bans a supplier from supplying goods that breach the legislation.
System (EMC):	Comprises several items of apparatus intended to function as a single unit.
Technical construction file (EMC, MY):	EMC: Describes the apparatus, procedures used to ensure conformity with the protection requirements, and a technical report or certification from a competent body. MY: Comprises drawings of machinery, tests, technical specifications used, methods used to eliminate hazards, instructions, and technical reports and tests of conformity with harmonized standards.
Technical documentation:	Established by the manufacturer under Modules A or B of the modular approach to attestation of conformity. The content is to be laid down by each directive but is likely to include a general description of the product, conceptual design and manufacturers' drawings and descriptions, the standards applied and solutions adopted to meet the essential requirements where standards have not been applied, and design calculations and test reports.

Technical file (MY, PPE):	Contains drawings of the machinery or equipment, calculations and tests, methods used to eliminate risks, instructions, and measures to maintain conformity with specifications.
Technical specifications (PP):	Specifications that define in an objective fashion the characteristics of the construction works, products, or services sought so that they fulfil the use for which they are intended. Characteristics may include quality, performance, safety dimensions, testing, packaging, marking, and costing.
Tender notice (PP):	Used in open and restricted procedures and, in some circumstances, negotiated procedures. Makes known the nature of the contract the contracting authority proposes to award. Also known as contract notice.
Tenderer (PP):	Supplier who submits a tender under open procedures.
Test purchases (CPA, CPR):	Purchases by enforcement authorities of samples of products for testing to see whether they comply with the legislation.
Testing laboratory (CPD):	An approved body which is a laboratory which measures, tests, calibrates, or determines the characteristics or performance of products.
Third countries:	Countries which are not members of the EC.
Thresholds (PP):	Value of a contract net of VAT at which the advertising provisions of the Public Procurement directives begin to operate.
Time limits (PP):	Minimum periods of time after the publication of tender notices during which a supplier can submit a bid or a request to participate in bidding.
Unit verification:	Module G of the modular approach to conformity assessment. Manufacturer draws up technical documentation. A notified body examines each individual item produced to check that there is conformity with the relevant directive.
Utilities:	Contracting entities operating in the areas of transport, water, energy, or telecommunications.

Abbreviations

AFNOR	Association Française de Normalization
BBA	British Board of Agrément
BIPE	Bureau d'Informations et de Prévisions Economiques
BS	British Standard
BSI	British Standards Institution
BSRIA	Building Services Research and Information Association
CCT	compulsory competitive tendering
CEN	European Committee for Standardization
CENELEC	European Committee for Electrotechnical Standardization
DIN	Deutsches Institute für Normung e.V.
DTI	Department of Trade and Industry
EC	European Communities
EEC	European Economic Community
ECISS	European Committee for Iron and Steel
ECU	European Currency Unit
EFTA	European Free Trade Area
EN	European Standard
ENV	European pre-standard
EOTA	European Organization for Technical Approvals
EOTC	European Organization for Testing and Certification
ETA	European technical approval
ETSI	European Telecommunications Standards Institute
GATT	General Agreement on Tariffs and Trade
GDP	Gross domestic product
HD	Harmonization document
IMES	International Marketing and Economic Services (UK) Ltd.
ISO	International Organization for Standardization
MOATs	Methods of Assessment and Test
NACCB	National Accreditation Council for Certification Bodies
NAMAS	National Measurement Accreditation Service
Official Journal	*Official Journal of the European Communities*
SME	small and medium-sized enterprises
UEAtc	European Union of Agrément
VAT	Value added tax

How to use this publication

STRUCTURE OF THE PUBLICATION

The publication has been organized into four parts:

Part A: Introduction	Section 1.
Part B: Technical harmonization	Sections 2, 3, 4, 5.
Part C: Public procurement	Sections 6, 7, 8.
Part D: Post-construction liability	Sections 9, 10, 11.

Part A: *Introduction* comprises an Overview which places the EC's quality management policies in the context of its Single Internal Market programme, summarises the policies examined in detail in Parts B-D, and draws out the principal implications of the policies for quality management in construction.

Parts B, C and D each concentrate on a different area of policy and its effects on quality management in construction.

Part B: *Technical harmonization* examines the major directives produced so far under the New Approach to Technical Harmonization and Standards which affect the construction industry. It also discusses the relevant directives produced on the health and safety of workers at work that principally affect the construction industry. Both types of directive are examined together due to the interface between them. New Approach directives are concerned with the manufacture of products that health and safety directives regulate in their use in work. The former lay down minimum requirements that products must satisfy before they may be placed upon the market. These include technical specifications, which can include specifications for quality control and quality assurance, and attestation of conformity procedures, which set levels of quality assurance. Technical specifications and attestation of conformity procedures can act as non-tariff barriers and so limit imports. The New Approach directives are intended to result in harmonized systems of product approval so that products that satisfy these can enjoy freedom of mobility within the EC.

Section 2 provides an overview of technical harmonization policy and its evolution. It examines the New Approach to Technical Harmonization and Standards, the organization of standardization work, and conformity assessment. It is not specifically concerned with the construction industry but rather with the broad range of technical harmonization policies that periodically produce measures that affect the industry. It enables the policies to be placed in their wider context.

Section 3 examines the principal New Approach directive to affect the construction industry, namely the Construction Products Directive.

Section 4 discusses the New Approach directives that have a bearing on building services, namely the Gas Appliances Directive, the Electromagnetic Compatibility Directive, which affects electrical engineering, and the Machinery Directive, which affects mechanical engineering.

Section 5 examines several New Approach directives concerned with the production of products bought by the construction industry. These are the amendment to the Machinery Directive, that encompasses lifting equipment, mobile machinery, and machinery for use underground, and the Personal Protective Equipment Directive. It discusses the directives concerned with safety on construction sites and the safe use of equipment, namely the Framework, proposed Temporary or Mobile Construction Site, Work Equipment, and Use of Personal Protective Equipment directives.

Part C: *Public Procurement* examines the directives dealing with the purchase of goods, services, and construction works by public bodies and utilities. These directives seek to ensure that there is a level playing field for potential suppliers from all parts of the EC and prevent Member States from favouring their own domestic firms. Their implications for quality management are twofold. The directives require the use of European standards where possible and these may contain requirements concerning quality control and quality assurance. They set limits on the technical references and information that can be sought from suppliers.

Section 6 examines the costs that result from governments using their purchasing power to discriminate in favour of domestic producers and how the EC has sought to control such practices.

Section 7 discusses the Public Works Directive, which is concerned with the procurement of construction works by public bodies. It explains the main principles in public procurement, including what contracts are affected, the procedures used in the award of contracts, the use of technical specifications, advertising rules, the economic and technical references that can be sought, the criteria for awards, and the remedies open to contractors wrongfully discriminated against.

Section 8 examines the remaining public procurement directives concerned with public supplies, the proposed Public Services Directive, and the directives that deal with procurement by utilities undertakings in the areas of energy, transport, water, and telecommunications. The latter affect such bodies irrespective of whether they are in public or private ownership. It focuses on the points of difference between them and the Public Works Directive.

Part D: *Post-construction Liability* examines what can happen after a construction product has been produced or a building or works erected.

Section 9 discusses product liability and how the Consumer Protection Act 1987 implemented the EC's Product Liability Directive. The Act has provided the basis for bringing into force New Approach directives in the UK, either by the making of safety regulations under Section 11 or by enacting similar provisions.

Section 10 discusses how the Construction Products Directive has been brought into force by the Construction Products Regulations 1991. It examines the powers being used to enforce the Directive and the potential impact of the Directive on the legal liability of construction professionals.

Section 11 considers the proposals that have been made for the harmonization of liabilities, warranties and insurance and the ways in which these are introducing into UK laws features of continental law, such as fixed time limits for the bringing of actions.

ALTERNATIVE WAYS OF USING THE PUBLICATION

The material in this publication has been organized so that it follows the development of the policies in a logical fashion. However, readers may wish to follow the material in a different sequence and each section has been written so that it is self-contained. Several other approaches to the material can be suggested.

Seven alternative pathways through the material are suggested below. They have been devised according to the function in the construction process:

- A Procurement
- B Design
- C Cost planning
- D Construction and installation
- E Construction products manufacture
- F Conformity assessment of construction products
- G Protection of health and safety of workers at work.

If the reader wishes to follow up all that is written about a particular topic, this can be done through the use of the Index. If information about a particular policy or piece of legislation is sought, the Table of Authorities identifies where particular documents are discussed. As the subject matter is constantly changing, it will be necessary for the reader to update the material. In order to assist in this, there is a statement of where the main policies stood when this publication was completed.

If readers wish to scan the material to determine which elements are of particular relevance to them, it is suggested that they could make use of Section 1, the Overview, which contains references to where subjects are treated in more detail. In addition, each section contains an overview and conclusions so that the reader can gain a flavour of what is covered in each. A glossary of the main terms used is also provided.

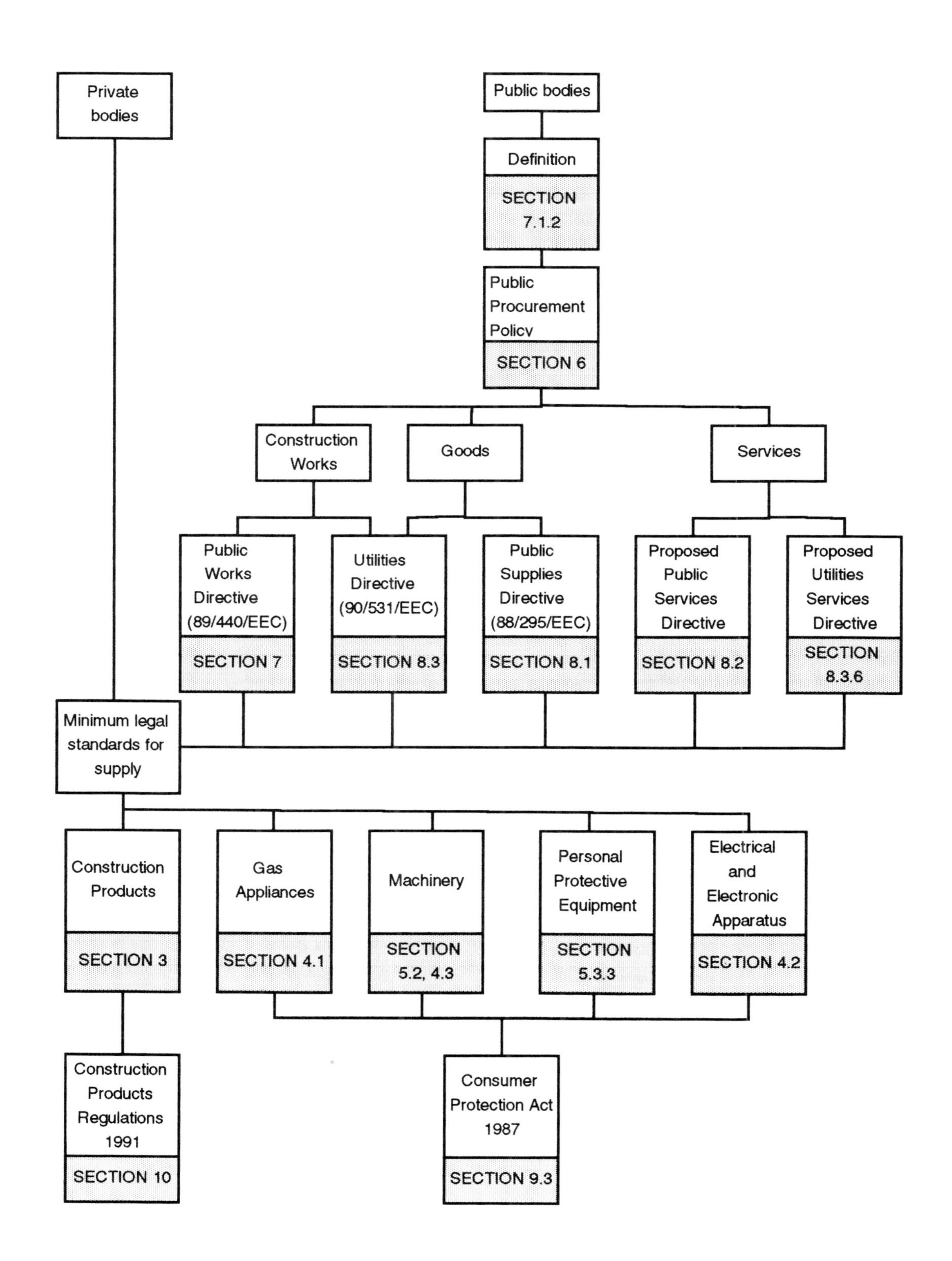

Figure 1 *Pathway A: Procurement*

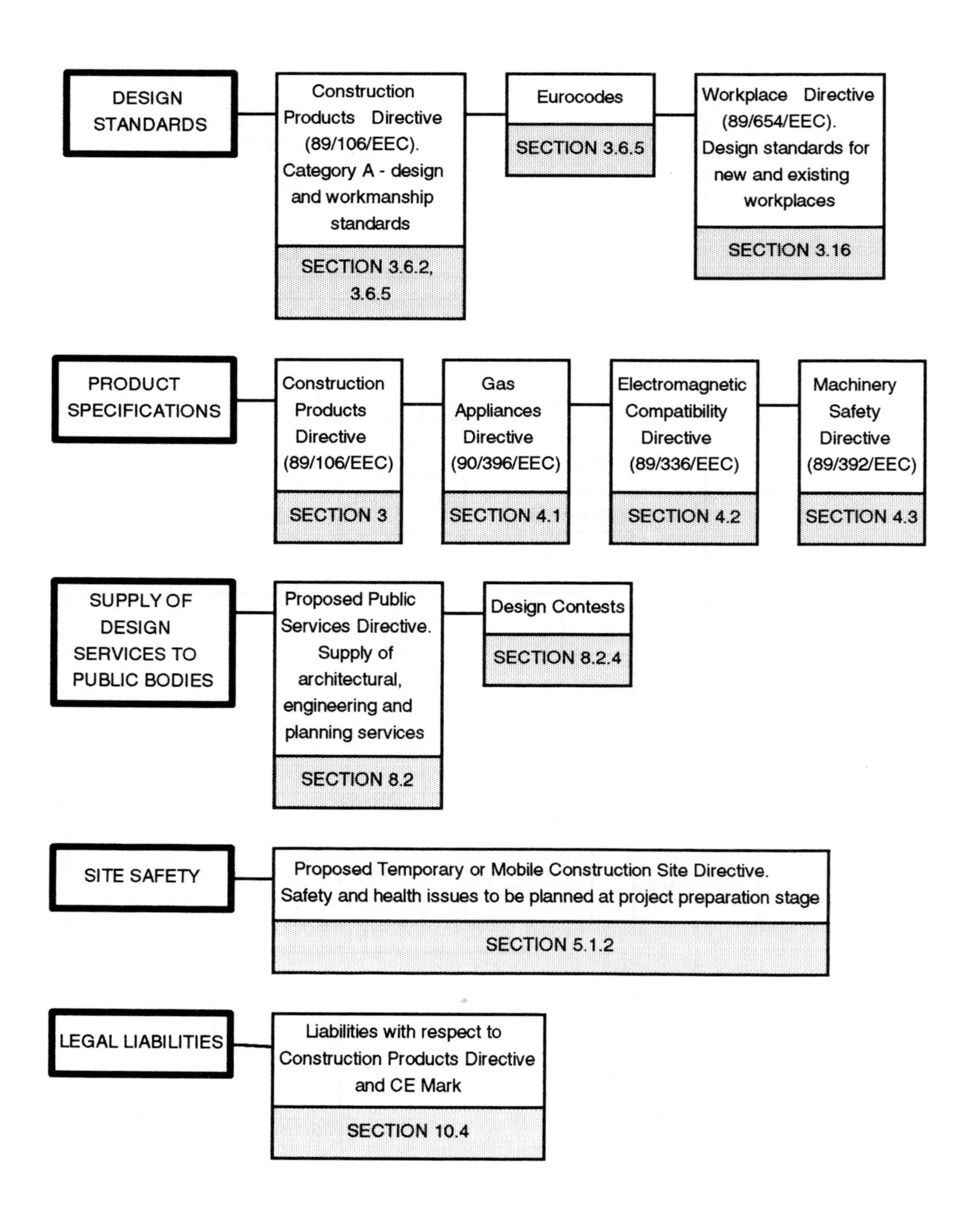

Figure 2 *Pathway B: Design*

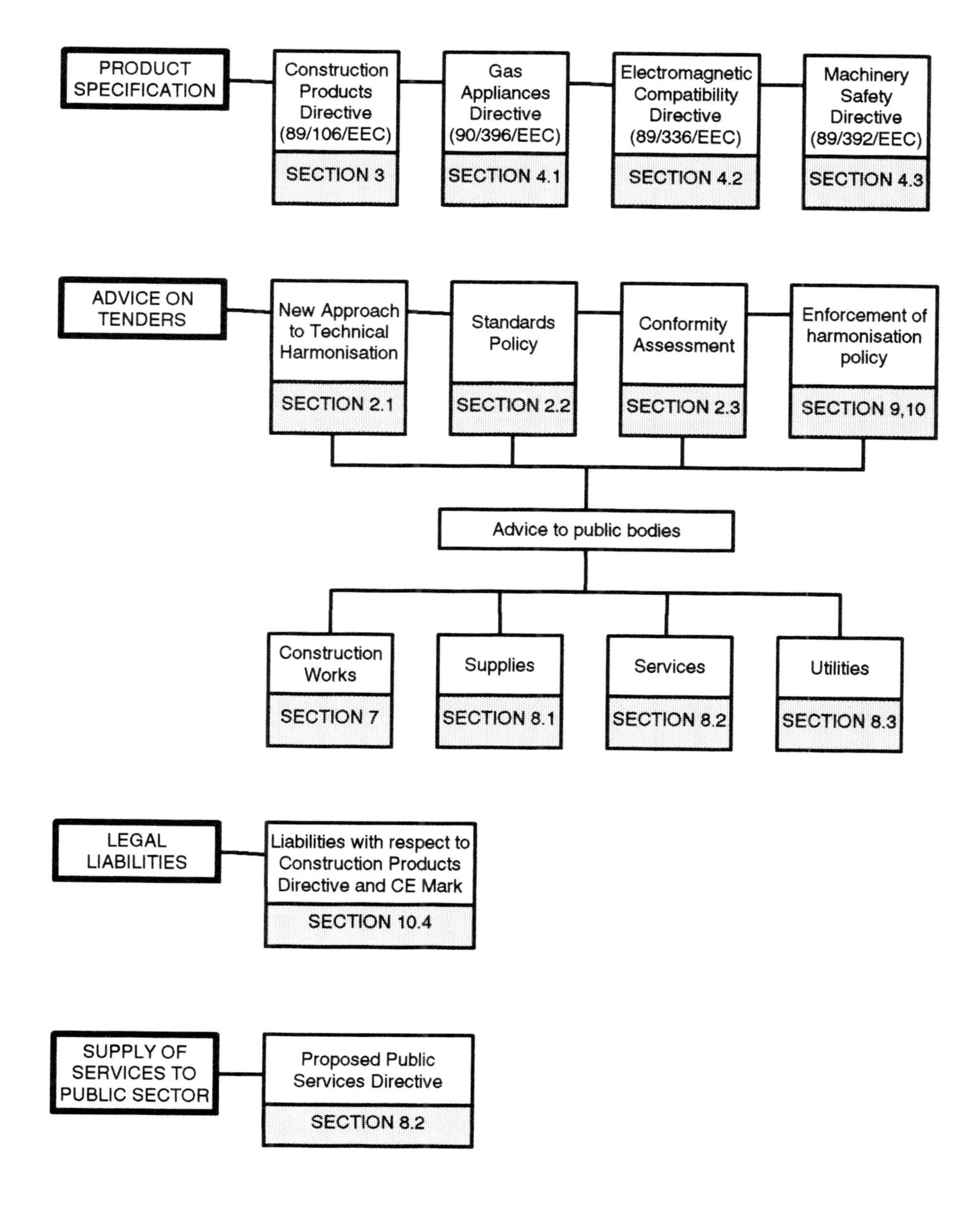

Figure 3 *Pathway C: Cost planning*

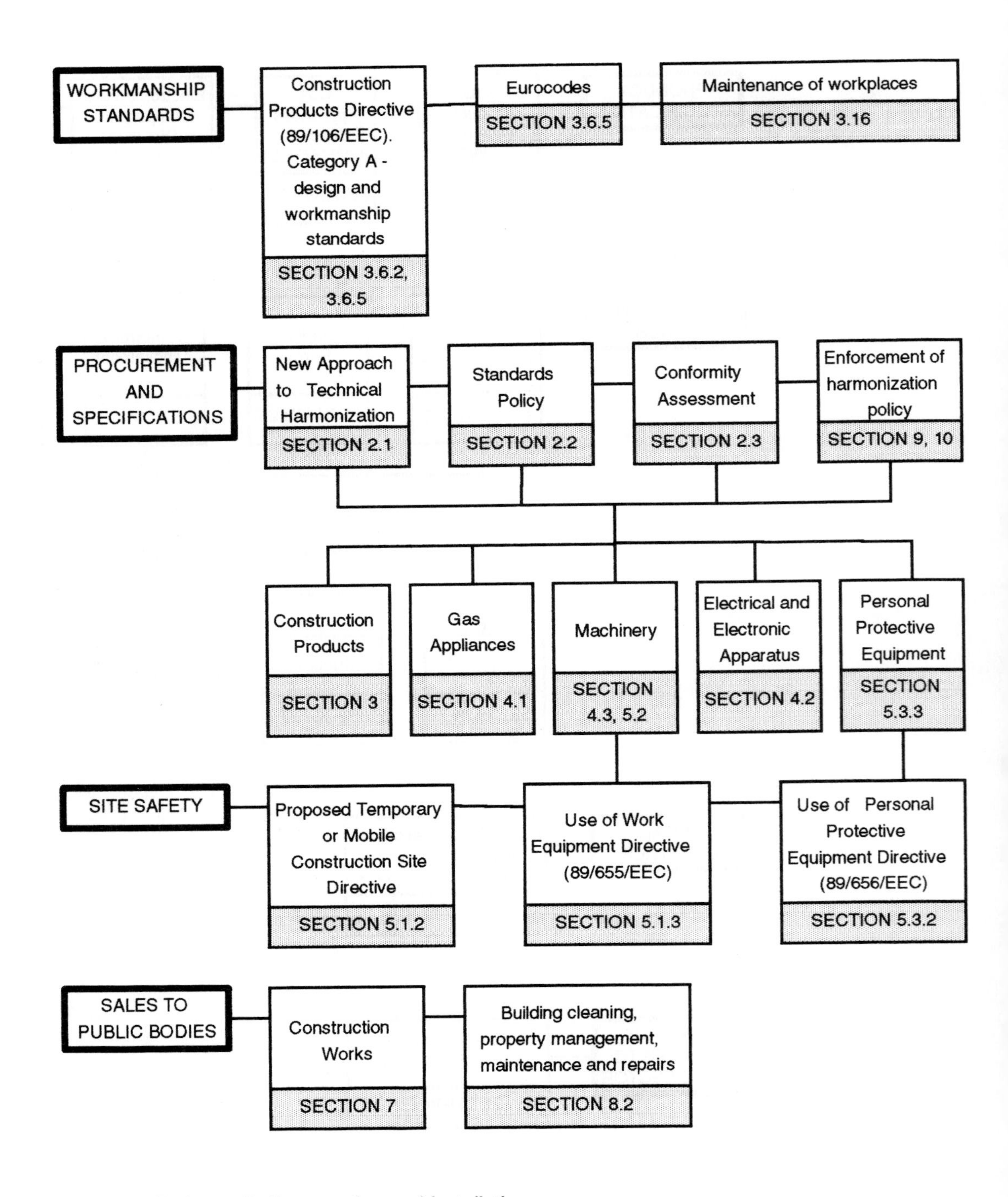

Figure 4 *Pathway D: Construction and installation*

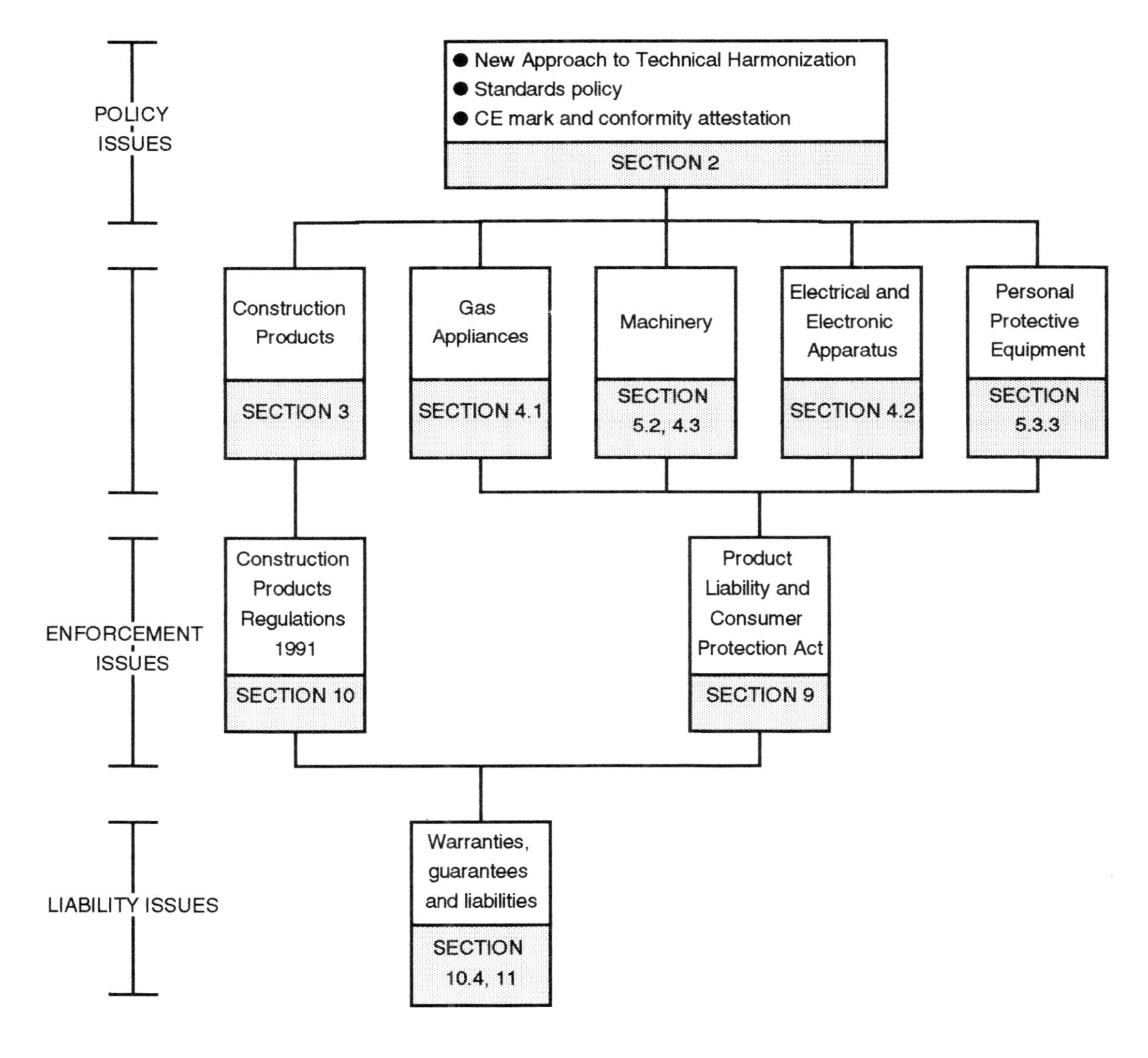

NOTE: Those who assemble or refurbish and bring into service machinery or electrical apparatus for their own use are regarded as being manufacturers.

Figure 5 *Pathway E: Construction products manufacture*

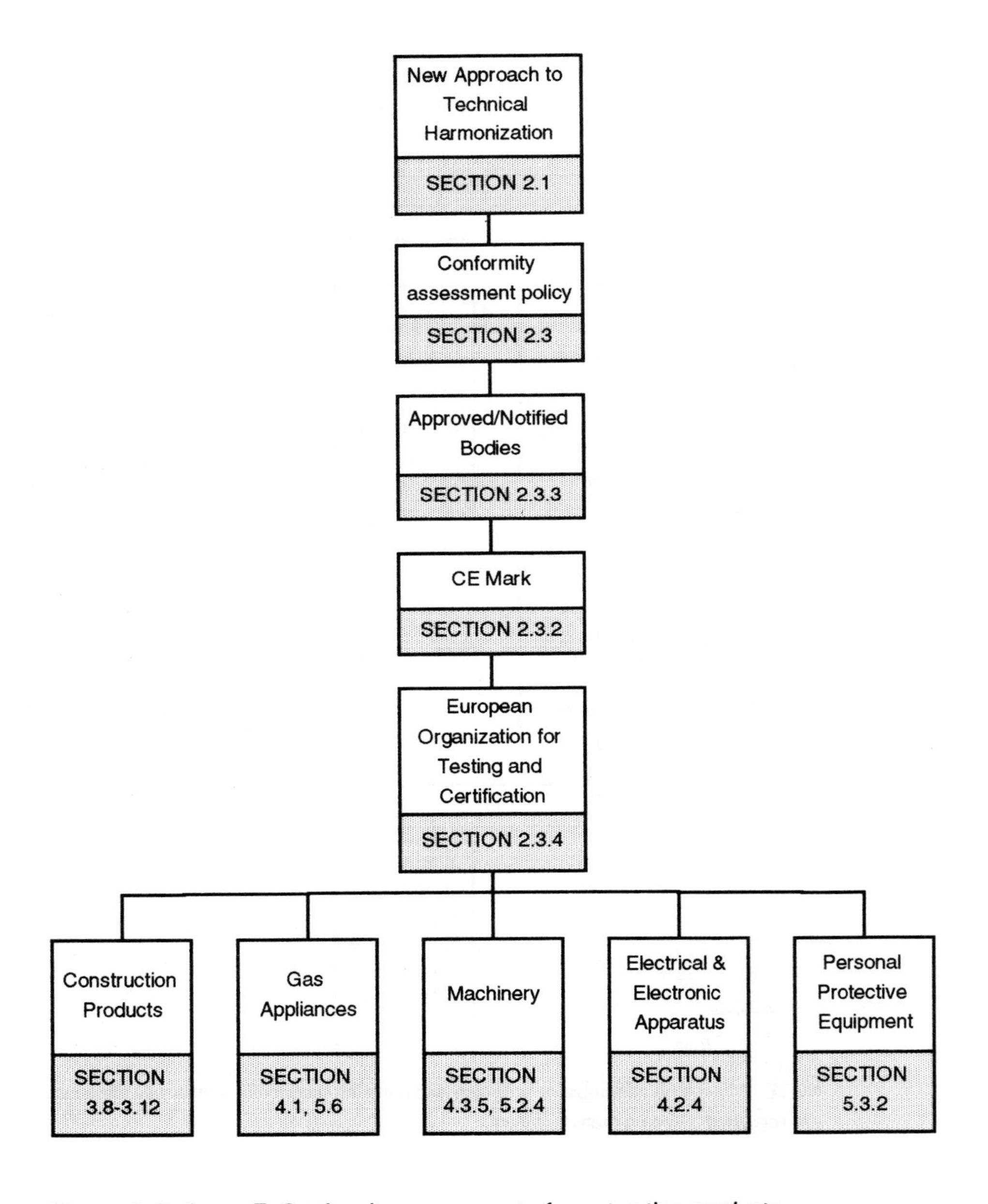

Figure 6 *Pathway F: Conformity assessment of construction products*

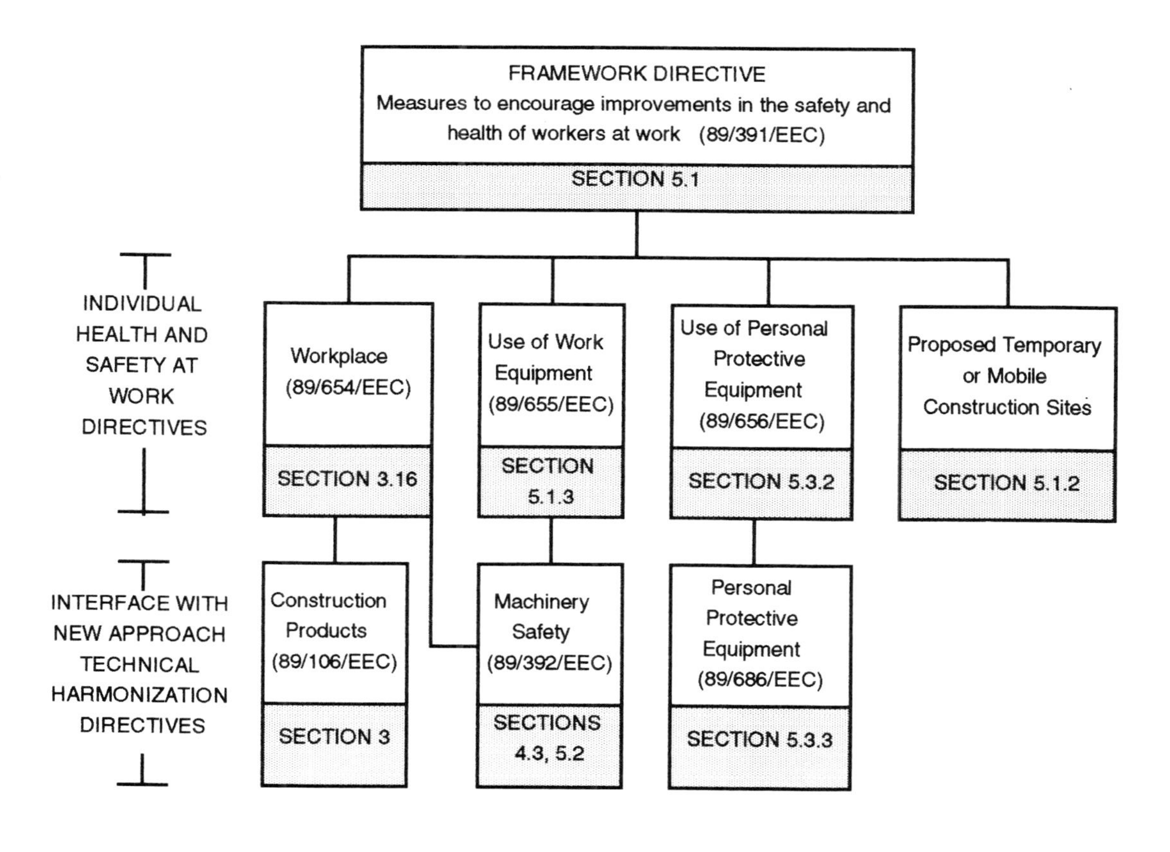

Figure 7 *Pathway G: Protection of health and safety of workers at work*

Part A Introduction

1 Overview

1.1 QUALITY MANAGEMENT AND THE SINGLE INTERNAL MARKET

Single Internal Market

1.1.1 This publication examines how the EC's policies to complete the Single Internal Market are likely to affect quality management in construction. In 1982 the EC adopted the objective of completing the Internal Market by the end of 1992. The intention was to remove the non-tariff barriers to trade that resulted from legal and administrative practices. This has involved the drafting of 282 measures, of which 232 so far have been agreed. Member States should have brought 159 measures into force to date. The UK has implemented 123, with only Denmark and France having implemented more[1]. Until now, Britain has largely been free to adopt whatever policies towards quality management that it thought fit. However, international treaties, of which the EC Treaty is probably the most significant, constrain the activities that are permitted within a country. This publication examines the extent to which EC policies aimed at securing a Single Internal Market affect the practice of quality management in the British construction industry and government support for it. It examines each of the main areas of EC policy that have an influence on quality management and discusses the extent to which they necessitate changes in quality management in Britain. It must be emphasized that the policies are continuing to evolve. A number of measures are still at a relatively early stage in their implementation and some have still to be adopted. This publication of necessity represents a snapshot taken at one point in time. In reality, the policies are subject to constant change and what is described here may be different from what eventually emerges.

SIM Policies

1.1.2 The policies being pursued to complete the Single Internal Market fall into three main groups:

- *The removal of physical barriers to trade.* These include removing frontier controls on individuals and goods and speeding up physical entry into a market.
- *The removal of technical barriers to trade.* These are the barriers caused by administrative controls and regulations over the supply of goods and services and the establishment of enterprises.
- *The removal of fiscal barriers to trade.* These are barriers caused by taxes on consumption, such as VAT and excise duties.

The measures that principally affect construction and quality management fall into the second group.

Quality management as a non-tariff barrier

1.1.3 The Single Internal Market programme contains a series of measures designed to remove non-tariff barriers to trade. Non-tariff barriers include standards, technical regulations, and administrative provisions which, intentionally or unintentionally, reduce imports of goods and services. For example, a foreign manufacturer might be prevented from tendering for a government contract because his product does not conform to a particular national standard, or has not received specific test or quality management system assessment certificates, even though it conforms to equivalent standards and has test and quality management system assessment certificates. Some non-tariff barriers act like a tariff by adding to the cost of imports, for example, by requiring products to be redesigned to meet different national standards. Others act as a quota by physically restricting entry, for example, by delaying importation until requisite product approvals are obtained. Standards, product approval systems, product conformity assessment, and quality management system assessment can all act as non-tariff barriers.

1.1.4 Three of the families of policies being pursued under the Single Internal Market Programme have a particular bearing on quality management in construction.

Technical harmonization

- *Technical harmonization of products.* Since 1985 the EC has adopted a number of technical harmonization measures that have been produced under the **New Approach to Technical Harmonization and Standards.** This involves setting minimum standards that products must satisfy before they may legally be placed upon the market. These include technical specifications and the procedures under which manufacturers attest that their products are in conformity with the requisite technical specifications. The technical specifications may include standards for testing and for the quality management of production. Attestation of conformity can involve systems of product approval and the assessment of product conformity or quality management systems. Five of the technical harmonization directives adopted to date have a particular bearing on construction, either because they concern construction products or products that the construction industry uses. 2.1.2

  - **Construction Products Directive** 3.0-3.17
  - **Gas Appliances Directive** 4.1
  - **Electromagnetic Compatibility Directive** 4.2
  - **Machinery Directive** 4.3, 5.2
  - **Personal Protective Equipment Directive.** 5.3

Health and safety at work

There is an interface between the New Approach directives and the family of directives concerned with the health and safety of workers at work. A **Framework Directive** was adopted in 1989, which contains general principles for the 5.1.1

prevention of occupational risks and the elimination of accident factors. This has been followed by a series of measures that are concerned with specific risks or the risks encountered in particular industries. The directives or proposed directives that have a particular bearing on the construction industry are:

- **Workplace Directive** 3.16
- **proposed Temporary or Mobile Construction Site Directive** 5.1.2
- **Work Equipment Directive** 5.1.3
- **Use of Personal Protective Equipment Directive.** 5.3.2

The New Approach directives are concerned with the manufacture of products and the health and safety directives are concerned with their safe use at work. As the philosophy behind the health and safety directives is one of planning for the avoidance of risk, establishing effective management systems to implement plans, the maintenance of proper records, and the monitoring and review of safety systems, this has many parallels with quality management.

Public procurement

- *Public procurement.* Public bodies are a major source of demand within the EC and are important clients of the construction industry. There can be no effective Single Internal Market unless firms from anywhere in the EC are able to bid for and to be awarded public contracts. Firms can be excluded from public contracts by a variety of devices, including the failure to advertise contracts, by not permitting sufficient time for a proper response to advertisements, and by the use of discriminatory criteria in the award of contracts. The devices include some that have a particular bearing on quality management, such as the use of technical specifications that are unique to a country, the requiring of specific test or quality management system assessment certificates, and the information sought in technical references. The EC has had public procurement directives in place to curb such abuses since the 1970s, but these are thought to have been ineffective. It has introduced a series of new directives to regulate public contracts. These include:

  - **a revised Public Supplies Directive** 8.1
  - **a revised Public Works Directive** 7.0-7.7
  - **Utilities Directive** 8.3
  - **proposed Public Services and Utilities Services Directives** 8.2, 8.3.6
  - **Remedies or Compliance Directives.** 7.6, 8.2.8, 8.3.7

The aim is to curb previous abuses by tightening up the procedures on public purchasing, to provide suppliers who have been discriminated against with more effective means of redress, and to extend the principles of public purchasing into new areas, such as purchasing by utilities and of services. In so doing, they introduce various measures that affect quality management, including setting out the rules that are to govern the use of particular technical specifications and determining the information that can be sought by way of technical references.

Post-construction liability

- *Post-construction liability.* A number of the measures examined in this publication have implications for legal liabilities once a construction product has been manufactured or a building or construction works constructed. These fall into two main categories:

  - Liabilities to the state that result from the enforcement of minimum standards under the New Approach directives. These are largely the responsibility of the Member States. In the UK the methods of enforcement have been derived from the **Consumer Protection Act 1987**, which brought into force the **Product Liability Directive of 1985**. 10.0-10.3 9.2-9.4

  - Changes in the legal relationships with other parties as a result of New Approach directives having implications for contracts or torts. 10.4

  The Commission has explored the differences in liabilities, warranties, and guarantees between the Member States, and legislation to harmonize these may follow in the future. 11.0-11.3

This publication does not examine, except incidentally, other aspects of the Single Internal Market programme such as social policy, the mutual recognition of qualifications, environmental policy, construction finance, indirect taxation, or the regulation of enterprises. In due course, these could also have a bearing on quality management in construction.

1.2 TECHNICAL HARMONIZATION

1.2.1 Technical harmonization policy in the EC seeks to ensure that differences in national standards, technical regulations, laws, and administrative provisions do not impede trade in products between Member States. Product standards, test standards, and quality management standards have the capability to prevent trade. Similarly, the organization of product conformity, product approval, and quality management system assessment can also act as barriers to trade.

Policies to prevent technical barriers to trade

1.2.2 The EC has pursued four main policies to prevent technical measures from being used as barriers to trade.

- *Prevention of new standards, technical regulations, and administrative provisions being added to the existing barriers to trade.* Under a directive adopted in 1983 (and amended in 1988), the Commission, the European Standardization Bodies, CEN and CENELEC, and the national standards organizations of the Member States are to be notified of national standards programmes and the Commission is to be notified of draft technical regulations. The introduction of measures that may act as a barrier to trade can be delayed and the measures modified. 2.2.2

- *Removal of existing barriers to trade caused by laws, administrative procedures, or technical regulations.* This is achieved by a policy of technical harmonization. Directives set minimum standards that products must satisfy before they may legally be placed upon the market. Products that meet these standards enjoy freedom of mobility throughout the Community without interference from Member States. 2.1.2

- *Ensuring that public bodies do not use technical specifications to discriminate against suppliers from other Member States.* The public procurement directives oblige public bodies to use European standards in their specifications wherever possible. 7.3

- *Encouragement of mutual recognition by bodies engaged in non-regulatory testing and certification of each other's test and conformity certificates.* The EC, together with EFTA, CEN, and CENELEC, founded the **European Organization for Testing and Certification** in 1990 to coordinate mutual recognition in the non-regulatory sphere. 2.3.4

'Old' approach to technical harmonization

1.2.3 Technical harmonization policies have been pursued by the EC since 1968 but relatively little progress was made before 1985. Two main reasons can be suggested for this: 2.1.1

- Until the **Single European Act of 1986** all decisions on technical harmonization needed the unanimous approval of all the Member States.

- The process by which technical harmonization directives were produced required all the details to be resolved before they could be adopted.

New Approach to Technical Harmonization

1.2.4 In 1985 the EC adopted a different approach to technical harmonization, namely the **New Approach to Technical Harmonization and Standards**. The New Approach has four main principles. 2.1.2

- That harmonization should be limited to the adoption of *essential safety requirements*. 2.1.2.3

- That technical specifications conforming to the essential requirements should be drawn up and, generally, this work should be entrusted to the European Standardization Organizations, CEN and CENELEC, who are to carry this out under mandate from the Commission.

- That compliance with the technical specifications drawn up should be voluntary so that manufacturers have the opportunity to satisfy the essential requirements by other means.

- That Member States must accept products that conform to the harmonized standards produced by CEN and CENELEC as satisfying the essential requirements and, subject to safeguard procedures, must not impede their being offered for sale on their territories.

Features of New Approach directives

1.2.5 The technical harmonization directives produced under the New Approach have a number of key elements in common. 2.1.2.5

- The scope of the directive is defined in terms of the products to be covered and the hazards to be adverted.

- The principle that products shall be placed on the market only if they do not endanger persons, domestic animals, or property, when properly installed and maintained, and used for the purposes for which they are intended.

- The definition of what constitutes a safe product through *essential safety requirements.*

- That products that conform with a *harmonized European standard*, drafted by CEN or CENELEC under mandate from the Commission, satisfy the essential requirements.

- That manufacturers are required to demonstrate that their products are in conformity with technical specifications through *attestation of conformity* procedures, which can include testing or certification by *approved* or *notified bodies* designated for this purpose by Member States.

- Products that have satisfied the attestation of conformity procedures may bear the *CE mark*, which entitles them to freedom of mobility within the EC.

- Member States shall police the use of the CE mark.

- Safeguard arrangements, by which Member States can intervene in the supply of a product when they have reason to suspect that a product does not comply with the essential requirements, even when it bears a CE mark.

- The appointment of Standing Committees, comprising representatives of the Member States and chaired by the Commission, to advise the Commission on, and to determine certain aspects of, the implementation of the directives.

New Approach directives

1.2.6 The five New Approach directives adopted to date to have a bearing on the construction industry are:

- ***Construction Products Directive, 1988***. This applies to any product produced for incorporation in a permanent manner in construction works. 3.0-3.17

- ***Electromagnetic Compatibility Directive, 1989***. This applies to any apparatus which is either liable to cause undue electromagnetic disturbance or whose performance is likely to be unduly affected by such disturbance. It affects building services that contain electrical or electronic components. 4.2

- ***Machinery Directive, 1989, and its first amendment, 1991***. These apply to assemblies of linked parts or components joined together for a specific application, at least one of which moves. They affect mechanical engineering. The first amendment extended the scope so as to include lifting equipment, mobile machinery, and machinery for use underground, so that the Directive covers construction plant. 4.3, 5.2

- ***Gas Appliances Directive, 1990***. This applies to appliances that burn gaseous fuels that are used in cooking, heating, providing hot water, lighting, or refrigeration and to their component parts. It does not apply to appliances used in industrial processes. 4.1

- ***Personal Protective Equipment Directive, 1989***. This applies to devices or appliances worn or held by an individual for protection against health and safety risks. 5.3

Essential requirements

1.2.7 Each of these directives contains *essential requirements* (though some of them call them *basic* or *protection requirements*). These define what is meant by a safe product. However, there are some significant differences of approach between the directives, both in terms of the amount of detail contained in the essential requirements and what exactly they apply to. The **Construction Products Directive** has six essential requirements, but these have certain unusual features not found in the other New Approach directives. 3.3, 4.1.3, 4.2.3, 4.3.3, 5.2.3, 5.3.3.3

- Construction products are to have such characteristics as to enable the construction works into which they are incorporated to satisfy the essential requirements, if properly designed and built. This means that the essential requirements are not applied directly to the products the Directive seeks to regulate. 3.3.1

- The essential requirements only apply if the construction works are regulated. If a Member State does not have regulations that apply an essential requirement to particular construction works, there is no potential barrier to trade for the Directive to eliminate and no requirement for a Member State to introduce regulations.

- The essential requirements do not contain sufficient information to enable standards to be derived from them. This is remedied by a series of documents, one for each essential requirement, known as the *interpretative documents*. 3.4

The other directives have more precisely drafted essential requirements. For example, the **Machinery Directive**'s essential requirements are 12 pages long in the original directive and have been added to by amendments.

Technical specifications

1.2.8 Conformance with the essential requirements is usually to be demonstrated by compliance with: 3.5

(i) A harmonized European standard drafted by CEN or CENELEC under mandate from the Commission and transposed into a national standard, *or*, 2.2.4

(ii) A national standard accepted by the Commission as conforming to the essential requirements.

There is some doubt as to whether there will be any significant use made of the latter provision. The **Construction Products Directive** provides for a third type of technical specification, the *European technical approval*. 3.7 This is a favourable technical assessment of the fitness for use of a product for an intended use. It is intended for the approval of innovatory products for which there are either no harmonized standards or which differ significantly from standards. They are to be granted by bodies designated for this purpose by Member States. Approvals bodies collectively form a single organization called the **European Organization for Technical Approvals**. The government has designated the British Board of Agrément as the sole UK body to issue European technical approvals for the time being. Other bodies, including private ones, may be designated in due course.

Harmonized European standards

1.2.9 Different types of harmonized European standards are likely to be produced under the directives. For example, there are two principal types of standard being drafted under the **Construction Products Directive**: 4.3.4 3.6.2

- **Category A**. These are standards for the design and execution of buildings and works and could include *Eurocodes*.

- **Category B**. These are product standards and include:

  - Standards for basic materials used in the manufacture of products, e.g. plastics.

- Standards for products with specific end uses, e.g. products for use in external walls.

- Horizontal standards in support of each essential requirement, applying several procedures, e.g. test methods.

Attestation of conformity

1.2.10 The objective of *attestation of conformity* is to enable the authorities to ensure that products are only placed on the market if they satisfy minimum legal standards. The exact procedures used vary between directives, as does the degree of choice in procedure allowed to manufacturers. However, the fundamental principle is that the minimum level of quality assurance is laid down by the EC and is not agreed voluntarily between producers and purchasers. *There is nothing in any of the directives that prevents a manufacturer from voluntarily offering a higher level of quality assurance than that provided for.* It is important that products that comply with the requirements of the directives should be capable of being identified by purchasers and by the governments who have responsibility for policing their markets. This is the function of the *CE mark*. Each of the directives identifies the circumstances in which the CE mark should be affixed to products, who is to be responsible for affixing it, the form it is to take, and what information is to accompany it. For the **Electromagnetic Compatibility** and **Machinery** Directives, there is also the provision that apparatus or machinery may not be brought into service unless it satisfies the essential requirements. For example, the owner or tenant of a building may bring electrical apparatus or machinery into service for his own use by installing or altering electrical or mechanical engineering aspects of a building, and a construction firm could do so where it assembles or adapts equipment for its own use. It is not yet clear whether such apparatus or machinery must also be subjected to the attestation of conformity procedures. Directives proposed since 1990 must make use of a standard set of eight procedures. The Commission has attempted to align the procedures of existing directives with those in the standard set.

3.8-3.10, 4.1.5., 4.2.4, 4.3.5, 5.2.4, 5.3.3.4-5.3.3.7

2.3.2, 4.1.6, 3.12

2.3.1

Approved, notified and competent bodies

1.2.11 Some of the aspects of attestation of conformity are to be carried out by the manufacturer and others by *approved*, *notified*, or *competent bodies*. These are independent bodies that can provide third-party certification of the product, the tests and inspections it has been through, or of the production system used to produce it. They are certification bodies or testing laboratories. The **Construction Products Directive** also has a third category of approved body, an inspection body. They are designated by Member States to carry out precisely defined activities under the directives. In the case of approved or notified bodies, the Commission is to be notified of their identity. The criteria that a body must satisfy to be designated is similar in each of the directives and largely follows those first laid down in the **Toy Safety Directive** in 1988:

2.3.3

3.11

2.3.3.2

- Having the available personnel, means, and equipment to carry out their tasks,

- Having personnel with the necessary technical competence and professional integrity,
- Being impartial,
- Being able to maintain professional secrecy,
- Having civil liability insurance or having their liability guaranteed by the state.

The latter condition is interpreted in the UK as meaning having professional indemnity insurance. Since 1989, the EC has supported the use of the **EN 45000** series of standards (BS 7501–7503, 7511–7514) concerned with the operation and assessment of testing laboratories and certification bodies. The EN 45000 series covers most of the criteria for approved bodies with the exception of civil liability insurance, though they also have requirements that go beyond the requirements of the directives. The UK government's policy is to select approved bodies from among those accredited by the **National Measurement Accreditation Service** (NAMAS) for test and calibration laboratories or the **National Accreditation Council for Certification Bodies** (NACCB) for certification bodies. 4.1.5.3

Quality management

1.2.12 The directives vary in their approach towards quality management. For example, the **Electromagnetic Compatibility Directive** does not explicitly mention quality management but it requires manufacturers to take all measures necessary to ensure that the apparatus produced complies with the technical specifications. By contrast, the **Construction Products Directive** requires manufacturers to have in place *factory production control*. This is defined by the Directive as meaning the permanent internal control of production by the manufacturer. The Standing Committee for Construction has adopted for guidance purposes a definition of factory production control that closely follows the requirements of **EN 29002** (BS 5750 : Part 2). 3.9.2

Transitional and interim arrangements

1.2.13 The New Approach directives introduce a framework for technical harmonization in an area to which elements of detail can be added incrementally. It is likely to be some time after a directive has been adopted before the full range of harmonized European standards necessary for its full implementation is produced. In consequence, each of the directives provides for some form of transitional or interim arrangements to enable it to come into operation before all the standards have been drafted. Four main approaches are to be found in the directives.

- *Defined transitional periods during which manufacturers may continue to place on the market products that conform to the national regulations in force when a directive comes into effect.* This provides manufacturers with a period of time in which to redesign their products, retool, and follow the necessary attestation of conformity procedures, while they can continue to supply their existing products. This approach is to be found in the **Gas Appliances**, 4.1.1.1, 4.2.1.1, 4.3.1.1, 5.3.1.1

Electromagnetic Compatibility, **Machinery**, and **Personal Protective Equipment directives.** The **Construction Products Directive** does not have a formal transitional period but national technical specifications and provisions for attestation of conformity are to remain in place until superseded by European ones. 3.15.1

- *Attestation of conformity procedures that apply where a product does not comply with harmonized European standards or there is only partial compliance.* This could happen as a result of there being no standards with which to comply. The solution is generally to require type-testing of a prototype by an approved body. Such procedures can be found in the **Gas Appliances**, **Electromagnetic Compatibility**, **Machinery**, and **Personal Protective Equipment directives**. It is possible that manufacturers may seek European technical approvals for their products under the **Construction Products Directive** if standards are not available. 4.1.5.4, 4.2.4.1, 4.3.5.2, 5.2.4.3, 5.3.3.6; 3.7

- *Provision for testing and certification to be carried out in one Member State* in accordance with the specifications of another Member State. The **Construction Products Directive** provides for a Member State to presume conformity with their national specifications where a product has satisfied tests and inspections carried out in accordance with its requirements by an approved body in another Member State. 3.15.2-3.15.3

- *Recognition by the Commission of national technical specifications as conforming to the essential requirements of a directive.* This would enable existing standards to be used as a means of demonstrating compliance with a directive. Each of the directives contains such provisions, but there is no indication that the Commission is to accord such recognition to national standards.

Problems with the New Approach

1.2.14 The New Approach to Technical Harmonization and Standards has the potential to change radically technical harmonization by speeding up the process and resulting in European rather than national specifications. This has not yet happened, though it could well do so once significant numbers of harmonized European standards become available for use. Four main problems have arisen with the New Approach to date: 2.1.3

- *There are differences between directives in the procedures adopted for attestation of conformity.* This could present problems for manufacturers when products must satisfy two or more directives before they can be placed upon the market. In 1990 the EC adopted a *modular approach* to attestation of conformity so that new directives must make use of modules selected from among a group of eight rather than including ones that are unique to them. There has 2.3.1

been some attempt to align certain procedures of the existing directives with these but, generally, it seems likely that the directives will be brought into line with the modules when they come up for revision.

- *There are differences between directives in the rules for the use of the CE mark.* The Commission has proposed a regulation to overcome this, which would be binding on all existing directives. The proposal is currently under discussion. 2.3.2

- *The length of time that is likely to elapse between the adoption of a directive and its full implementation, including the drafting of the requisite harmonized European standards.* The Commission has argued that part of the problem is due to the way in which standardization is organized and has proposed a series of measures to change it. These measures have not been greeted enthusiastically by the standardization bodies and it is not clear what action, if any, will result. 2.2.5

- *There are differences in detail in the ways in which the directives are being brought into force by Member States.* Although it is too early to be certain that this will present a problem, there are important areas in each directive which lie within the competence of Member States. These include the policing of the CE mark. There is no reason why Member States should do this in the same way so that actions that may be a criminal offence in one country may not be in another or offences might be punished in a different way. Manufacturers could exploit differences between Member States.

1.3 LEGAL IMPLICATIONS OF THE INTRODUCTION OF THE TECHNICAL HARMONIZATION DIRECTIVES

1.3.1 EC directives have to be brought into force in a Member State by the actions of its government. These actions may be legislative or administrative. Bringing the New Approach directives into force within the UK involves a mixture of both types of action: legislative, principally statutes and subsidiary regulations, and administrative, including the designation of approved bodies and the instruction of local authorities in their role in enforcement.

Consumer Protection Act 1987

1.3.2 The model for legislation is the **Consumer Protection Act 1987**, which brought into force the **Product Liability Directive of 1985**. Section 11 of the Act allows the Secretary of State to make *safety regulations*, which may contain provisions with respect, for example, to the content, design, testing, and inspection of goods and the instructions that accompany them. The Act creates a number of offences, including supplying consumer goods which fail to comply with general safety requirements and failing to carry out tests or procedures required by safety regulations. The powers of enforcement include prohibition notices, notices to warn, suspension notices, the forfeiture of goods, and the

9.2-9.3

9.3.5

9.3.6

obligation to provide information or produce records. Contravention of notices, breaching safety regulations, or supplying false information can lead to fines and/or imprisonment, and the reimbursement of the enforcing authority's costs. There are rights of appeal against suspension notices and the detention of goods, with compensation being payable by the authorities where goods have been seized when there has been no contravention of a safety provision. Enforcement is by the weights and measures authorities in Great Britain (district councils in Northern Ireland). They can make purchases, test goods, enter premises, and seize goods or records. Customs officers can detain imports for two working days. 9.3.7

Consumer Protection Act as a model

1.3.3 Two distinct approaches have been adopted towards the use of the **Consumer Protection Act** as the means of bringing the technical harmonization directives into force in the UK: 9.3.8

- *The making of safety regulations under Section 11 of the Act.* The weights and measures authorities are able to use their powers under the Act to enforce the regulations. This is the approach adopted for the Gas Appliances Directive.

- *The making of regulations under the European Communities Act 1972, which largely follow the provisions of Parts II and IV of the Consumer Protection Act and grant similar powers to the enforcement authorities as they enjoy under this Act.* This is the approach adopted in the **Construction Products Regulations 1991.**

Construction Product Regulations

1.3.4 The **Construction Product Regulations** are crucially concerned with product standards and the validation of those standards. The emphasis is on standards, not upon legal liability. Nevertheless, there is provision for enforcement. Indirectly there are potential implications for civil obligations and, thus, liability of the participants in the construction process. The CE mark is a claim by a manufacturer that when a product is incorporated in construction works in a proper manner for the intended use, it will enable the works to comply with the six essential requirements of mechanical resistance and stability, safety in case of fire, hygiene and environmental health, safety in use, protection against noise, and energy economy and heat retention. The regulations create offences for misuse of CE marks. Enforcement authorities, the local weights and measures authorities in Britain (district councils in Northern Ireland), are given a range of powers similar to those enjoyed under the **Consumer Protection Act** to deploy against suppliers of goods which do not satisfy the essential requirements. These include prohibition notices, notices to warn, suspension notices, forfeiture, notices requiring information, test purchases, search, and detention, all of which are aimed at detecting and inhibiting the supply of such goods as well as providing for punishment of offences. The Commission must be notified of action taken against products by Member States and this is enforced in the UK 10.1 10.1.5-10.1.7 10.3 10.3.5

for construction products by a government circular to local authorities.

Legal liabilities

1.3.5 Regulations such as the **Construction Products Regulations** are not primarily intended to regulate legal relationships between parties. Nevertheless, there are potential implications for the civil obligations and, thus, liability of the participants in the construction process which proceed from the introduction of the regulations. The use of the CE mark is not mandatory for construction products. Failure to specify or use a CE marked product cannot therefore be an automatic breach of contract nor a tort by a designer or a builder. A non-CE marked product could be validly used if its technical performance enabled the essential requirements to be satisfied as appropriate. However, it would be hard to argue that failure to meet one or more of the essential requirements is irrelevant in assessing a professional's standard of skill and care in specifying a product. A designer would need to be satisfied of the adequacy of a non-CE marked product in enabling the essential requirements to be met. The specification of a CE marked product does not necessarily mean that the product is appropriate to the task, or that the designer has satisfied his/her obligations. A particular design task may well require standards higher than the general fitness standard of the essential requirements and, of course, standards relating to other criteria beyond the coverage of the essential requirements. The specification of a CE marked product is not conclusive proof that the specifier has fulfilled his/her legal obligations of reasonable care and skill. Failure to specify a CE marked product is not conclusive proof of failure to fulfil such obligations, but may be indicative of failure in the absence of justification.

10.4

Mathurin Report

1.3.6 The position of participants in the construction process is the subject of continuing change. The **Mathurin Report** (1990) to the Commission recommended the harmonization of liabilities between developers and producers, harmonization of financial protection for home owners, and uniformity in public works contract documents and building control documentation. The progress of the Mathurin proposals has been stalled by conflicts between the (mainly southern European) Member States, who favour Mathurin's mandatory property-insurance-backed harmonization, and the (mainly northern European) Member States, which have varying degrees of reservations. The UK is in the latter category. Despite this hold-up, further steps toward uniformity have been made with the **European Communities (Recognition of Professional Qualifications) Regulations 1991** and the draft **Services Liability Directive**, which contains the decennial liability of building producers as advocated by Mathurin. An attempt has been made to break the impasse between the supporters and opponents of Mathurin's proposals for uniformity. Division DG 111/D in Brussels commissioned four Drafting Groups in 1991 to produce a draft Directive. The October 1991 deadline for this was not achieved, but during 1992 it is anticipated that the reports will form the basis for discussion on the proposed Directive.

11.2

1.4 INTERFACE BETWEEN THE TECHNICAL HARMONIZATION DIRECTIVES AND THE HEALTH AND SAFETY AT WORK DIRECTIVES

1.4.1 The New Approach directives set down legal minimum standards which must be satisfied before products can be placed upon the market. The health and safety at work directives concern the use of those products. Thus, there is an interface between the two types of directive and the necessity to ensure that they are compatible. The main interfaces are:

Machinery Directive	&	**Use of Work Equipment Directive**
Personal Protective Equipment Directive	&	**Use of Personal Protective Equipment Directive**
Construction Products Directive	&	**Workplace Directive**

Framework Directive

1.4.2 The **Framework Directive** sets out general principles for the prevention of occupational risks and the elimination of accident factors. These include avoiding risks, evaluating risks that cannot be avoided, combating risks at source, and the development of coherent prevention policies. Satisfying these implies that employers will have effective management systems for safety planning, for implementing safety decisions, and for monitoring and review. The systems needed to achieve this are likely to have many features in common with quality management systems and to incorporate a similar management philosophy. 5.1.1

Work Equipment and Personal Protective Equipment Directives

1.4.3 The safety directives concerned with **Work Equipment** and **Personal Protective Equipment** make employers responsible for ensuring that equipment is suitable for its intended use. This implies that they will familiarize themselves with the essential requirements that the equipment must comply with, the meanings of attestation of conformity, and the information, markings, and warnings that manufacturers must provide. Clearly, they should not make use of equipment that does not display evidence of attestation of conformity where this should have been provided. The technical harmonization directives set out the essential requirements with which equipment must comply, including warnings, instructions, and markings, and the attestation of conformity provisions that must be satisfied. Where employers have assembled or adapted equipment for their own use, it must comply with the essential requirements. 5.1.3, 5.3.2

Workplace Directive

1.4.4 The **Workplace Directive** sets out minimum health and safety requirements for workplaces, including requirements concerning their stability, electrical installations, emergency routes, fire-fighting, temperatures, lighting, sanitary equipment, danger areas, and rest rooms. New and modified premises will also have to incorporate requirements concerned with ventilation, floors, walls, ceilings, windows, roofs, traffic routes, loading bays, first aid rooms, and outdoor workplaces. Thus, this Directive will 3.16

have an impact upon design standards. It also lays down standards for the construction materials that can be used, for example, for floors in areas in which toxic liquids might be spilled.

1.5 INTERFACE BETWEEN THE TECHNICAL HARMONIZATION DIRECTIVES AND THE PUBLIC PROCUREMENT DIRECTIVES

Reasons for public procurement directives

1.5.1 The EC first introduced public procurement directives to regulate public purchasing in the 1970s with the **Public Works Directive of 1971** and the **Public Supplies Directive of 1977**. Their aim was to open up public procurement in each Member State to competition from firms from anywhere within the EC. Public expenditure represents such a major part of the national economies of the EC that discrimination in favour of one's own nationals could considerably distort trade. There is evidence that Member States have not always followed the requirements of these directives, for example, through using technical specifications that favour domestic producers. Relatively few contracts are awarded to firms from other Member States. Consequently, a new series of public procurement directives have been adopted or proposed to make good these apparent deficiencies. 6.1 6.2

Public procurement directives

1.5.2 The new public procurement directives adopted or proposed are:

- A revised **Public Supplies Directive**, dealing with the purchase of goods, which was adopted in 1988. 8.1

- A revised **Public Works Directive**, dealing with the purchase of construction works, which was adopted in 1989. 7.0-7.7

- A **Utilities Directive**, adopted in 1990, which extends the principles of the public procurement of goods and construction works to entities operating in the water, energy, transport, and telecommunications sectors, irrespective of whether they are in public or private ownership. 8.3

- A proposed **Public Services Directive** and a parallel proposed **Utilities Services Directive**, which are intended to extend the principles of public procurement to the purchase of services. Services include architectural, engineering, building maintenance, and property management services. 8.2, 8.3.6

- A family of **Remedies** or **Compliance** Directives, one for each procurement directive, which are intended to provide means of redress for those firms who believe that they have been wrongfully excluded from the award of a contract. 7.6, 8.2.8, 8.3.7

There are some differences between the Directives in the precise rules, but the same basic principles apply.

Public bodies

1.5.3 The public procurement directives apply to public bodies. In much of the EC, it is clear what a public body is. In the UK this is more difficult as there is no body of public law. Public bodies are central and local government and bodies which draw the majority of their finance from or are controlled by public bodies. This means, for example, that universities are regarded as being public bodies. The Directives also apply to private bodies that derive funding from public sources. Certain types of contract are excluded from their scope, including those concerning security. 7.1.3

Procurement procedures

1.5.4 Public bodies can seek suppliers by one of three means. 7.2.1, 8.1.3.1, 8.3.3

- *Open procedures*, under which any interested supplier may tender,
- *Restricted procedures*, under which those suppliers invited to tender can do so,
- *Negotiated procedures*, under which the authority deals directly with a supplier. This can only be done under certain very limited circumstances, for example, if there are no appropriate tenders, or when the work can only be carried out by a particular contractor for artistic reasons, or for reasons of extreme urgency brought about by unforeseen events, such as flood damage. 7.2.2

Technical specifications

1.5.5 There are requirements concerning the use of technical specifications and these apply to all contracts, including those that are too small for the contracting authority to be required to follow the advertising rules. Where possible, technical specifications are to be by reference to *European standards*. Departure from these is permitted only under certain limited circumstances, such as the innovatory nature of the product or where their use would oblige a contracting authority to acquire products that are incompatible with those already in use. In the latter case, there must be a clearly defined and documented strategy to bring this situation to an end. In the absence of European specifications, there is a hierarchy of alternatives set out in order of preference in the Directives. Trademarks can be used only where there is no alternative and must be qualified by the expression 'or equivalent'. Thus, it is intended that the New Approach directives will generate the standards to be used in public procurement. 7.3

Thresholds

1.5.6 The Directives lay down rules as to how the larger contracts are to be advertised so that there is fair and open competition. The contracts affected are:

- Public works ≥ 5 million ECU 7.1.3.1
- Public supplies ≥ central government 130,000 ECU, local government 200,000 ECU 8.1.2.1, 8.3.2
- Services ≥ 200,000 ECU, except for architecture, where the proposed Directive will apply to public works affected by the **Public Works Directive**. 8.2.3

There are rules concerning how contracts are to be valued and concerning the division of contracts into lots. The Directives provide for certain notices to be issued advertising contracts, for the advertising of them in the *Official Journal*, and the minimum time periods that must be allowed to elapse between advertisements and the final acceptance of bids. All these are intended to provide for a level playing field. 8.1.2.2, 7.1.3.2, 8.3.4, 7.4.1, 7.4.2,

Award procedures

1.5.7 Contracts can be awarded on the basis of: 7.5.2, 8.3.5

- lowest price, *or*,
- most economically advantageous bid.

If the latter is to be used, this must be stated in the advertisements and the criteria for judging economic advantage disclosed in the rank order in which they are to be applied. The authority cannot decide to use this basis only once the bids are received or to decide the criteria in the light of the bids.

Economic and technical references

1.5.8 The Directives lay down the references that may be sought from suppliers. These fall into two categories.

- *Economic and financial*. There are few restrictions on the information that may be sought. This includes bankers' references and extracts from accounts. 7.5.2
- *Technical references*. Only certain types of information can be sought, e.g. educational and professional qualifications, works carried out, plant and tools, technical support. The precise information that can be sought differs between the **Public Works Directive** and the **Public Supplies Directive**, with the latter being more explicit about the information that can be asked for about quality management. References under the former include educational and professional qualifications and the technical support available to a contractor. The **Public Supplies Directive** states that it is permitted to ask questions about quality control, the competence of technicians responsible for quality control, and about certification bodies. Under the proposed **Public Services Directive**, contracting authorities can require the production of certificates drawn up by independent bodies conforming to the **EN 45000** series of standards attesting to the conformity of a contractor's quality system to the **EN 29000** series (BS 5750). Utilities can require contractors to obtain certification from third parties. 7.5.3 8.1.4 8.2.6

Approved lists can still be kept but cannot be used to exclude firms who also meet the criteria for a contract. Contractors can be excluded from the award of a contract for various reasons, including insolvency, the failure to pay taxes, or professional misconduct. 7.5.3.1

Remedies Directives

1.5.9 The **Compliance Directive for Public Works and Supplies** requires Member States to set up procedures so 7.6

that decisions on the award of public contracts can be reviewed rapidly. They must be open to any person with an interest in obtaining a contract who has been, or risks being, harmed by an alleged infringement. The review procedures must include the power to take interim measures, the ability to set aside unlawful decisions, and the power to award damages. The review procedures do not have to result in the automatic suspension of a contract award. In the UK action is to be taken by a supplier before the High Court, but only after the contracting authority has been informed of the complaint. The court can suspend the contract, set aside the award, or award damages but, once a contract has been entered into, it can only award damages. The Commission can intervene where it believes there to have been an infringement of Community provisions. Member States are obliged to provide it with an annual report on their review procedures and a report every two years on the contract awarded.

European and harmonized European standards

1.5.10 The directives contain the requirement to use *European standards* where possible. The standards produced by CEN and CENELEC under mandate from the Commission as a result of the New Approach directives are *harmonized European standards*. Difficulty has arisen as to whether the requirement to use European standards should be interpreted to mean a requirement to use harmonized European standards. Until the latter have been drafted, it will not be clear what their scope will be. In principle, they could be restricted to covering just the essential requirements. For construction products, this would mean that many valued attributes would not form part of the harmonized standards. Under such circumstances, it is difficult to see how a public body could achieve value for money in its purchases. A further complication is caused by Article 6 (1) of the **Construction Products Directive**. This requires Member States to take steps to ensure that public bodies, private bodies acting as public undertakings, and private bodies acting as public ones by virtue of their monopoly position do not by rules or conditions impede free trade in products that comply with the Directive. This would appear to indicate that they ought to use harmonized European standards in their specifications since products that comply with these will satisfy this Directive. The Directive will also lay down levels of quality assurance by determining the attestation of conformity procedures that particular products must satisfy. If a public body sets a higher level of assurance, can it be said to be impeding the free mobility of products that satisfy the Directive? If the answer is yes, governments, like that in the UK, will not be able to support the adoption of quality management by the construction industry by discriminating in their purchasing in favour of firms who have quality management systems. The **Construction Products Directive** is the only New Approach directive to contain such an article, so the problem only arises with respect to products that fall within its scope.

7.3.1.3

7.7.3

There are no definitive answers as to whether Article 6 (1) prevents public bodies from using standards other than European ones or setting levels of quality assurance other than those prescribed by the attestation of conformity procedures.

1.6 EC POLICY TOWARDS QUALITY MANAGEMENT

UK quality management policy

1.6.1 Since the 1982 White Paper, *Standards, Quality and International Competitiveness*[2], the UK has developed a quality infrastructure with the following features:

- The use of **EN 29000** series (BS 5750) as the standard for assessment of quality management systems,
- Third-party certification of quality management systems by independent certification bodies,
- The accreditation of certification bodies engaged in product approvals, product conformity assessment, quality management system assessment, and the assessment of personnel engaged in quality management system assessment by the National Accreditation Council for Certification Bodies (NACCB),
- The accreditation of testing laboratories and calibration laboratories by the National Measurement Accreditation Service (NAMAS),
- The use of the **EN 45000** series of standards for the assessment and operations of certification bodies and testing laboratories.

EC quality management policy

1.6.2 Unlike the UK government, the EC has not until recently had a clear policy towards quality management. Instead, there have been a series of contradictory changes in policy. For example, the Council Resolution establishing the **New Approach to Technical Harmonization and Standards** in 1985 stated that national bodies authorized to issue marks or certificates of conformity (i.e. approved or notified bodies) should carry out their duties in accordance with ISO Guides. The Commission's initial proposal for a **Construction Products Directive**[3] implied that the appointment of approved bodies would follow the corresponding ISO Guide, according to whether they were inspection, certification, or testing bodies. These provisions were replaced in the final version of the Directive, adopted in 1988, by criteria for approved bodies taken from the **Toy Safety Directive**, which make no reference to the ISO Guides. It also included a requirement for manufacturers to adopt 'factory production control' as part of the procedures for attestation of conformity. Although the Directive defined this as being 'the permanent internal control of production exercised by the manufacturer' and talked of the elements being 'documented in a systematic manner', with the documentation ensuring 'a common understanding of quality assurance', it stopped short of adopting **EN 29002** as the definition of factory production control. However, in the

2.3.3.2

3.9.2

Resolution in 1989 on a **Global Approach to Conformity Assessment**, the Council adopted as guiding principles the use of the **EN 29000** series of standards on quality assurance and of the **EN 45000** series of standards for specified bodies working in conformity assessment. The latter are the equivalent of the ISO Guides. The current policy can be interpreted as being supportive of quality management, subject to the qualification that quality management should not be used to the disadvantage of those Member States whose quality infrastructures are not as well developed as others. Since then, guidance papers produced by the Standing Committee for Construction on the implementation of the **Construction Products Directive** have defined factory production control so that it is closely related to **EN 29002** and aligned the criteria for approved bodies more closely with the **EN 45000** series of standards. However, it should be noted that these papers have no legal status and are merely a consensus view as to how the Directive should be interpreted.

2.3.3.3

Table 4

3.11.3-
3.11.4,
Table 5

Impact of EC quality management policy

1.6.3 EC policy on quality management affects export opportunities for British goods and the market for imports into the UK through the creation of a Single Internal Market free from tariff and non-tariff barriers to trade. *The primary impact of EC policy, though, is on how British goods are traded in the British market by determining the minimum legal conditions under which they can be placed on the market.* These include the technical specifications that they must satisfy and, through attestation of conformity provisions, the minimum level of quality assurance. Thus, for those products that fall within the scope of a New Approach directive, the law sets out minimum standards that must be satisfied and minimum levels of quality assurance. There is an important contrast between present EC policy on product approval and that which has traditionally been pursued in the UK. The EC system is a more regulated one than that to which manufacturers in the UK have been used. While such a change is likely to present few problems for those firms who have adopted the disciplines of a quality management system, it represents a fundamental shift in attitudes for those firms who have not.

1.6.4 It is open to a manufacturer to accept voluntarily more onerous requirements than the directives require. Thus, there is no reason why a manufacturer should not have a quality management system that provides a level of assurance in excess of the minimum required under EC law. Where a directive requires there to be a quality management system that is less onerous than the requirements of the **EN 29000** series, a manufacturer may still adopt a system that satisfies this standard if desired. A directive may not require third-party product testing or third-party certification of the quality management system as part of its attestation of conformity provisions, but this does not prevent a manufacturer adopting these if desired.

1.6.5 The situation described in this publication is far from complete. Even if no new policies are added, it will be many years before all the elements required for a fully operational system, for example European standards, are in place. As implementation takes place, so the policies evolve and, sometimes, change. Moreover, the history of the EC provides examples of where harmonization or the development of common policies has produced a situation that has led to further harmonization. The EC Treaty provides an on-going imperative towards further integration in order to satisfy its political aspirations. One possible area where this could occur is in the technical harmonization of construction products. This has largely been concerned with the means by which products are approved so that they can be placed on the market throughout the EC. Thus, it has been concerned with the removal of barriers to entry into a market. It has not primarily been concerned with the use of construction products. A product may gain entry into a market but still not be sold because of barriers to its use. It seems quite possible that the EC will, in the future, take measures to harmonize the regulations and practices that govern the use of construction products. Such measures would have direct consequences for the quality management systems of designers and construction firms. However, this has not happened yet.

1.7 IMPACT ON THE CONSTRUCTION PROCESS

Impact on different stages of the construction process

1.7.1 Different policies impact on different stages of the construction process.

- *Decision to build.* Only one of the measures has a direct effect on the client. The proposed **Temporary or Mobile Construction Sites Directive** makes the client responsible for sending the authorities prior notice if the planned duration of works is to be at least 30 days. There are indirect effects in that the client is ultimately responsible for ensuring that the design of the construction works is fit for its intended use. For example, if the building is to be a workplace, then the client needs to ensure that it is so designed as to satisfy the requirements of the **Workplace Directive**, since, if it does not, no tenant will be found for it.

  5.1.2
  3.1.6

- *Design and specification.* Various of the New Approach directives have implications for those responsible for specification. These directives contain essential requirements, provisions for the drafting of harmonized standards, and procedures for the attestation of conformity of products. Designers must be familiar with these if they are to ensure that their specifications are fit for their intended purpose. Designs must be compatible with the products available. The **Construction Products Directive** with its category A standards and the **Workplace Directive** are likely to result in design standards. The proposed **Temporary or Mobile Construction Sites Directive** requires health and safety issues to be taken into account when making architectural and organizational decisions in the

  3.6.2, 3.16.3
  5.1.2

planning of projects. The proposed **Public Services Directive** will set the rules under which public bodies may obtain design and cost planning services. 8.2

- *Appointment of contractor and management of the contract.* The **Public Works** and **Utilities Directives** contain rules that govern the appointment of contractors and also certain management issues that may arise in a contract, for example, whether the contractor should be employed to carry out additional works that have become necessary. These apply to public sector clients, including utilities companies in private ownership. 7.0-7.5, 8.3

- *Procurement.* The New Approach directives are concerned with the minimum requirements that products must satisfy in order to be placed upon the market. Those concerned with procurement must ensure that the products obtained comply with the designers' specifications and are fit for their intended purpose. 3.0-3.12, 4.1, 4.2, 4.3 They must therefore be familiar with the essential requirements, European technical specifications, and attestation of conformity procedures. Similarly, those 5.2, 5.3 responsible for the procurement of machinery and personal protective equipment must ensure that it is fit for the purpose. The **Workplace Directive** provides 3.16 guidance as to what products may be regarded as being fit in certain situations. The **Public Supplies** and **Utilities Directives** contain the rules that govern the 7.0-7.5, 8.3 procurement of goods by the public sector and privately owned utilities.

- *Construction/installation/assembly.* The New Approach 3.0-3.12, directives contain essential requirements that are to be 4.1, 4.2, 4.3 satisfied when the product is properly installed or the equipment or apparatus is taken into service. This implies that those responsible for construction, installation or assembly will take steps to ensure that this is done. They are responsible for the safe use of the machinery and personal protective equipment that 5.2, 5.3 their employees are required to use and for the safe organization of construction work and the construction 5.1 site.

- *Inspection and acceptance.* The **Electromagnetic** 4.2.4, 4.3.5 **Compatibility** and **Machinery Directives** require that apparatus or machinery is not taken into service until it satisfies the essential requirements. This would appear to necessitate inspection of whether this is the case and a decision on their acceptance. The **Simple Pressure Vessels Directive** requires there to be safety clearance before pressure vessels are brought into service, but it is not yet clear whether there will be similar 3.3 requirements for machinery or electrical apparatus. The **Construction Products Directive** requires that construction products should enable construction works to satisfy the essential requirements. This raises the question of whether the products are being used in their proper context. All the New Approach directives have 3.8-3.11, attestation of conformity procedures that involve some 4.1.5, 4.2.4, form of implicit or explicit inspection and acceptance, either by the manufacturer or else by a third party, such as an approved or notified body. 4.3.5, 5.2.4, 5.3.3

- *Operational management and maintenance.* The construction works continue to require management and maintenance after those responsible for their initial construction have handed them over. The New Approach directives talk in terms of the products satisfying the essential requirements subject to normal maintenance. This would appear to imply maintenance requirements. The **Workplace Directive** has requirements concerning the maintenance of workplaces. The **Personal Protective Equipment** and **Machinery Directives** affect the equipment used by maintenance operatives. The proposed **Public Services Directive** contains rules by which public bodies may place maintenance contracts. 3.16 5.2, 5.3 8.2

Impact on quality management systems of designers, contractors and clients

1.7.2 None of the legislation discussed in this publication obliges designers, those involved in construction, assembly, or installation, those responsible for property development or property management, or public bodies who procure construction works or construction services to introduce a quality management system. The decision whether or not to adopt quality management, and, if so, whether to seek certification, remains a voluntary one, just as it has been under the policies pursued by the UK government. Organizations active in these areas will continue to decide whether to adopt quality management or not on the basis of their perception of their own best interests. Factors such as marketing advantages, the potential for cost savings, and pressure from purchasers, will continue to influence this decision. However, the legislation does introduce new and potentially onerous requirements, for example in the areas of health and safety and public procurement procedures. There are penalties for failing to comply with these. The question that these groups should address is whether they need to have a quality management system so that they are better able to meet such obligations and to avoid potential penalties. It is not mandatory for them to do so but they may find it to be the most appropriate response to new obligations. For example, it is difficult to see how employers can hope to meet their obligations under the **Health and Safety at Work directives** without introducing documented systems to plan for the avoidance of risks to their workers, to ensure the effectiveness of their actions, and to monitor and review their activities. In so doing they will put in place systems that have many similarities in philosophy and practice to quality management systems. As there are no legislative requirements on the groups identified in this section to adopt quality management, there are no obligations for their quality management systems to follow any particular form. However, as the legislation has implications for the way in which they carry out their activities, this must feed back into their quality management systems.

Impact on quality management systems of manufacturers

1.7.3 For manufacturers of construction products the situation is different. The New Approach directives set out what must be done before products can be placed upon the market. In some cases, such as the **Construction Products** and **Gas Appliances Directives**, the Directives require manufacturers to adopt quality management systems. In others, such as the **Electromagnetic Compatibility Directive**, it is difficult to see how the obligations laid on them could be met without there being an effective quality management systems. There is no obligation on a manufacturer to adopt a quality system that satisfies the relevant part of the **EN 29000** series (BS 5750), though this is deemed to satisfy the requirements. However, the systems specified, in some cases, come very close to having much the same requirements. Some of the guidance documents interpreting legislation such as the **Construction Products Directive** set out what the quality manual should contain and, thus, what the operating procedures should address. There is nothing in the New Approach directives adopted to date that will prevent a manufacturer from voluntarily adopting a higher level of quality assurance than that specified for his product. Thus, a manufacturer could, if so desired, seek a BSI kitemark for the product when, for example, it is legally permissible for a product to be placed on the market on the basis of a manufacturer's declaration of conformity with the requisite technical specifications.

3.9, 4.1.5

4.2.4

Impact on quality management systems of monitoring bodies

1.7.4 For those monitoring bodies who are designated as approved or notified bodies for attestation of conformity under one of the New Approach directives, there is the expectation that they will usually satisfy the requirements of the appropriate standard in the **EN 45000** series, which means that they must have a quality system. Although the criteria adopted in the directives makes no mention of the **EN 45000** series, this is the logical conclusion from the **Global Approach Resolution** and is the line that tends to be taken in guidance documents. The British government has stated that it expects the bodies it designates to be NAMAS or NACCB accredited.

2.3.3.3, 3.11

1.8 IMPACT ON THE UK'S QUALITY INFRASTRUCTURE

1.8.1 The construction industry generally shares the quality management infrastructure with other industries. There are certain exceptions to this, principally the system by which innovatory construction products are approved. The construction industry is therefore affected by policies which are not just concerned with it but industry as a whole. The UK's system of quality management is built around the principles of the certification of producers and the accreditation of certification bodies and testing laboratories. The value of any assurance given to the purchaser that quality is being achieved is enhanced if the claims made are subject to verification by an independent third party. The credibility of the third parties is assured if they are also subject to independent assessment by government-backed accreditation bodies.

Impact on NAMAS

1.8.2 The accreditation activities of the National Measurement Accreditation Service accord with the principles set out in the **Global Approach Resolution** so that the laboratories that it accredits generally satisfy the requirements of the directives. No major changes in its operations are therefore likely to be necessary as a result of EC policy. Greater attention, though, will have to be paid to the question of the amount of professional indemnity insurance that laboratories should carry.

Impact on NACCB

1.8.3 The NACCB accredits certification bodies concerned with product approval, product conformity assessment, quality management system assessment, and the assessment of personnel engaged in quality management system assessment. The EC has yet to develop policies concerning personnel involved in quality management system assessment. These are indirectly touched upon in the directives concerned with the mutual recognition of qualifications and in the criteria for the selection of notified or approved bodies. It is an obvious step to move from determining the criteria for approved or notified bodies to defining what is meant by the technical competence of the persons who work for them, but it has yet to be taken. It would appear that NACCB practices with respect to the accreditation of certification bodies engaged in quality management system assessment and product conformity assessment largely meet the requirements of the directives for approved or notified bodies. There is an issue of the amount of professional indemnity insurance a certification body should carry. The **Construction Products Directive**'s procedures for European technical approvals and the designation of approvals bodies have necessitated NACCB developing its accreditation procedures for product approvals bodies. In due course, the government will be able to designate private bodies as European technical approvals bodies in addition to the British Board of Agrément. The **Construction Products Directive** makes reference to a type of approved body called an inspection body. The UK does not currently have a scheme for the accreditation of inspection bodies that is distinct from that for certification bodies.

1.8.4 The general conclusion is that, since 1982, the UK has largely developed the quality infrastructure necessary to ensure compliance with the directives issued under the New Approach to Technical Harmonization and Standards. Relatively little of this infrastructure requires major modification to meet the requirements of the directives. There is no reason why this infrastructure should not continue to be used on a voluntary basis where there is a commercial need as well as for regulatory work under EC legislation.

1.9 FURTHER READING

As this publication concentrates on a few limited aspects of EC policies, it is suggested that the reader who is interested in a wider perspective consults two other publications:

- Cecchini, P., Catinat, M. and Jacquemin, A., *The European Challenge: 1992 – The Benefits of a Single Market*, Gower, 1988, discusses the Single Internal Market programme and summarizes the research undertaken by the Commission into its potential benefits.

- Spencer Chapman, N.F. and Grandjean, C., *The Construction Industry and the European Community*, BSP Professional Books, 1991, examines how a wide range of EC policies affect the construction industry and explains how a number of EC institutions function.

References: 1 Overview

1. Department of the Environment, *Euronews Construction*, No. 18, May 1992.

2. *Standards, Quality and International Competitiveness*, Cmnd 8621, 1982.

3. Proposal for a Council Directive on the approximation of the laws, regulations and administrative provisions of the Member States relating to construction products, COM(86) 756 final, 8 January 1987.

Part B Technical harmonization

2 Technical harmonization and standards policy in the EC

2.0 OVERVIEW

2.0.1 Technical harmonization has been an aim of the EC since its creation. Differences in national standards and the failure to recognize other countries' tests and certificates as equivalent to one's own can act as barriers to trade. Manufacturers have to meet additional cost and suffer delays before their products can be sold in other markets within the EC. Domestic suppliers are protected from foreign competition as a result. The process of technical harmonization has been a slow one, with relatively few directives having been adopted before 1985. Each directive required the minutiae of standards and tests to be drafted and unanimity was required for them to be adopted. The Low Voltage Directive of 1973 offered an alternative approach by delegating the drafting of the standards needed for harmonization to expert groups. At the time, it did not lead to a change in harmonization policy but, more recently, it has provided the model that has been followed.

2.0.2 In 1979, a European Court ruling in the Cassis de Dijon case stated that Member States could only block the importation of goods produced lawfully in another Member State on certain limited grounds, such as the protection of the consumer. Thus, harmonization should be unnecessary to secure the removal of barriers to trade except in the limited area of lawful restrictions. In consequence, technical harmonization is now primarily concerned with issues of safety as these provide the major justification that can be put forward by a government seeking to restrict imports from elsewhere in the EC. However, the precise meaning of the term safety is a matter of debate. In particular, there is an issue as to whether it should include consumer and environmental protection.

2.0.3 In 1983, the EC took steps to prevent new barriers from being created by the drafting of new national technical regulations and standards by the adoption of a directive providing for the Commission to be notified of national standards programmes and new technical regulations. This Directive imposed a standstill on Member States producing standards in areas in which European standards are being drawn up and enables the Commission to delay and seek modifications to technical regulations that might introduce new barriers. The Directive was extended in 1988 so that Member States cannot now adopt technical regulations on subjects covered by a proposal for a directive or regulation.

2.0.4 The removal of existing barriers was the subject of a Council Resolution in 1985 which introduced a New Approach to Technical Harmonization and Standards. Technical harmonization directives produced under this resolution follow a common format. They are concerned with safety and define essential safety requirements that products must satisfy before being placed on the market. Conformity with the directives may be demonstrated by compliance with harmonized European standards or with national standards accepted by the Commission as embodying the essential requirements. The Commission mandates the European standardization bodies CEN and CENELEC to draft the necessary standards. Manufacturers demonstrate that their products comply with technical specifications by attesting to their conformity with them. The procedures include the certification of tests and production systems by bodies designated by Member States. Products that satisfy the requisite directives bear the CE mark and are guaranteed freedom of mobility throughout the EC. The directives put in place a framework for harmonization in a specific area, which is completed later by more detailed work. A directive can come into operation in stages as the necessary technical work is done. Qualified majority voting arrangements, put in place by the Single European Act of 1986, further speed up the process of harmonization.

2.0.5 The New Approach has resulted in the production of a number of directives including those on Construction Products, Machinery, Gas Appliances, Personal Protective Equipment, and Electromagnetic Compatibility. However, some problems have arisen with the approach. The different

directives have not adopted common procedures for the attestation of conformity or consistency in the use of the CE mark. There have also been delays in the production of harmonized standards. There has been a debate as to whether conformity attestation ought to involve the adoption by manufacturers of quality assurance systems based on the EN 29000 series (BS 5750), with procedures for the attestation of conformity being carried out by bodies accredited as working to the EN 45000 series (BS 7501, BS 7511, or BS 7512). These issues were discussed in an EC document, A Global Approach to Certification and Testing, which appeared in 1989. This has led to a Council Resolution on a Global Approach to Conformity Assessment in 1989, which supported the generalized use of the EN 29000 and EN 45000 series and a modular approach to conformity assessment. A Council Decision in December 1990 adopted a modular approach to conformity assessment. New Approach directives proposed subsequent to this measure can select appropriate modules for attestation of conformity procedures, but may not create their own. This should bring to an end the variations in procedures between directives. Regulations are expected to be produced on the use of the CE mark.

2.0.6 The Commission has also sought to encourage the mutual recognition of certification and testing in the non-regulatory sphere. The Council Resolution of 1989 on a Global Approach to Conformity Assessment adopted as a guiding principle the promotion of mutual recognition agreements in this sphere and supported the use of the EN 29000 and EN 45000 series of standards in both the regulatory and non-regulatory spheres. A European Organization for Testing and Certification was launched in 1989 to oversee and encourage mutual recognition agreements. The Commission proposed a number of changes intended to speed up the production of European standards in a Green Paper in October 1990. Although the Commission's primary interest lies in the use of standards for regulatory purposes, the proposals, if implemented, would have implications for the production of voluntary standards.

2.1 TECHNICAL HARMONIZATION DIRECTIVES

2.1.1 Introduction

2.1.1.1 The EC has had a policy of securing technical harmonization since 1968. Different national standards, technical regulations, and administrative provisions can act as barriers to trade by requiring manufacturers to seek separate approvals for their products for the different national markets. This delays imports until approval has been given and creates uncertainty for buyers and sellers. The policy of completing the Single Internal Market aims at the removal of such barriers.

2.1.1.2 The process of technical harmonization has been a slow one. Between 1969 and 1985 the EC adopted just 270 technical standards directives while, by way of comparison, DIN, the German standards body, has over 20 000 standards and produces on average 1400 standards per annum[1]. Two main reasons can be advanced for this:

- *Until the Single European Act of 1986*[2] *all decisions on EC legislation required unanimity as each Member State could apply a veto to those measures it did not support.* The amended Article 100A of the Treaty provides for the Council to act by a qualified majority on proposals from the Commission for approximations of laws, regulations, and administrative actions other than those concerned with fiscal matters, the free movement of persons, and the rights and interests of employed persons. Seventy-six votes are allocated to the Member States and 54 votes in favour constitutes a majority. France, Germany, Italy, and the UK have 10 votes each, Spain 8, Belgium, Greece, the Netherlands, and Portugal 5 each, Denmark and Eire 3 each, and Luxembourg 2. Thus, harmonization can only be blocked by a substantial dissenting minority and not by an individual Member State. The Single European Act requires the EC to adopt measures to achieve the Single Internal Market by the end of 1992 and so provides a legal impetus towards technical harmonization measures.

- *The process by which technical harmonization took place required all the details to be resolved before the legislation could be adopted.* For example, the directive on the approximation of laws relating to the classification, packaging and labelling of dangerous preparations contains seven pages showing how concentration levels for health hazards should be computed[3]. There was no process by which the framework for harmonization could be put in place with the details added later at times that vary according to the ease of the specific tasks to be undertaken. One exception occurred in the electrotechnical sector. The Low Voltage Directive of 1973[4] invoked the principle of delegation of competence to draft standards to the standards institutions and, thus, of the implemention of a directive in stages as technical drafting in each area is completed.

It became apparent that, if technical harmonization was to take place at a faster pace, then new procedures would need to be adopted to achieve this.

2.1.2 New Approach to Technical Harmonization and Standards

2.1.2.1 The EC's approach to standardization stems from the ruling in the *Cassis de Dijon* case. In 1976 a German importing firm was prevented from selling the French liqueur, Cassis de Dijon, in the Federal Republic as it had an alcohol content of only 15–20%. German law required spirits to have one of at least 32%. The European Court ruled in 1979 that this minimum alcohol restriction served no purpose in the general interest but was a quantitative restriction on imports. It concluded that there was no valid reason why goods that were lawfully produced and marketed in one Member State should not be introduced into another. The ruling suggests that Member States can only block imports produced lawfully elsewhere in the EC on the grounds of the effectiveness of fiscal supervision, the protection of public health, the fairness of commercial transactions, and the defence of the consumer[5, 6]. Thus, measures for technical harmonization are concerned with protecting the public, this being the principal valid reason why a Member State may use technical measures to control imports.

2.1.2.2 In July 1984 the Council approved a policy for standardization[7]. It supported standardization as a means to ensure that products could be freely marketed within the EC and to improve their competitiveness in both the internal and external markets. It recognized that the alternative methods adopted by Member States for protecting health and safety were equally valid, but each made use of different techniques. These can act as a barrier to trade. It set out as principles:

- That Member States should check technical regulations and withdraw those that are obsolete or unnecessary, including those that are *de facto* standards as well as those that are *de jure*.

- That there should be mutual recognition of the results of tests and the operations of certification bodies.

- That there should be an extension of Community practice in technical harmonization and an expansion of the capacity to standardize.

2.1.2.3 The July 1984 Conclusions led in May 1985 to the Council Resolution on a New Approach to Technical Harmonization and Standards[8]. This set out guidelines for technical harmonization directives and called on the Commission to give the production of technical harmonization proposals priority. The Resolution set out four principles for technical harmonization.

- That harmonization should be limited to the adoption of essential safety requirements so that products which conform to these can have freedom of movement within the EC.

- That the drawing up of technical specifications for the production and placing on the market of products conforming to the essential requirements should be entrusted to organizations competent in standardization. This means bodies that have the staff and technical infrastructure for the work, the capacity to involve interested parties in the work, and procedures by which the standards produced can be transposed into national ones. In practice, this usually means CEN and CENELEC, though other bodies could also be used. The quality of the standards are to be ensured by the standardization bodies receiving mandates for this work from the Commission and the standards being verified by a standing committee of representatives from the Member States.

- That the technical specifications are to be voluntary and not mandatory. This leaves it open for manufacturers to satisfy the essential requirements directly rather than indirectly through conformance with standards.

- That Member States must accept products that conform to harmonized standards as satisfying the essential requirements, though safeguard procedures would enable them to challenge any standards, certificates, or products that they have reason to believe do not comply with the essential requirements.

2.1.2.4 The principal justification for proposals for directives under the New Approach is that Member States have responsibility for ensuring the safety of persons, domestic animals, and property, and that national provisions for the discharge of this require harmonization in order to ensure the freedom of mobility for goods. However, the wording of the Resolution does leave open the possibility of intervention by Member States, and therefore of a need for harmonization, on other grounds as well. It states

> Member States have the responsibility of ensuring safety on their territory (in the home, at the workplace, etc.) of persons, domestic animals and goods, or the respect of other essential protection requirements in the general interest such as health, consumer or environmental protection etc., with regard to the hazards covered by the Directive itself (*).
>
> (*) For reasons of convenience and ease of drafting the rest of this document refers only to safety.

This could be taken to imply that when a New Approach directive uses the term 'safety', it also encompasses health, consumer, and environmental protection. It is believed that there are differences between Member States as to which is the more appropriate interpretation, with the UK leaning towards the view that safety does not encompass other factors.

2.1.2.5 The Resolution sets out ten main elements for these directives.

(I) The scope of the directive in terms of the products to be covered and the hazards it is intended to avert should be given.

(II) There should be a general clause that goods should be placed on the market only if they do not endanger persons, domestic animals, or property when properly installed and maintained and used for the purposes for which they are intended. Member States are prohibited from setting up their own systems of control of products prior to their being placed upon the market.

(III) Essential safety requirements are to be defined. They should be formulated so that certification bodies can certify products as conforming to the essential requirements in the absence of standards.

(IV) Products that conform with the essential requirements are to have freedom of mobility within the EC.

(V) Member States are to presume conformity with the essential requirements where a product satisfies a harmonized European standard or, on an interim basis, a national standard accepted by the Commission as conforming to the essential requirements.

(VI) The Commission is to manage the list of standards accepted as conforming to the essential requirements. The advice of the Standing Committee (see (IX) and (X) below) is sought where the Commission or a Member State has reason to believe that a standard may not conform.

(VII) Under a safeguard clause, Member States can take action against products they have reason to believe may compromise safety, even if the products have followed the requisite procedures for attestation laid down in a directive. Action can be because of deficiencies in a standard, non-conformance with a standard, or the incorrect application of a standard.

(VIII) The means by which the conformity of products with the essential requirements may be demonstrated are to be identified. These include third-party tests and certificates and declaration of conformity by a manufacturer, with or without third-party surveillance. Member States are to notify the Commission of the bodies authorized to issue marks or certificates of conformity. These bodies must carry out their duties in accordance with international practices and principles, especially ISO Guides.

(IX) A Standing Committee of representatives of the Member States and chaired by the Commission is to be set up.

(X) The Standing Committee is to advise on standards and the implementation of the directive. In most cases, the Standing Committee to be used is that set up under the Directive 83/189/EEC[9], which is discussed in Section 2.2.2.2 below.

2.1.2.6 In practice, there have been some variations from these principles in individual directives. For example, the essential requirements for construction works in the Construction Products Directive[10] are not sufficiently precise to enable conformance with them to be assessed, resulting in the creation of a body of documents, the interpretative documents, which give concrete form to them. The Construction Products Directive has its own Standing Committee for Construction. The Machinery and Personal Protective Equipment Directives[11, 12] make use of the Standing Committee set up under 83/189/EEC for advising the Commission on standards, but have also established a joint standing committee to advise on their implementation. Some of the more recent New Approach directives, such as the Machinery Directive, include transitional periods during which products can be placed on the market if they comply with national provisions in place on the implementation date. The earlier ones, such as the Construction Products Directive, have no formal transitional period but, in this case, the Directive has special provisions that apply in the absence of harmonized technical specifications.

2.1.2.7 Construction has been seen by the Commission as a priority area for this New Approach since there are large numbers of national standards but few European ones. Standardization has also been seen as a means of combating growing import penetration into the EC. BIPE *et al.*[13] have suggested that the removal of trade barriers in construction products could reduce costs by up to 4% and result in an increase in production of between 2.5 and 10%. However, they have argued that regulations concerned with building processes cause more barriers to trade than those dealing with building products. The technical harmonization directives have been primarily concerned with the latter.

2.1.3 The implementation of the New Approach

A series of New Approach directives has been proposed or adopted since the Resolution was passed. Those that particularly affect the construction industry are the Construction Products, Gas Appliances, Electromagnetic Compatibility, Machinery (including the amendments concerned with mobile machinery and lifting equipment), and Personal Protective Equipment Directives. The main problems to have arisen to date with the approach are:

- Length of time taken for the directives to be fully implemented,
- Differences between directives in the procedures adopted for attestation of conformity,
- Differences between directives in the rules for the use of the CE mark to indicate conformity with essential requirements.

These issues are examined below and the ways in which the EC has sought to deal with them are discussed. It is believed that a fourth problem is emerging, namely the differences in the ways in which the directives are brought into force by the Member States. There are areas of each directive which are left to Member States to determine, for example, how to police the use of the CE mark. Thus, for example, it is quite possible for different Member States to create different offences or for similar offences to be subject to different punishments. Distortions in trade could arise if manufacturers exploit such differences. Whether this problem is a significant one will only become apparent as the Member States bring the directives into force.

2.2 ORGANIZATION OF STANDARDIZATION WORK

2.2.1 Introduction

2.2.1.1 New Approach directives lay down the essential requirements, the ways in which conformity with these can be demonstrated, and the procedures for attesting to a product's conformity. The production of harmonized standards is delegated to CEN and CENELEC, while Member States are responsible for establishing procedures for policing the market, for the selection of approved or notified bodies, and communicating to the Commission those national standards that they believe comply with the essential requirements. The preparation of mandates for the production of harmonized standards, the drafting of the standards, and the interpretation of aspects of the directives, such as the activities approved bodies are actually to carry out, inevitably takes time and resources. In addition, manufacturers may have to redesign products to comply with the new standards and will have to follow the new procedures for attestation of conformity. The evidence indicates that the EC is experiencing problems in completing all the requirements stemming from New Approach directives within their original timescales. The Commission has recognized the need to accelerate the delivery of European standards and has noted that the 'demand for European standards is outstripping supply'[14].

2.2.1.2 This section examines how work on standardization is organized within the EC. Much of the work undertaken by the standards bodies, to which the drafting of harmonized standards for regulatory purposes is delegated, is undertaken by volunteers. Most of their work takes the form of drafting standards, for which their members see a useful role in the market place, and which may be used by manufacturers and specifiers on a voluntary basis. Although the standards bodies have the necessary technical expertise and experience of drafting standards to fulfil the function of drawing up mandatory standards, the grafting of this process on to their other functions raises a number of questions. These include:

- Whether it is appropriate to assign to volunteers what are, in effect, delegated legislative powers, even though the draft standards they produce are subject to review by a legislative body, the Council.

- Whether the working practices of these bodies can be adapted to satisfy the requirements of a legislative timetable.

- What the relationship should be between mandatory and voluntary standards and, in particular, whether both elements can coexist within the same standard, or whether the mandatory elements must be in a separate standard.

2.2.1.3 The directives drawn up to complete the Single Internal Market have left an element of ambiguity in the terminology they employ with respect to European standards and, thus, the precise function of mandatory and voluntary standards. The New Approach directives refer to *harmonized European standards*, namely standards drawn up under mandate from the Commission. The public procurement directives require public bodies to make use of European specifications where possible in procurement, which include standards drawn up by the European standards bodies on a voluntary basis, that is, *European standards*. The UK regulations implementing the Public Works and Public Supplies Directives also follow this terminology and so require public bodies to make use of European specifications which include European standards rather than exclusively harmonized European standards[15, 16]. The issue is further complicated by Article 6 (1) of the Construction

Products Directive, which requires Member States to ensure that the free movement of products that satisfy the Directive shall not be impeded by rules or conditions imposed by public bodies or private bodies acting as a public undertaking or acting as a public body on the basis of a monopoly position. Compliance with the Construction Products Directive can be by conforming to harmonized European standards. If these are narrowly concerned with the six essential requirements (see Section 3.3) and if public bodies must make use of these rather than European standards, it is difficult to see how they will be able to secure value for money in their purchasing, since their requirements go into areas that are not the subject of the essential requirements.

2.2.2 Interchange of information on standards and regulations

2.2.2.1 One way in which the use of technical standards and regulations can be prevented from acting as a barrier to trade is for Member States to be obliged to notify the Commission of the standards and regulations they introduce and for the Commission to be able to prevent the introduction of any that are likely to be discriminatory. This is the intention of the Directive on the Provision of Information in the Field of Technical Standards and Regulations[17]. The Directive provides for the Commission, CEN and CENELEC, and the national standards institutions of the Member States to be notified of the standards programmes of the national standards institutions. The current UK institutions designated for this purpose are BSI and the British Electrotechnical Committee (BEC)[18]. The Commission is to receive draft standards, other than those that transpose European or international standards into national ones. Member States must also communicate to the Commission any draft technical regulations and a statement of the grounds that makes their introduction necessary. They are to take into account the comments of the Commission and other Member States on their drafts, the introduction of which can be delayed if the Commission or a Member State produces a detailed opinion that a measure creates barriers to trade.

2.2.2.2 The Directive established a Standing Committee, composed of representatives of the Member States and chaired by the Commission, to advise the Commission on standards and the system by which there is interchange of information on standards and standards programmes. It can propose that the Commission requests that the European standards institutions draw up a European standard. Since 1988, its terms of reference have included identifying where harmonization appears necessary and, in certain circumstances, the undertaking of harmonization measures[17]. The Committee is consulted by the Commission on requests to the standards institutions to draw up harmonized standards. It plays an important role under most of the directives produced under the New Approach to technical harmonization in advising the Commission on matters concerning standards, particularly whether harmonized standards satisfy the essential requirements for health and safety contained in these directives. The exception is the Construction Products Directive, which has its own Standing Committee for Construction that performs this role, though the Standing Committee continues to monitor the overall position.

2.2.2.3 The Directive introduced a standstill procedure on the drafting and amending of national standards. Member States must ensure that their standards institutions do not draw up or introduce standards in areas in which a European standard is being drafted. Since 1988 they have also been obliged to refrain from adopting technical regulations on subjects covered by a proposal made to the Council for a directive or a regulation. Thus, the Directive provides a means by which the creation of new barriers to trade resulting from standards and technical regulations can be prevented by ensuring that all interested parties are informed of the work being undertaken in this area and by providing a means by which such measures can be delayed or modified. Unfortunately, the system has not always worked effectively as information about national standards activity has 'often been incomplete, tardy and unclear'[18].

2.2.3 Role of CEN and CENELEC in standardization work

2.2.3.1 The Comité Européen de Normalization (CEN) was set up in 1960 by the EC and EFTA to promote standardization at a regional level. It comprises the national standards bodies of each of the EC and EFTA countries. CENELEC was set up in 1972 with similar responsibilities with respect to the electrotechnical field. They now have common rules. CEN manages the European Committee for Iron and Steel Standardization (ECISS), which is funded by the European Steel and

Coal Community (one of the EC's three Communities), to carry out standards work for iron and steel.

2.2.3.2 In 1984 the Commission reached an agreement with CEN and CENELEC over the future conduct of standardization work and their role within it[19]. While the Commission reserved the right not to make use of these bodies, it undertook to:

- Use European standards in technical harmonization,
- Mandate and finance CEN and CENELEC to undertake standardization work relating to harmonization and not to draw up technical specifications in areas in which they were working,
- Disseminate European standards and to use them in its own tendering arrangements,
- Seek the opinion of CEN and CENELEC on standardization issues.

For their part CEN and CENELEC undertook to:

- Maintain a standards infrastructure,
- Permit the Commission to participate in technical committees,
- Involve interested parties in standardization work,
- Unify their voting procedures for the adoption of standards,
- Ensure that European standards are transposed into national ones.

The last undertaking has involved the introduction of a standstill agreement so that their members will not introduce new standards in areas in which CEN and CENELEC are working and to withdraw and refrain from the introduction of divergent national standards so as to ensure that the national standards bodies do not pre-empt the introduction of European standards.

2.2.4 Working methods of CEN and CENELEC

2.2.4.1 The European Standards bodies produce three types of standards document[20]:

EN European standards that are transposed into identically worded national standards,

HD Harmonization documents that are transposed into national standards, which are worded differently between countries, but have a similar effect,

ENV European pre-standards or drafts used as prospective standards experimentally for an initial period of up to three years.

The prefix 'pr' before the documents mean that they are awaiting formal voting. The outcome of a standardization mandate from the Commission should be the production of an EN or HD that conforms with the essential requirements of a directive.

2.2.4.2 The CEN standards programme is controlled by the Technical Board comprising members of the national standards bodies. Programming committees coordinate and plan standardization activities in a sector. Technical committees (TCs) are formed by the Technical Board to prepare standards when there are no acceptable international standards but a demand for them exists, or in response to a mandate from either the Commission or the EFTA secretariat. Their terms of reference include target dates for critical stages in the project. The chairman is expected to guide the committee towards a consensus and the secretary ensures that the committee functions efficiently. The secretariat of a technical committee has a good deal of control over the functioning of the committee and the eventual outcome of the project, and so is sought after. The three major standards organizations, DIN (Germany), AFNOR (France), and BSI (UK), have been dominant in gaining appointment as secretaries of technical committees. Much of the work of technical committees is done by subcommittees, with participation by the Commission and experts. Correspondence rather than meetings are used where possible. Working groups are set up for specific short-term tasks and undertake much of the work in producing drafts of standards. The link with interested parties in each Member State is through the national standards body, such as the British Standards Institution.

2.2.4.3 The Technical Board is able to establish the degree of standardization in a particular area before work commences on standardization by means of the questionnaire procedure. The questionnaire has the effect of initiating CEN's standstill agreement, though this can also be done by the first meeting of a technical committee. Under this agreement, members do not publish new or revised standards that are not in line with an EN or HD, or one in preparation, or take any other action that could prejudice harmonization, though they may circulate drafts of their own standards for comment.

2.2.4.4 Technical Committees seek to reach a consensus on issues and there is a voting procedure. This includes weighting the votes of Member States. The votes of EC countries are weighted in conformity with the Single European Act. If the minimum conditions for acceptance of a draft standard are not achieved, then the EC votes are counted separately. The minimum conditions for acceptance are:

- a simple majority of members in favour, *plus*
- at least 25 affirmative weighted votes, *plus*
- at most 22 negative weighted votes, *plus*
- at most 3 members voting negatively.

If two of the UK, France, Italy, and Germany and one other state (other than Luxembourg) vote against, the proposition is lost on negative weighted votes, hence the need for consensus for progress. Conditional voting is not permissible. Once a standard has been passed, members must give the EN the status of a national standard and withdraw any conflicting ones. It should be noted that the majority voting conditions in CEN and CENELEC are more restrictive than qualified majority voting under the Single European Act. The Commission has asked unsuccessfully for this to be removed(14).

2.2.4.5 There have been criticisms of the European standards bodies from some quarters. BSRIA has identified a number of weaknesses with the system(21). Other than the input of staff members of the national standards bodies, it is dependent upon voluntary inputs, with all that is implied about who is able to participate and how representative they may be. Input into the process comes through the national member, so the effectiveness of a country's contribution depends upon the efficiency and zeal with which its national standards body functions. Decisions may be the result of procedural manipulation and attempts to achieve consensus are subject to reversals of decisions as they are reviewed by more senior persons in each country.

2.2.5 The Commission's Green Paper on Standardization

2.2.5.1 The Commission's concern at the slow pace at which standards were being produced resulted in a Green Paper in October 1990(14). This was primarily concerned with the production of standards, though one of the reasons for the slow pace is the delay in giving mandates to CEN and CENELEC. The Commission argued that European standardization should be given a higher priority, especially by industry, which, it argued, should provide more funding for the standardization bodies, be willing to suggest priorities, and release experts for standardization work. It is largely concerned with the role of European standards in support of the technical harmonization directives produced under the New Approach rather than with the use of standards in the voluntary sphere or with the mutual recognition of testing and certification between Member States.

2.2.5.2 A number of changes were proposed to the ways in which standards are produced.

- There could be changes in procedures in order to speed up the process. These could include the use of drafting secretariats to accelerate drafting, more systematic use of majority voting using the EC's qualified majority voting system, shorter public inquiry and comment periods, and more active encouragement of sectoral associated standards bodies. In particular, the standardization bodies could give greater priority to mandated work and to performance rather than descriptive standards.

- A new European Standardization System could be established comprising a European Standardization Council made up of major economic interest groups to determine strategic matters, a European Standardization Board of representatives of the national standards bodies to manage the system, the European standardization bodies, and the national standards bodies. The new system would be recognized in Community law by a Council Decision.

- The work and management of European standardization bodies could be opened up to interested parties, such as trade unions, consumers, and industrialists.

- Long-term stability could be ensured through a new approach to the financing of standardization work. This could include more revenue from the sale of European standards being directed to the European standardization bodies, more direct funding from industry, and a long-term commitment to the financial support of standardization by public authorities.

- Standards databases could be developed and Directive 83/189/EEC on information about standards could be reinforced to combat incomplete and late returns.

- European standards could exist in their own right without the necessity for transposition into national standards and could be identified as such in national catalogues.

2.2.5.3 The Green Paper met with a mixed response from standards bodies. The Joint Presidents' Group of CEN, CENELEC, and the European Telecommunications Standards Institute (ETSI) argued in favour of systematically increasing the efficiency with which European standards are delivered, increasing coordination on a voluntary basis, and increasing access to their work, but were opposed to a major restructuring in the short term. ETSI broadly welcomed the Green Paper proposals, with relatively few reservations, while CEN and CENELEC raised more fundamental objections. These included drawing attention to the extent to which their work lies in the voluntary rather than the mandatory sphere, whereas the Green Paper is largely concerned with the latter. They also drew attention to the importance of international standards, the need to avoid excessively bureaucratic new structures, and the importance of participation in the standards drafting process of small and medium-sized enterprises (SMEs) through input to their national standards bodies. All three bodies were opposed to a move towards greater use of majority voting rather than consensus in drafting. BSI has argued that the shortcomings in European standardization include some that are the responsibility of the Commission and questioned whether the proposals in the Green Paper would improve efficiency. It argued that it was not so much standards but different national testing and certification practices that need to be addressed if barriers to trade are to be removed(22). Thus, no consensus as to whether the Green Paper represents the appropriate way forward has yet emerged. As a result, there has been no agreement that the changes proposed in it should be introduced.

2.2.5.4 After a period of consultation, the Council produced a Resolution on the role of European standardization in the European economy(23). This reaffirmed the EC's support for the development of European standards. It reiterated previous policy on the role of the European standards organizations in technical harmonization, but argued that the public interest required there to be a partnership between them and the EC. It welcomed the steps they had taken to improve efficiency, openness, and cooperation with third countries but highlighted for further action:

- The strengthening of coordination between the European standards organizations,
- Continuing the dialogue between the European standards organizations and other interested parties, including industry,
- The need for Member States to ensure that their standards organizations comply with the rules of the European standards organizations and take effective part in their discussions.

2.3 CONFORMITY ASSESSMENT

2.3.1 The Modular Approach to Attestation of Conformity

2.3.1.1 The guidelines in the Resolution introducing the New Approach (see Section 2.1.2.4) are imprecise on the question of attestation of conformity. As a result, each directive has adopted its own approach. These are not necessarily compatible, either in terms of the terminology employed or, more importantly, the procedures. The result could be that the incompatibilities in procedures between Member States are replaced by incompatibilities between directives.

A product can only be placed on the market, and enjoy free mobility within the EC, if it satisfies the essential requirements for all appropriate directives. For example, an electrically operated garage door is a construction product, being permanently incorporated in construction works, and must satisfy the Construction Products Directive[10]. It is a piece of machinery, comprising linked parts of which at least one moves and must, therefore, satisfy the Machinery Directive[11]. It is subject to the Electromagnetic Compatibility Directive by virtue of its power source[24]. Assuming that there is an appropriate European technical specification with which it can comply for it to be demonstrated that it is in conformance with the essential requirements, it must satisfy one of the four procedures for the attestation of conformity under the Construction Products Directive (see Section 3.10). The procedure depends upon the decision of the Commission. The Directive states that the choice depends on how critical the product is for the construction works to satisfy the essential requirements and the degree of variability in the product itself. Probably this will involve a declaration of conformity by the manufacturer by the second or third possibility, i.e. the manufacturer exercising factory production control and there being initial type-testing, either by the manufacturer or an approved body. The procedures under the Electromagnetic Compatibility Directive (see Section 4.2.4) depend upon whether there has been full compliance with standards that conform to the essential requirements or not. Where there has been compliance, there has to be a declaration of conformity by the manufacturer, which is to be held at the disposal of the authorities for 10 years. If there has not been compliance, a technical construction file must be produced and held for 10 years and a competent body must certify the apparatus. Attestation of conformity under the Machinery Directive (see Section 4.3.5) also depends upon whether there has been conformance with standards that comply with the Directive. If there has been, the manufacturer has a choice of sending a technical file to a notified body or sending it to a notified body for verification that the standards have been correctly applied and the issuing of a certificate of adequacy for the file. If complying standards have not been fully applied, there must be an EC type-examination of a prototype by a notified body. The manufacturer will want to organize the process of attestation of conformity so that the requirements of the different directives can be met without retesting by different bodies. This means making use of approved or notified bodies who are designated for work under all of the relevant directives and ensuring that his responses and documentation embrace the requirements of each directive. However, at the very least, the differences between directives add to the manufacturer's compliance costs and, probably, do little to assist the purchaser in determining whether the product is fit for its intended use.

2.3.1.2 The Council has taken steps to resolve the problems caused by different attestation procedures between directives through the Council Decision in December 1990 to adopt a modular approach to the attestation of conformity[25]. The Decision requires that procedures for conformity assessment must be selected from among the modules, and departure from the modules will only be permitted in certain specific and limited circumstances. This will not bring immediate relief since it will not apply to existing directives until they come up for review. Each directive has a review period, for example, the Commission must produce proposals for amendments to the

Construction Products Directive by 31 December 1993. At this point, it would be possible to make this Directive compatible with the modular approach.

2.3.1.3 The Decision makes it clear that the objective of a conformity assessment procedure is to enable the public authorities to ensure that the products placed on the market comply with the essential requirements set out in the directives. Products that satisfy the requirements of the relevant directives will bear the CE mark. The Decision contains eight modules. Some apply at the design stage, some at the production stage, and some at both stages. The choice of module will depend upon the type of product, the nature of the risks involved, and the infrastructure within a sector, such as the existence of third parties. Where a directive provides the manufacturer with the possibility of using modules based on quality assurance techniques, the manufacturer must also be able to have recourse to a combination of modules not using quality assurance, and vice versa, except where a directive requires compliance with specific procedures. The Decision also clarifies the position with regard to notified and approved bodies. Member States are to have a continuing obligation to ensure that the notified bodies they designate for tasks under New Approach directives have the necessary technical qualifications. Notified bodies that can prove their conformity with harmonized standards (i.e. the EN 45000 series[26]) shall be presumed to conform to the requirements of the directives. Member States whose notified bodies are unable to prove their conformity with the EN 45000 series may be requested to provide the Commission with information on how the selection was carried out. Notified bodies may subcontract work subject to the competence of the subcontractor, assessed by its conformity with the EN 45000 series, and the ability of the notified body to exercise effective responsibility for the work carried out on its behalf.

2.3.1.4 Certain modules can stand alone as they apply at both the design and production stages. Some will usually be used only in conjunction with other modules as they are concerned with either the design or production phases. The permitted combinations of conformity assessment procedures are set out in Table 1. Modules A, G, and H are to be used on their own, with the possibility of supplementary provisions. Module C is designed to be used in conjunction with B. Modules D, E, and F will also normally be used in conjunction with B, but can also be used on their own in special cases as, for example, when dealing with certain products of 'very simple design and construction'. The modules do not contain any very radical departures from the procedures already to be found in individual New Approach directives. However, they offer a common set of procedures so that terminology, methods, and interpretations of requirements should be consistent between directives. If a product is subject to more than one directive, the manufacturer will be able to select the most onerous procedure with the confidence that the requirements from other directives have been subsumed into it without there being supplementary requirements to be met.

The modules are as follows:

A *Internal production control.* Attestation is primarily based on the results of internal checks by the manufacturer. The manufacturer establishes *technical documentation* which is kept for at least 10 years after the last product has been manufactured. If the manufacturer is not established in the EC, the responsibility to keep the documentation available falls on the person who places the product on the market. The content of the technical documentation is to be laid down by each directive but is likely to include a general description of the product, conceptual design and manufacturer's drawings and descriptions, the standards applied and the solutions adopted to meet the essential requirements where standards have not been applied, and design calculations and test reports. The manufacturer shall take all measures necessary to ensure that production takes place in conformity with the technical documentation. He affixes the CE mark and draws up a written declaration of conformity. As a supplement, a notified body may supervise tests on the product or carry out random tests at intervals to check the conformity of the product with a directive's requirements. If a notified body has been involved, the manufacturer affixes the body's identification symbol during manufacturing on the responsibility of the notified body.

B *EC type-examination.* The manufacturer produces *technical documentation* similar to that produced in Module A and presents it to a notified body with his application for EC type-examination and a specimen of the product. The application includes a declaration that the

Table 1 Conformity assessment procedures in Community legislation

	A. (Internal control of production)	C. (conformity to type)	D. (production quality assurance)	E. (product quality assurance)	F. (product verification)	G. (unit verification)	H. (full quality assurance)
DESIGN	Manufacturer Keeps technical documentation at the disposal of national authorities Aa. Intervention of notified body	B. (type examination) Manufacturer submits to notified body ● Technical documentation ● Type Notified body ● Ascertains conformity with essential requirements ● Carries out tests, if necessary ● Issues EC type-examination certificate				Manufacturer ● Submits technical documentation	EN 29001 Manufacturer ● Operates an approved quality system (QS) for design Notified body ● Carries out surveillance of the QS ● Verifies conformity of the design (') ● Issues EC design examination certificate (')
PRODUCTION	A. Manufacturer ● Declares conformity with essential requirements ● Affixes the CE mark Aa. Notified body ● Tests on specific aspects of the product (') ● Product checks at random intervals (')	Manufacturer ● Declares conformity with approved type ● Affixes the CE mark Notified body ● Tests on specific aspects of the product (') ● Product checks at random intervals (')	EN29002 Manufacturer ● Operates an approved quality system (QS) for production and testing ● Declares conformity with approved type ● Affixes the CE mark Notified body ● Approves the QS ● Carries out surveillance of the QS	EN29003 Manufacturer ● Operates an approved quality system (QS) for inspection and testing ● Declares conformity with approved type, or to essential require-ments ● Affixes the CE mark Notified body ● Approves the QS ● Carries out surveillance of the QS	Manufacturer ● Declares conformity with approved type, or with essential requirements ● Affixes the CE mark Notified body ● Verifies conformity ● Issues certificate at conformity	Manufacturer ● Submits product ● Declares conformity ● Affixes the CE mark Notified body ● Verifies conformity with essential requirements ● Issues certificate of conformity	Manufacturer ● Operates an approved QS for production and testing ● Declares conformity ● Affixes CE mark Notified body ● Carries out surveillance of the QS

(') Supplementary requirements which may be used in specific directives.

Source: Council Decision of 13 December 1990 concerning the modules for the various phases of the conformity assessment procedures which are to be used in the technical harmonization directives (90/683/EEC), *Official Journal*, L 380 vol 33, 31 December 1990.

same application has not been lodged with any other notified body. The notified body verifies that the type has been manufactured in conformity with the technical documentation and tests that the specimen conforms to the relevant standards or the essential requirements.

If the type meets the provisions of the directive, the notified body issues an *EC type-examination certificate*. The manufacturer must inform the notified body of any modifications and keep the technical documentation and the certificate for at least 10 years.

C *Conformity to type*. The manufacturer takes all measures necessary to ensure that production conforms to the EC type-examination certificate and draws up a declaration of conformity and affixes the CE mark. The declaration is to be kept for 10 years. As a supplement, a notified body may supervise tests on the product or carry out checks at random intervals. In this case, the notified body's identification symbol is affixed to the product by the manufacturer during manufacture on the responsibility of the notified body.

D *Production quality assurance*. The manufacturer operates an approved *quality system* for production and there is final product inspection and testing in accordance with the EC type-examination certificate. The quality system is assessed by a notified body. The quality system must be documented and this includes its objectives, the organizational structure, responsibilities of management, manufacturing processes, the methods of assuring quality, examinations and tests, quality records, and how product quality and the effectiveness of the system is to be monitored. It is presumed that there is conformity with these requirements if the quality system implements EN 29002 (BS 5750: Part 2)[27], supplemented as necessary to take into account the specific nature of the products involved. The manufacturer undertakes to fulfil his obligations under the system, to maintain it, and to inform the notified body of changes to the system. The notified body continues to keep the quality system under surveillance by periodic audits and unannounced visits. The manufacturer keeps documentation of the quality system for 10 years after the ending of manufacture, affixes the CE mark, and draws up a written declaration of conformity. The CE mark is accompanied by the identification symbol of the notified body. If the module is used independently of Module B, the manufacturer must draw up technical documentation as specified in Module A as an alternative to the EC type-examination.

E *Product quality assurance*. The manufacturer operates an approved quality system for final product inspection and testing in accordance with the EC type-examination certificate. The quality system must meet similar requirements to that in Module D except that, for a system to be presumed to be in conformity with the requirements of this module, it must satisfy EN 29003 (BS 5750: Part 3)[28], supplemented as necessary to allow for the specific features of the product. Surveillance of the system by the notified body is similar to that for Module D. The manufacturer affixes the CE mark and draws up a written declaration of conformity, with the notified body's identification symbol accompanying the CE mark. If the module is used independently of Module B, the manufacturer must draw up technical documentation in accordance with the requirements of Module A as an alternative to the EC type-examination.

F *Product verification*. The manufacturer takes all measures necessary to ensure that manufacturing conforms to the EC type-examination. The notified body checks conformity of the product with the requirements of the directive. The manufacturer can choose between this being done statistically, by sampling from production in accordance with the requirements of a directive, or by the individual examination of each item produced. The notified body draws up a written *certificate of conformity* and affixes its mark to the products. The manufacturer affixes the CE mark and draws up a declaration of conformity. If the module is used independently of Module B, the manufacturer must draw up technical documentation in accordance with the requirement of Module A as an alternative to the EC type-examination.

G *Unit verification*. The manufacturer draws up technical documentation similar to that required by Module A. The notified body examines each individual item produced for conformity with the relevant directive. It draws up a *certificate of conformity* and affixes its identification mark to the product. The manufacturer draws up a declaration of conformity and affixes the CE mark.

H *Full quality assurance*. The manufacturer must operate an approved quality system for design, manufacture, and final inspection and testing. The quality system must satisfy similar requirements to that in Module D, except that it must also include technical design specifications, design control and verification techniques, and how design quality is monitored. It is presumed that the quality system meets these requirements if it implements EN 29001 (BS 5750: Part 1)[(29)], supplemented as necessary by measures appropriate to the specific products involved. The notified body carries out surveillance of the quality system by means of audits and unannounced inspections. The manufacturer draws up a declaration of conformity and affixes the CE mark, which is accompanied by the identification symbol of the notified body. As a supplement, the manufacturer may lodge an application for the examination of the design by a notified body. If the design meets the requirements of the directive, the notified body issues an *EC design examination certificate*.

2.3.2 The CE mark

2.3.2.1 Products that conform to the essential requirements of New Approach directives must be capable of being identified both by purchasers and by the governments that have the responsibility for policing the markets so as to ensure that unsafe products are not supplied. This is the function of the CE mark, the proposed form of which is shown in Figure 8. The New Approach directives identify the circumstances in which the CE mark should be affixed to products, who is to affix it, the form it should take, and any information that is to accompany it, and make Member States responsible for ensuring that it is being used in a proper manner.

2.3.2.2 The EC has put in place an infrastructure that provides the purchaser with redress should the CE mark be wrongly applied. In 1985 it adopted a directive approximating the laws on liability for defective products[(30)], which has resulted in a harmonized system of product liability throughout the EC. The UK implemented the Directive through the Consumer Protection Act 1987[(31)] (see Sections 9.2 and 9.3). A defect is said to exist 'if the safety of the product is not such as persons are generally entitled to expect' (S. 3(1)). This includes the risk of damage to property as well as of personal injury and death. In determining what purchasers can expect, the Act takes account of the

> manner in which, and the purposes for which, the product has been marketed, its get-up, the *use of any mark in relation to the product* and any instructions for, or warnings with respect to doing or refraining from doing anything with or in relation to the product (S. 3(2)(a) italics added).

The definition of a defect would appear to encompass the misuse of the CE mark, the identification symbol of a notified body, or any other mark or instruction produced under a New Approach directive. There is a defence that the defect was due to compliance with an EC obligation.

2.3.2.3 Unfortunately a number of problems have arisen with the CE mark, in particular:

- *Purchaser perceptions as to the information it conveys.* The CE mark does not show that a product is fit for all the purposes claimed by a manufacturer. It merely shows that the essential requirements of relevant directives should have been met. Thus, for example, the CE mark on floor tiles means that they have been designed and manufactured so that pedestrians should not slip over on them, which satisfies the essential requirement in the Construction Products Directive of safety in use (see Section 3.3.5). It is not a guarantee of colour fastness, which is not an essential requirement under this Directive. However, if the colour should not prove to be fast, the CE mark is a guarantee that the process of degradation will not poison users as the essential requirement of hygiene, health, and the environment should have been met. At best, other quality marks will be needed to cover those aspects of fitness for purpose which lie outside the scope of the essential requirements. There is a risk that the CE mark may be brought into disrepute if products comply with the essential requirements but fail to achieve other aspects of fitness for purpose.

- *There are differences between directives as to who is responsible for affixing the CE mark.* It is necessary to study the directive in question in order to establish where responsibility lies. For example, for gas appliances it is the manufacturer, except where there has been verification by a notified body, when the notified body affixes the mark[32]; for machinery it is the manufacturer or his authorized representative in the Community or the person placing the product on the market, even when a notified body has been involved in attestation of conformity. For toys, it is the manufacturer or his authorized representative in the Community[33].

- *There are differences between directives as to what the CE mark is to look like and what additional information is to accompany it.* The Toy Safety Directive does not contain any guidance as to what the mark is to look like; the Machinery and Simple Pressure Vessels Directives[34] have different shapes for the letters, with the former also including information on their dimensions. The Machinery Directive[11] states that the CE mark is to be accompanied by the last two figures of the year in which the mark was affixed, the name and address of the manufacturer, designation of series or type, and serial number if any. In addition, there are to be instructions concerning, for example, foreseen use, assembly, operation, adjustment, and maintenance. The Construction Products Directive[10] requires the CE mark to be accompanied by the identity of the producer, the characteristics of the product, the last two digits of the year of manufacture, the identification symbol of any inspection body involved, and the number of the EC certificate of conformity. The Toy Safety Directive[33] just requires the name and address of the manufacturer, or his authorized representative, or the importer into the Community to accompany the CE mark.

- *Some directives allow products to be placed on the market without bearing the CE mark, whereas others require all products that conform to a directive to bear it.* The Construction Products Directive[10] allows products which play a 'minor part' with respect to health and safety to be placed on the market and these are not to bear the CE mark. Similarly, the Simple Pressure Vessels Directive[34] allows vessels for which the multiple of working pressure times capacity is 50 bar/litre or less to be placed on the market without bearing the CE mark. By contrast, personal protective equipment of 'simple design', where the user can assess the level of protection against the minimal risks concerned, bears the CE mark.

As the Commission has said, 'This leads to a great deal of confusion and does not enable economic operators to know exactly what their marking obligations are under the various Community regulations.'[35]

2.3.2.4 The Commission has proposed a regulation concerning the affixing and use of the CE mark[36]. A regulation is directly binding on the laws of the Member States and, unlike directives, does not permit national variations. The proposal has met with a number of objections and the date when it is likely to be adopted is uncertain. The main features of the proposal are:

- That the CE mark is to mean that a product conforms with all legally binding EC provisions applicable to it and that appropriate conformity assessment procedures have been carried out. The measures listed in the proposal are the New Approach directives adopted to date and one that is at the common position stage. This would seem to imply that breaches of old approach directives would not appear to invalidate the use of the CE mark.

- That the size and form of the CE mark and what it is to be attached to will be determined. The manufacturer will have some discretion, for example, to determine the colour for aesthetic reasons.

- The mark is to be accompanied by the last two digits of the year in which the mark was affixed and a numerical identification of the notified body involved in the production phase. The use of a number in the latter is intended to conceal the country of origin. No identification appears of any notified body involved in the design phase. If more than one notified body is involved in the production, one of them is to coordinate their activities and only its identification is to appear.

- Information, such as a pictogram, relating to the use of the product can be affixed. Other marks may also be affixed providing they do not reduce the visibility or legibility of the CE mark.

- Marks that may be confused with the CE mark are to be prohibited, but it is proposed that there should be a transitional period to 31 December 1999 so that offending registered trade marks can be withdrawn.

- The mark is to be affixed by the manufacturer, his authorized representative established in the Community, or the person responsible for placing the product on the market.

- Member States are to prevent the misuse of the mark with national provisions to prevent this from happening being put in place by 1 January 1993. Penalties for misuse are to be determined by individual Member States so that some variation within the EC is possible.

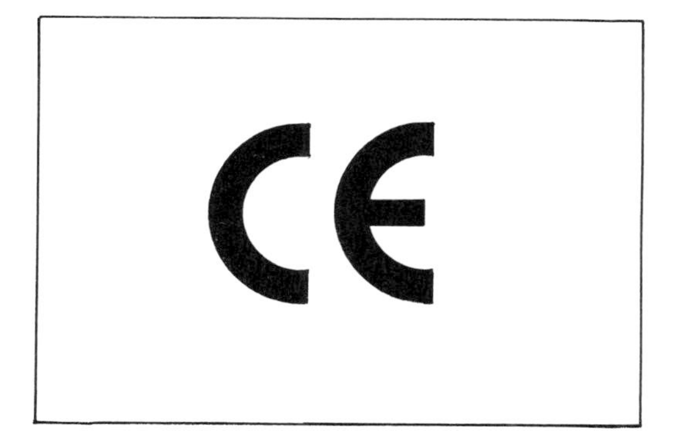

Figure 8 *The proposed CE mark*

Source: Proposal for a Council Regulation (EEC) concerning the affixing and use of the CE mark of conformity on industrial products (COM(91) 145 final), *Official Journal* C 160, 20 June 1991

Notes: *The initials are to consist of semicircular letters.*
The length of the bar inside the '€' is to be at least 80% of the outer radius of the semicircle.
The CE mark is to be at least 5 mm in height with the thickness of the initials being at least one-fifth of the height of the mark.

If adopted, the proposal would become binding immediately on all directives, including those that have already been adopted and implemented.

2.3.2.5 The UK has raised a number of objections to the proposal, some of which are to the principles in it and some to the solutions adopted to particular problems. The proposed Regulation is much less detailed than many of the national provisions to implement the directives that it supersedes and this could lead to administrative complications. It has failed to take into account that certain directives, such as the Construction Products Directive, would appear to permit products that comply with them to be placed on the market without bearing the CE mark, though this is a matter about which the UK government and the Commission disagree. With the identification of just the year of affixing the mark, it may be difficult to obtain necessary information about the product, and whether it actually satisfies the essential requirements or has been through the requisite procedures for attestation of conformity. A case can be made for arguing that the directives to which compliance is claimed are identified. It remains to be seen whether the proposal for one notified body to coordinate the activities of others can be made to work and there must be reservations about not identifying those involved in the design phase. Where products must comply with more than one directive, at least one of which contains provision for self-certification, there could be a danger of the coordinating body appearing to operate in areas in which it has not been designated. The process may also prove to be discriminatory against those manufacturers who legitimately use a procedure for attestation of conformity which does not involve a notified body being active in the production phase. The DTI has argued that while measures to take action against misuse of the mark are needed immediately, the transition period for confusing trade marks should be extended[37].

A measure to provide order and consistency in the use of the CE mark is clearly needed both by manufacturers, who need to be able to understand their obligations under different directives, and by purchasers, who need to be able to understand what information is being conveyed.

2.3.3 Third-party assessment bodies

2.3.3.1 At the heart of conformity assessment is the role to be played by independent bodies that can provide third-party certification of the product itself, the tests and inspections it has been through, and of the production system used to produce it. Though the terminology employed by different directives is not consistent, three types of third-party assessment body are recognized by New Approach directives:

- *Notified or approved or approved inspection bodies.* These are designated by Member States as competent to carry out particular activities and their identity is notified to the Commission. The Construction Products Directive[10], uniquely, classifies them into inspection and certification bodies, and test laboratories.

- *European technical approvals bodies.* These are designated by Member States under the Construction Products Directive to test products and issue certificates (see Section 3.11.1). The products are innovatory ones for which standards either do not exist or for which existing standards are inappropriate. Other New Approach directives also have procedures for dealing with innovatory products but these generally involve type-testing by an approved body rather than the setting up of a separate category of product approvals body.

- *Test laboratories, certification and inspection bodies who are not notified to the Commission.* Some directives contain conformity attestation procedures that do not have to be undertaken by approved bodies. For example, the Electromagnetic Compatibility Directive[24] uses the term 'competent bodies' to refer to bodies that have to meet the same criteria as approved ones, but whose identity does not have to be notified to the Commission.

2.3.3.2 The EC's policy towards approved bodies has been through several different shifts of direction. The Council Resolution on the New Approach to Technical Harmonization[8] stated that the bodies authorized to issue marks or certificates of conformity should carry out their duties in accordance with ISO Guides. This approach found its way into the earlier drafts of some of the New Approach directives. Thus, the Commission's proposal for a Construction Products Directive[38] envisaged that the approved bodies would need to observe the relevant ISO Guides in order that confidence would be developed such as to support mutual recognition of their results. Subsequently references to international standards were deleted. Instead, less precise criteria for approved bodies were introduced into the Toy Safety Directive[33] and transposed, largely unaltered, into other New Approach directives. These are:

- Having the available personnel, means, and equipment to carry out their tasks,

- Having personnel with the necessary technical competence and professional integrity,

- Being impartial,

- Being able to maintain professional secrecy,

- Having civil liability insurance or having their liability guaranteed by the state. In the UK this is interpreted to mean having professional indemnity insurance.

The fulfilment of the first two conditions must be verified at intervals by Member States.

2.3.3.3 The policy was reversed with the encouragement of the use of international standards for approved bodies with the adoption by the EC of its *Global Approach to Conformity Assessment.*

The Resolution adopted in December 1989[39] accepted as a guiding principle the use of the EN 45000 series in accreditation systems. The EN 45000 series of standards substantially follow the international standards. EN 45001 (BS 7501) *General Criteria for the operation of testing laboratories* is based on ISO Guides 2, 25, 38, 43, 45, and 49, EN 45011 (BS 7511) *General Criteria for certification bodies operating product certification* is based on ISO Guides 28 and 40, and EN 45012 (BS 7512) *General Criteria for certification bodies operating quality system certification* is based on ISO Guides 40 and 48. The result has been that the implementation of the New Approach directives have returned to the use of international standards. Thus, the Standing Committee on Construction has suggested that 'Compliance with the criteria . . . may be satisfactorily demonstrated by means of assessment against the requirements derived from the relevant standards in the EN 45000 series.'[40]

However, not all the clauses in the EN 45000 series form part of the legal requirements of the directives. While the EN 45000 series meets these requirements, with the exception that approved bodies must have civil liability insurance, it goes into more detail as to what has to be fulfilled and has additional clauses that have no equivalent in these requirements. A body with accreditation to the EN 45000 series should be able to fulfil these requirements, but a body that fulfilled the requirements for approved bodies would not necessarily meet all the standards for accreditation to the EN 45000 series.

2.3.3.4 The criteria for notified bodies have undergone further development in the more recent New Approach directives, such as the Hot-water Boilers Directive[41] and the proposed Recreational Craft Directive[42]. These explicitly refer to 'minimum criteria' to be taken into account by Member States when designating notified bodies. There are seven criteria and they are more explicit than those used in the Toy Safety Directive:

- *Independence.* A notified body, its director, and the staff involved in verification may not be the designer, manufacturer, supplier, or installer of what they inspect nor be the authorized representative of any of these. They must not be involved in construction, marketing, or maintenance of the product. However, there may be exchanges of technical information between them and the manufacturer.

- *Professional integrity.* Verification must be carried out with the highest degree of professional integrity and technical competence. The notified body and its staff must be free from all pressures and inducements that might influence their judgement.

- *Technical competence.* The notified body must have at its disposal all the necessary staff and facilities to enable it to perform its functions.

- *Staff competence.* The staff responsible for inspection must have sound technical and professional training, satisfactory knowledge of the tests, and the ability to draw up certificates and reports.

- *Impartial staff.* The impartiality of the staff must be guaranteed. Their remuneration must not depend upon the number of tests carried out or on the results of such tests.

- *Liability insurance.* The notified body must take out liability insurance unless its liability is assumed by the State.

- *Professional secrecy.* The staff of the notified body must be bound to observe professional secrecy, except in relation to the authorities of the Member State in which it carries out its activities.

The effect of these modifications to the criteria for notified bodies is to cause them to be more closely aligned with the requirements of the EN 45000 series than was previously the case.

2.3.4 Mutual recognition of testing and certification

2.3.4.1 Much of the work on attestation of conformity is not concerned with regulatory matters but is undertaken voluntarily. Firms often seek certification of their products or production systems out of choice rather than compulsion. Organizations and individual bodies reach mutual recognition agreements for each other's test and conformity certificates in order to avoid the need for multiple reassessment. The EC has sought to encourage mutual recognition and has argued that agreements should be transparent and that there should be a source of information on the working of agreements available to new groups seeking to achieve mutual recognition.

2.3.4.2 The Commission's response has been to establish a body in conjunction with EFTA, CEN, and CENELEC to oversee voluntary systems for mutual recognition of testing and certification, the European Organization for Testing and Certification, which was set up in 1990[43]. This is intended to coordinate mutual recognition work, disseminate information on mutual recognition, and to assist the Commission and the European standardization bodies on conformity assessment. The Commission has proposed that it takes over responsibility for CENELEC's certification agreements, though CENELEC has argued against this[44]. EOTC is in an experimental stage between 27 November 1990 and 31 December 1992, during which it intends to develop the most appropriate legal and administrative form for its activities, including its possible establishment as a body legally independent from its four founders. It will also be necessary for there to evolve by experience the precise relationship it will have with the regulatory sphere since there must be some interaction between voluntary and mandatory standards in testing and certification.

2.3.4.3 EOTC consists of:

- *A council*, which coordinates its activities and is responsible for transferring information; it contains representatives of the EC, EFTA, CEN, and CENELEC, the conformity assessment community, consumers, trade unions, and industrialists.

- *Specialized committees*, which are discipline orientated; they provide expertise, develop technical instruments, and promote mutual recognition agreements.

- *Sectoral committees*, which recognize agreement groups, promote agreements, and provide information about them.

- *Agreement groups*, which design and maintain mutual recognition agreements.

2.3.4.4 Agreement groups can be product, service, or discipline orientated, and comprise their signatories[45]. Agreements must meet certain criteria:

- They must include participants from at least three EC or EFTA countries, though they can also include participants from outside these countries as well.

- The agreement must be open to other EC and EFTA participants who meet the eligibility criteria applied to existing participants and who are willing to abide by the same rules as existing participants.

- The participants must satisfy the criteria of the relevant standard in the EN 45000 series.

- The achievement of mutual recognition of calibration or test results, inspection reports, product certificates, or the certification of quality systems in accordance with the EN 29000 series and/or the harmonization of procedures for calibration, testing, inspection, and certification (and/or accreditation).

It is not certain how EOTC will be financed in the long term. If funding is to come from agreement groups, it is not clear what benefits they will enjoy from the structure that they could not obtain without it. The benefits from avoiding trade barriers are ones that will accrue to the EC and EFTA as a whole rather than to individual agreement groups. This would point to the desirability of funding for EOTC coming from EC and EFTA sources rather than from agreement groups.

2.4 CONCLUSIONS

2.4.1 The EC has taken some major steps towards the removal of technical barriers to trade since it adopted the New Approach to Technical Harmonization in 1985. New Approach directives enacted to date include those for Construction Products, Electromagnetic Compatibility, Gas Appliances, Machinery, and Personal Protective Equipment, all of which have an impact on the construction industry. They have a number of features in common including:

- *The defining of essential requirements that products must satisfy in order to be deemed safe.*
- *The production of harmonized European standards by the European standardization bodies under mandate from the Commission as the principal technical specifications by which conformity with the essential requirements may be demonstrated.*
- *Attestation of conformity procedures by which it may be demonstrated that there has been compliance with the technical specifications.*
- *The use of the CE mark to identify products that comply with the provisions of relevant directives.*

2.4.2 The process of technical harmonization has been speeded up by the ability to use qualified majority voting and by delegating the resolution of technical issues to expert groups so that these can be resolved after a directive has been adopted. However, certain problems have developed, principally:

- *The length of time taken for directives to be fully implemented, which is, in part, a result of the time needed to produce mandates and to draft standards. The Commission made proposals in a Green Paper in 1990 to speed up this process but they have yet to be accepted and it is not clear when, or if, these will be acted upon.*
- *Differences in the attestation of conformity procedures between New Approach directives. A modular approach to conformity attestation was adopted in 1990, but it cannot affect existing directives until they come up for review.*
- *Differences in the rules for the use of the CE mark between New Approach directives. The Commission has promised a regulation to resolve discrepancies. Its proposals have met with objections from Member States and it is not clear when agreement will be reached.*

2.4.3 The Commission has also been active in the area of the mutual recognition of tests and certificates. It was one of the founders with EFTA, CEN, and CENELEC of the European Organization for Testing and Certification to coordinate and encourage the mutual recognition of test and conformity certificates by organizations and individuals. Agreements under the EOTC umbrella must satisfy certain minimum criteria, such as the use of the EN 29000 and EN 45000 series of standards, have participants from at least three EC or EFTA countries, and be open to other participants on the same terms as existing members.

References: 2 Technical harmonization and standards policy in the EC

1. Woolcock, S., Hodges, M. and Schreiber, K. (1991), *Britain, Germany and 1992: The Limits of Deregulation*, Royal Institute of International Affairs.

2. *The Single European Act signed at Luxembourg and the Hague 17 and 28 February 1986*, Cmnd 9758 (1986), enacted into UK law by the European Communities (Amendment) Act 1986, c 58.

3. Council Directive of 7 June 1988 on the approximation of the laws, regulations and administrative provisions of the Member States relating to the classification, packaging and labelling of dangerous preparations (88/379/EEC), *Official Journal*, L 187, 16 July 1988.

4. Council Directive of 19 February 1973 on the harmonization of the laws of the Member States relating to electrical equipment designed for use within certain voltage limits (73/23/EEC), *Official Journal*, L 77, 26 March 1973.

5. Court of Justice of the European Communities, *Case 120/78 Cassis de Dijon* [1979] ECR, 649.

6. Lawlor E. (1988), *Individual Choice and Higher Growth: The task of European consumer policy*, Commission of the European Communities.

7. Council Conclusions of 16 July 1984 on Standardization, *Official Journal*, C 136, 4 June 1985.

8. Council Resolution of 7 May 1985 on a new approach to technical harmonization and standards (85/C 136/01), *Official Journal*, C 136, 4 June 1985.

9. Council Directive of 28 March 1983 laying down a procedure for the provision of information in the field of technical standards and regulations (83/189/EEC), *Official Journal*, L 109, 26 April 1983.

10. Council Directive of 21 December 1988 on the approximation of laws, regulations and administrative provisions of the Member States relating to construction products (89/106/EEC), *Official Journal*, L 40, 11 February 1989.

11. Council Directive of 14 June 1989 on the approximation of the laws of Member States relating to machinery (89/392/EEC), *Official Journal*, L 183, 29 June 1989.

12. Council Directive of 21 December 1989 on the approximation of the laws of the Member States relating to personal protective equipment (89/686/EEC), *Official Journal*, L 399, 30 December 1989.

13. Bureau d'Information et de Prévisions Economiques and their fellow members of Euroconstruct (1988), *The 'Cost of Non-Europe' in Building Products*, Commission of the European Communities. English-language version published by the National Economic Development Office, 1989.

14. Commission of the European Communities (1990), *Commission Green Paper on the Development of European Standardization: Action for Faster Technological Integration in Europe*, COM(90) 456 final.

15. The Public Supply Contracts Regulations 1991, SI 1991, No 2679, Regulation 8.

16. The Public Works Contracts Regulations 1991, SI 1991, No 2680, Regulation 8.

17. Council Directive of 22 March 1988 amending Directive 83/189/EEC laying down procedures for the provision of information in the field of technical standards and regulations (88/182/EEC), *Official Journal*, L 81, 26 March 1988.

18. Commission Decision of 3 May 1990 amending the lists of standardization institutions set out in the Annex to Council Directive 83/189/EEC (90/230/EEC), *Official Journal*, L 128, 18 May 1990.

19. *General Guidelines for the Cooperation between the Commission of the European Communities and the European Standardization Bodies, the European Committee for Standardization (CEN) and the European Committee for Electrotechnical Standardization (CENELEC)*, 27 September 1984.

20. This section is based on CEN/CENELEC (1990) *Internal Regulations: Part 2: Common Rules for Standards Work.*

21. Building Services Research and Information Association (1990) *Technical Implications of New EC Codes, Standards and Legislation.*

22. CEN/CENELEC/ETSI (1991) *Response of Joint President Group to the Commission's Green Paper on Standardization*, 26 April; CEN (1991) *The CEN Strategy for the development of European standardization : CEN Response to the EC Commission Communication COM 90/456 final*, 15 April; CENELEC (1991) *CENELEC commentary on the Commission's communication on the development of European standardization*, 91/24183; CENELEC (1991) *CENELEC technical commentary on the Commission's communication on the development of European standardization*, 91/24185; ETSI (1991) *ETSI meets the challenge: the official ETSI response to the Commission Green Paper on the development of European standardization action for faster technological integration in Europe*, 4 April; BSI (1991) *The Future of European Standardization: The BSI Response to the European Commission Green Paper.*

23. Council Resolution of 18 June 1992 on the role of European standardization in the European economy (92/C 173/01), *Official Journal*, C 173, 9 July 1992.

24. Council Directive of 3 May 1989 on the approximation of the laws of the Member States relating to electromagnetic compatibility (89/336/EEC), *Official Journal*, L 139, 23 May 1989.

25. Council Decision of 13 December 1990 concerning the modules for the various phases of the conformity assessment procedures which are intended to be used in the technical harmonization directives (90/683/EEC), *Official Journal*, L 380, 31 December 1990.

26. British Standards Institution (1989) *EN 45001: 1989 (BS 7501: 1989) General Criteria for the operation of testing laboratories*; *EN 45002: 1989 (BS 7502: 1989) General Criteria for the assessment of testing laboratories*; *EN 45003: 1989 (BS 7503: 1989) General Criteria for laboratory accreditation bodies*; *EN 45011: 1989 (BS 7511: 1989) General Criteria for certification bodies operating product certification*; *EN 45012: 1989 (BS 7512: 1989) General Criteria for certification bodies operating quality system certification*; *EN 45013: 1989 (BS 7513: 1989) General Criteria for certification bodies operating certification of personnel*; *EN 45014: 1989 (BS 7514: 1989) General Criteria for suppliers' declaration of conformity.*

27. British Standards Institution (1987) *EN 29002: 1987 (BS 5750: Part 2, 1987; ISO 9002: 1987) Quality Systems – Specification for production and installation.*

28. British Standards Institution (1987), *EN 29003: 1987 (BS 5750: Part 3; 1987: ISO 9003: 1987) Quality Systems – Specifications for final inspection and test.*

29. British Standards Institution (1987) *EN 29001: 1987 (BS 5750: Part 1, 1987, ISO 9001: 1987) Quality Systems – Specification for design/development, production, installation and servicing.*

30. Council Directive of 25 July 1985 on the approximation of the laws of the Member States relating to product liability (85/374/EEC), *Official Journal*, L 210.

31. Consumer Protection Act 1987, c 43.

32. Council Directive of 29 June 1990 on the approximation of the laws of the Member States relating to appliances burning gaseous fuels (90/396/EEC), *Official Journal*, L 196, 26 July 1990.

33. Council Directive of 3 May 1988 on the approximation of the laws of the Member States concerning the safety of toys (88/378/EEC), *Official Journal*, L 187, 16 July 1988.

34. Council Directive of 25 June 1987 on the harmonization of the laws of the Member States relating to simple pressure vessels (87/404/EEC), *Official Journal*, L 220, 8 August 1987.

35. Commission of the European Communities (1990), *Working Document concerning the CE mark regulations*, CERTIF 90/3.

36. Proposal for a Council Regulation (EEC) concerning the affixing and use of the CE mark of conformity on industrial products (COM(91) 145 final), *Official Journal*, L 160, 20 June 1991.

37. Department of Trade and Industry (1991), *CE Mark Proposed Council Regulation: A Consultative Document.*

38. Proposal for a Council Directive on the approximation of the laws, regulations and administrative provisions of the Member States relating to construction products (submitted to the Council by the Commission), COM(86) 756/3 final.

39. Council Resolution of 21 December 1989 on a global approach to conformity assessment (90/C 10/01), *Official Journal*, C 10, 16 January 1990.

40. Standing Committee for Construction (1991), *Guidelines for the Designation of Approved Bodies in the field of the Council Directive 89/106/EEC on construction products*, Guidance Paper No. 6, CONSTRUCT 90/065.

41. Council Directive 92/42/EEC of 21 May 1992 on efficiency requirements for new hot-water boilers fired with liquid or gaseous fuels, *Official Journal*, L 167, 22 June 1992.

42. Proposal for a Council Directive on the approximation of the laws, regulations and administrative provisions of the Member States relating to recreational craft (92/C 123/07), *Official Journal*, C 123, 15 May 1992.

43. Commission of the European Communities (1989), *Memorandum of Understanding between EC Commission and CEN/CENELEC for the setting up of the European Organization for Testing and Certification*, Certif 89/1.

44. Details of the CENELEC certification agreements can be found in British Standards Institution (1987) *International Certification and Approval Schemes*, 3rd edition.

45. European Organization for Testing and Certification (1991), *Guidelines for the Recognition and Publication by EOTC of Agreement Groups*, adopted by the Council on 24 May 1991.

3 Construction Products Directive

3.0 OVERVIEW

3.0.1 The Construction Products Directive was adopted on 21 December 1988. Member States should have taken action to bring it into effect within their territories by 27 June 1991 but this has yet to happen. Denmark has transposed the measure into its national law. In the UK the main method of implementation is by means of the Construction Products Regulations 1991, which came into force on 27 December 1991. This will be supported by administrative action in areas such as the designation of approved bodies and the transposition of harmonized European standards into British ones. Administrative action has already included a circular from the Department of the Environment on the responsibilities of trading standards officers and building control officers under the Regulations. The full implementation of the Directive will not be complete until harmonized European standards have been produced and European technical approvals are available. Mandates to produce the former and guidelines for the latter cannot be finalised until the interpretative documents have been formally approved and published. However, provisional mandates have been issued and the preparation of technical specifications has already commenced.

3.0.2 The Directive is one of a series of directives produced under the New Approach to Technical Harmonization and Standards. Their aim is to ensure that products that meet defined minimum standards can enjoy freedom of mobility throughout the EC. This is to be achieved by the harmonization of those laws, regulations, and administrative provisions that may impede free trade so that each Member State has a system of regulation that is compatible with that of all the others. The Directive has several unique features that differ from other New Approach directives. These include its own Standing Committee for Construction to manage its implementation and advise on technical issues and a unique procedure for the approval of innovatory products. The purpose of the Directive is to achieve freedom of mobility for construction products within the EC. At the present time, the main impediments are seen by the Commission as being the different national systems of product approval that construction products must satisfy. These result in delays and costs while products have to be taken through the appropriate approvals mechanisms in each country before they can be placed on the market. The Commission has argued that, while different countries have their own approaches to product approval, they all have a common objective, namely the protection of the health and safety of the population and of their property. In principle, it should be possible to achieve this objective by a common system of control. Thus, the barriers to trade from having different systems would be removed.

3.0.3 The principal features of the Construction Products Directive are:

- *Definition of six essential requirements for construction works so that construction products are deemed safe if they are capable of enabling the works in which they are incorporated to satisfy these, providing that the works have been properly designed and constructed. The essential requirements are mechanical resistance and stability, safety in the case of fire, hygiene, health and the environment, safety in use, protection against noise, and energy economy and heat retention.*

- *A series of interpretative documents, which give concrete form to the essential requirements, provide the basis upon which harmonized technical specifications can be drawn up and form the link between the essential requirements and product specifications.*

- *Establishment of procedures by which technical specifications, such as harmonized standards and technical approvals, can be developed by expert bodies under powers delegated for this purpose by the Commission.*

- *Creation of procedures by which it can be attested that products comply with these technical specifications.*

- ***Use of the CE mark to identify those products that have been attested to be in conformity with the technical specifications.***

- ***Prohibition on Member States impeding the freedom of mobility of products that bear the CE mark and the obligation on them to ensure that the CE mark is applied in a proper manner.***

- ***Provision, in the absence of European technical specifications, for the acceptance by Member States of certificates and tests carried out elsewhere in the Community to their specifications as being equivalent to those undertaken on their own territory.***

- ***Creation of a Standing Committee for Construction, comprising representatives of the Member States, to advise the Commission on the implementation of the Directive and to determine certain technical issues.***

3.1 INTRODUCTION

3.1.1 The Construction Products Directive[1] is intended to remove the barriers to trade in construction products that result from different national systems of regulations, laws, and administrative provisions by establishing a harmonized system. It has been brought into force in the UK by the Construction Products Regulations 1991[2]. The Commission argued that each national system had as its objective ensuring the safety of persons and property and that all were technically equivalent. They represented different solutions to a common problem. Therefore, they could be replaced by a common system, providing that it shared the original objective and was technically equivalent to the existing national systems. The system of regulation is to be harmonized, not standardized, so that Member States will not have completely identical systems. Each must introduce measures to ensure that its national system is consistent with the Directive. For certain limited parts, such as the route to the attestation of conformity that individual products may take, it is understood that the Directive is to be supported by regulations, which will be binding on Member States. But in other areas, for example, how Member States ensure that the CE mark is applied in a proper manner, there are likely be some national variations in the ways in which the Directive is implemented. A system of product regulations needs to include standards, systems of product approvals, methods of verifying that products meet specifications, methods of identifying approved products, and systems for ensuring that approved products are used in a proper manner. The Directive contains provisions to ensure that there is harmonization in each of the first four of these areas but not the fifth[3]. Previously, each Member State had its own systems for each aspect.

3.1.2 The Directive owes its origins to research that pointed to cross-border trade in construction products being hampered by inconsistencies between national standards and procedures for attestations of conformity[4]. Standards and product approvals may act as a barrier to trade in a similar fashion to a tariff or a quota. Like a tariff, they may raise the costs of imported goods so as to provide domestic producers with an advantage in their home market. Delays in gaining product approvals may act as a quota by denying access to a market for a period of time. The consequences of these actions may be to provide domestic producers with a degree of protection. Prices may be higher than would be the case with free trade, and inefficient industrial structures and manufacturing processes may survive behind the protective wall of national standards and regulations. The Commission also hoped that the Directive would help to promote innovation and, by influencing international standards, aid the export of construction products outside the EC[5].

3.1.3 The research[4] indicated that not all the barriers to trade are the result of governmental regulations and administrative provisions. Barriers also exist as a result of the preferences of those working in the construction industry, the ways in which they have been trained, and their familiarity with particular products. Such cultural barriers are less susceptible to removal by means of directives than are those resulting from regulations and administrative provisions.

3.2 SCOPE

3.2.1 A construction product is defined by the Directive as being 'any product produced for incorporation in a permanent manner in construction works including both buildings and civil engineering works'.

The definition is wide-ranging and can include any item that is produced with the intention that it should contribute to the function of a building or civil engineering works. The definition refers to permanent incorporation within construction works. This is interpreted in the UK to exclude from the scope of the Directive items which are easily removable, such as fire extinguishers and light bulbs[6]. Temporary elements or works, such as scaffolding, are also outside the remit of the Directive. It is expected that their use will be subject to the provisions of the proposed directive on Temporary or Mobile Construction Sites[7] once it has been enacted (see Section 5.1.2) and that their production will be the subject of a proposed directive on temporary structures. Products supplied for the first time prior to the Directive coming into force (27 December 1991 for the UK) are not covered, so that the Directive will not operate retrospectively. Products supplied after 27 December 1991, which were produced in accordance with designs prepared prior to that date, are regarded as having been supplied for the first time after the implementation date. Second-hand products are also excluded, having been subject to it when supplied as new. However, both second-hand products and those supplied before the implementation date will continue to be regulated in their use by the Building Regulations. The Directive does not apply to construction products produced for export outside the EC.

3.2.2 Products may also be subject to other directives. For example, many building services products must also comply with the requirements of the Electromagnetic Compatibility Directive. If the various overlapping directives are to function efficiently, it would imply that the Commission ought to ensure that there is compatibility between their requirements. A product must satisfy the requirements of all relevant directives before it can bear the CE mark.

3.3 ESSENTIAL REQUIREMENTS

3.3.1 The Directive charges Member States with the responsibility of ensuring that construction products are placed on the market only if they are fit for their intended use. Products are deemed to be fit if they have 'such characteristics that the works in which they are incorporated, assembled, applied, or installed, can, if properly designed and built, satisfy the essential requirements . . . where such works are subject to regulations containing such requirements'.

The latter phrase is an important qualification as it means that there is no requirement on Member States to introduce regulations concerning the essential requirements if no regulations currently exist. If there are no regulations, there cannot be a barrier to trade for the Directive to remove. Therefore, the Directive applies to a construction product only if two conditions are fulfilled:

(i) at least one of the essential requirements must bear upon the product in use.

(ii) the construction works must be subject to regulations, such as the Building Regulations, which impose the essential requirements upon them.

An implication is that the Directive could apply to a product in one Member State but not to an identical product in another Member State[8].

3.3.2 The phrase 'if properly designed and built' has the effect of extending the influence of the Directive over the design team and those responsible for construction or installation, as well as over product manufacturers, and this is reflected in the interpretative documents and standards mandates derived from the Directive. The objective is to ensure that construction products enable construction works to satisfy the essential requirements. In this, the Directive recognizes that construction products generally do not have a stand-alone performance but are an integral part of the works. Their design must be compatible with the methods used in the design of the works and their characteristics can determine the design of the works. The overall performance and safety of completed works depends upon coherence of codes and standards[9]. Only construction products are traded between Member States and not construction works. Therefore, the Directive focuses attention on these. Member States retain the responsibility for ensuring that construction works are safe. It is open to debate whether genuine freedom of trade can result from harmonizing the regulation of the approval of construction products while leaving the possibility of barriers to trade arising from national regulation of their use.

3.3.3 It should be emphasized that the Directive does not reduce the responsibilities of building control officers and approved inspectors to ensure the fitness of products for use in works. They must continue to satisfy themselves that products are fit for their intended use, whether or not they comply with the Directive or bear the CE mark[6]. Products that comply with the Directive may be inappropriate or incorrectly used. The UK's Building Regulations have been amended so that products that comply with the Directive are regarded as 'proper materials'.

3.3.4 The Directive applies to construction products that have been 'placed on the market'. This has not been followed in the UK Regulations which use the term 'supply' instead. To say that a product has been placed on the market implies that it is made available to another party by means of a commercial transaction. This would appear to exclude from the scope of the Directive construction products that are made available by other means, including donations and producing a product for one's own use (see Section 10.2.2). In this respect, the UK Regulations are broader in scope than the Directive.

3.3.5 Construction products are considered to be suitable for use in construction works if the works that incorporate them satisfy six essential requirements. How the works are to achieve this is left to Member States to determine. There is no obligation on them to have any regulations concerning the essential requirements. The essential requirements given in Annex I of the Directive and Schedule 2 of the UK Regulations are:

- *Mechanical resistance and stability.* Construction works must be designed and built so that loadings acting on them during construction or use will not result in collapse, major deformations to an inadmissible degree, damage to other parts of the works or to fittings or installed equipment, or damage disproportionate to the event causing it.

- *Safety in the case of fire.* Construction works must be designed and built so that, in the event of fire, the load-bearing capacity of the structure is maintained for a specific period of time, the spread of fire and smoke within the works and to neighbouring works is limited, the occupants are able to leave or be rescued, and the safety of rescue teams is not compromised.

- *Hygiene, health and the environment.* Construction works must be designed and built so that they do not threaten the health of their occupants or those of neighbouring works. Specifically, health must not be threatened by the giving-off of toxic gases, the presence of dangerous particles or gases in the air, the emission of dangerous radiation, the pollution of water or soil, the failure to eliminate waste water, smoke, or liquid wastes, or the presence of damp.

- *Safety in use.* Construction works must be designed and built so that they do not present an unacceptable risk of accident to those who use them, for example, by slipping, falling, collision, burns, electrocution, or explosion.

- *Protection against noise.* Construction works must be designed and built so that the noise perceived by their occupants or people nearby is below a level that threatens health, and permits them to sleep, rest, and work in satisfactory conditions.

- *Energy economy and heat retention.* Energy economy in use shall be low, having regard to climatic conditions of the location and the occupants.

3.3.6 The essential requirements must be capable of being satisfied for an 'economically reasonable working life', subject to 'normal maintenance' being undertaken. The working life is the period during which performance of the works fulfils the essential requirements. All relevant costs during the life cycle are taken into account, including environmental costs and the consequences of failure. The Directive recognizes that diminishing returns set in as the costs of protection against risks of decreasing likelihood rise relative to their potential benefit. Thus, the products are to be fit for their intended use 'account being taken of economy'. Normal maintenance is the set of measures applied to enable the works to fulfil their functions during their working lives and includes cleaning and inspections. The requirements are concerned with actions which are foreseeable.

3.3.7 The essential requirements are intended to describe what is necessary for health and safety in functional terms, though the inclusion of energy economy stretches the meaning of safety. They are not intended to provide detailed rules for the design of products. This is the function of the technical specifications that are to be produced from the essential requirements. However, the Directive differs from other New Approach directives in the vagueness of the essential requirements. They are closer to constituting a mission statement than being a formula for construction technical specifications. It is the role of the interpretative documents to provide the basis for technical specifications.

3.4 INTERPRETATIVE DOCUMENTS

3.4.1 The interpretative documents are intended to give concrete form to the essential requirements. There is one document for each of the six essential requirements. They are a unique feature of this Directive, none of the other New Approach directives having anything comparable. They are compiled on the instruction of the Commission and are subject to approval by the Standing Committee for Construction. They will become the legal basis for interpretation of the essential requirements and, thus, whether standards or products meet the essential requirements. They will be given legal form by being formally adopted by the Standing Committee for Construction and being published in the *Official Journal*. As no final mandates for harmonized standards can be given or guidelines for European technical approvals issued without the interpretative documents being in place, they are the key to the full implementation of the Directive. However, provisional mandates can be given so that work on technical specifications has started before the legal mandate has been issued. It is believed that over 1000 individual standards are in preparation(8). It had originally been intended that the interpretative documents would be issued a year prior to the Directive's implementation date. The failure to do so has delayed the coming into force of the parts of the Directive concerned with technical specifications, attestation of conformity, and the CE mark.

3.4.2 The documents, or the technical specifications that stem from them, can create different classes or levels of requirement. In this way, they can take account of differences in geographical or climatic conditions in the EC, ways of life, or prevailing levels of protection. Member States will be permitted to select different classes or levels of performance for use within their jurisdiction. However, such differences should not constitute a barrier to trade since the levels or classes are common throughout the EC.

3.4.3 Draft interpretative documents have been produced for comment. They follow a common format. There are certain elements which are identical in each case(10):

- An explanation of the function of interpretative documents,
- A statement about classes or levels of performance,
- Definitions of general terms, e.g. normal maintenance, economically reasonable working life,
- How working life and durability are to be treated.

In addition, each interpretative document has certain unique elements, principally:

- An explanation of its specific essential requirement, e.g. families of risk types considered in safety in use,
- Definitions of specific terminology,

- The basis for verification of satisfaction of the essential requirement,

- The requirements for technical specifications and for guidelines for European technical approvals for both works and products (i.e. category A and category B standards).

The draft interpretative documents are currently being revised so as to remove information that is not related to the relevant essential requirement. That for Energy Economy and Heat Retention provides an indication of what the interpretative documents will eventually look like. There have been problems in specifying in an operational sense how safety in the case of fire was to be determined. This led to debates as to whether a CE mark could be given to a product that could not be demonstrated as satisfying one of the essential requirements. The result has been delays in finalizing the documents and having them approved, translated, and published in the *Official Journal*.

3.5 TECHNICAL SPECIFICATIONS

3.5.1 There are various ways in which it can be demonstrated that construction products comply with the essential requirements. In practice, compliance will normally be by means of conforming to:

- A national standard transposing a harmonized European standard,

- A European technical approval,

- A national specification that complies with the relevant essential requirements. They could include international standards as well as national ones. The acceptability of such specifications is determined by the Commission, who have indicated that they are reluctant to follow this route.

3.5.2 Products that comply with these technical specifications are able to bear the CE mark, which means that Member States are not permitted to impede their free mobility. This implies that Member States must ensure that any regulations having a bearing on construction products, such as building regulations and town and country planning regulations, do not impede products bearing the CE mark.

3.6 HARMONIZED STANDARDS

3.6.1 Harmonized standards are to be produced by the European standards organizations, CEN and CENELEC, on the basis of mandates given to them by the Commission. The Standing Committee for Construction is to approve the draft standards as complying with the essential requirements and the mandates given. Mandates will be concerned with the essential requirements but there is also the possibility that standards may include other aspects of performance. There is an issue of whether harmonized European standards should just be concerned with the essential requirements or whether they should also define fitness for purpose in its wider sense. The resolution of the issue is of some importance since it will define the minimum standard for the supply of construction products and has implications as to whether public bodies will have to purchase products that satisfy simply the essential requirements or whether they will be able to specify higher grades. The issue has still to be determined. Standards may contain different classes or levels of performance in accordance with the interpretative documents. Construction has been identified as being an area in which there are relatively few European or international standards[5].

3.6.2 The Standing Committee for Construction recognizes that there are two possible types of standard that CEN and CENELEC could be asked to produce[11]:

- *Category A*. These are standards for the design and execution of buildings and works. They are needed if there is to be a definition of when construction products enable the construction works into which they are incorporated to meet the essential requirements.

- *Category B.* These are standards that relate to construction products. They will be concerned with definitions, performance requirements, and conformity requirements. They will include specifications of the tests that will have to be carried out to ensure that there is conformance with the standard, including the types of tests, their frequency, the sampling to be employed, and how the results are to be analysed. Three types of category B standard have been identified:

  - Standards for basic materials used in the manufacture of products, e.g. timber, plastics,

  - Standards for products with specific end uses for which the mandates could follow the international CI/SfB classification system, e.g. products for use in external walls,

  - Horizontal standards in support of each essential requirement applying to several products, e.g. test methods.

The distinction between category A and B standards corresponds to the different responsibilities of Member States under the Directive. Only category B standards are used in the attestation of conformity of construction products and their marking with the CE mark demonstrates that they are in conformity with the technical specifications. Member States are obliged to ensure that the CE mark is used correctly.

3.6.3 The Standing Committee for Construction has prepared a model for standardization mandates to be issued by the Commission to CEN or CENELEC under the Directive. Until the interpretative documents have been adopted only provisional mandates can be issued. The model for mandates contains the following elements:

- *The legal basis for the mandate.* This explicitly draws attention to their function in relation to the requirements of the Public Works and Utilities directives with respect to technical specifications. A mandate may also specify any other relevant directives. The resolutions of the Standing Committee for Construction and the Standing Committee created by 83/189/EEC should be identified.

- *The product for which a standard is required (for category B standards) or the aspect of reliability of building or civil engineering works (for category A standards).*

- *The factors that should be taken into account in the preparation of the standard.* For category A standards these include relevant essential requirements under the Construction Products Directive and any other directive, common terminology, type of verification and control, differentiation according to probability of failure and its consequences, any levels or classes, the treatment of durability, the intended degree of harmonization, relevant differences in geographical or climatic conditions or ways of life, safety and protection elements, and assumptions concerning the quality of products and workmanship and their control. For category B standards these include the scope of the standard, its relation to and compatibility with other standards, the conditions of intended use of the product, performance, testing, dimension, and characteristics, standards, terminology, any specific conditions with respect to the essential requirements, the treatment of durability, relevant classes or levels of performance, relevant procedures for attestation of conformity, and indications on the marking of the product.

- *How the mandate is to be executed.* This includes the working programme, progress reports by CEN, a timetable for the work, and consultation arrangements with Member States.

- *The financial support to be given by the Commission.*

It is possible that the formal mandate for a standard may not be issued until well into the drafting process, work having been commenced on the basis of a provisional mandate. This is because there must be an interface between a standard and the attestation of conformity procedures. It is likely that the precise requirements for attestation will not become apparent until the standard is being drafted yet these should be part of the mandate. It seems likely that an interactive process may be used in drawing up mandates in which the provisional mandate may be revised in the light of work done on drafting the standard. A formal mandate may therefore not be issued until the drafting is well under way.

3.6.4 Various approaches could be adopted towards mandating the standards organizations to produce harmonized standards. It is necessary that the EC produces a comprehensive set of standards as quickly as possible if a Single Internal Market for construction products is to become a reality. Four approaches have been suggested to the Standing Committee on Construction:

- *Product specifications and design rules could be generated from the interpretative documents.* The problem with this approach is that not all the interpretative documents are specific about products. Some set out general principles and cover a range of different products. They are more concerned with assemblies of construction products rather than with the products themselves in order to ensure that buildings and works, and not merely products, should be safe.

- *A list of the standards needed could be compiled from national lists.* While this would produce a clear-cut list, there would need to be a good deal of work done in comparing national product standards and to identify the areas not covered by national regulations.

- *The priorities should reflect the current work of CEN and CENELEC and their technical committee structure.* The disadvantage here is that the current work of the standards bodies reflects the priorities of what is, essentially, a voluntary system. Voluntary committees would need to be persuaded to work on regulatory work rather than on what they have chosen.

- *Priority should be given to building products for which cross-border trade is possible.* These could be checked against product/use tables and priority given to those areas in which CEN already has work under way.

The approach that is likely to be adopted is the last one, as this would be the most compatible with issuing provisional mandates ahead of adoption of the interpretative documents.

3.6.5 The requirement that construction products should enable the buildings and works into which they are incorporated to satisfy the essential requirements means that the Directive may generate design and execution standards (category A standards). CEN is already mandated by the Commission to produce Eurocodes. These could be one form that category A standards might take, though others would also be possible. Table 2 lists the areas for which Eurocodes are being produced. There have also been proposals for Eurocodes for aluminium structures and off-shore structures. Eurocodes are concerned with design principles and how designs are to be executed. They identify the product standards that construction products must satisfy and minimum standards of workmanship. Once the Eurocodes have been published as ENVs, it is expected that building control procedures in Britain will be amended so that Approved Documents identify them as appropriate guidance for design[6]. Harmonized design standards will also be generated by the directive concerned with the minimum safety and health requirements for the workplace, which is discussed in Section 3.16 below.

Table 2 Eurocodes

1	General principles
2	Design of concrete structures
3	Design of steel structures
4	Composite construction
5	Timber structures
6	Masonry
7	Foundations
8	Structures in seismic regions
9	Actions and loadings

3.7 EUROPEAN TECHNICAL APPROVALS

3.7.1 Harmonized standards are not appropriate in all cases due to certain products or their uses being innovatory. In such cases, product standards may not yet have been produced or are not capable of being produced. Regulatory systems usually have some device by which innovatory products can be granted approval for use in certain circumstances. The Directive provides a route whereby innovatory products can demonstrate their compliance with the essential requirements through a process known as *European technical approval* (ETA). Each New Approach directive has some equivalent system, usually by means of an EC type-examination, but that for the Construction Products Directive is more precisely organized than for other directives. This may be a reflection of the fact that ETAs are replacing the well-organized system of agrément approvals.

3.7.2 An ETA is 'a favourable technical assessment of the fitness for use of a product for an intended use'. It may be granted for products for which there is no harmonized or recognized standard or which differ significantly from such standards. For example, if a harmonized European standard existed for a water pipe covered in a range of plastics, but a manufacturer developed a system in a new plastic, an ETA could be considered as the way of demonstrating that it would enable the essential requirements to be met. The precise boundary between the areas covered by standards and ETAs will to some extent depend upon the speed with which CEN develops standards(12). If the development of standards is tardy, manufacturers may press for ETAs to be awarded in order to secure a CE mark for their products. ETAs are expected to have a limited life of up to five years before they are superseded by a harmonized standard or made obsolete by technical change, though they can be renewed. The Commission can issue mandates for guidelines for ETAs for individual products or families of products. These deal with matters such as specific requirements of the product with respect to the essential requirements, test procedures and their assessment, inspection and conformity procedures, and the period of validity of an ETA. Where no mandate has been issued, assessment is to be made by reference to the essential requirements and interpretative documents. The Standing Committee for Construction will identify subject areas for ETAs. To date, they have identified five product groups for ETAs, namely roofs (liquid waterproofing), external insulation (thick/thin rendering), structural glazing, prefabricated partitions, and anchor bolts(13). Further listings are expected in due course. The European Organization for Technical Approvals Technical Board is preparing a list of subject areas in which it considers ETAs could be issued. More than 120 subject areas are under discussion(14). It is believed that there has been no discussion of whether ETAs should be extended to include the installation of approved products by approved installers. Thus, at present, there would appear to be no plans for the development of European equivalents to, say, the British Board of Agrément's approved installers schemes for cavity wall insulation, chimney linings, roofing, and concrete repairs. This is in contrast to standards for which category A standards are envisaged.

3.7.3 ETAs are granted by approved bodies authorized for this purpose by the Member States. A list of the approvals bodies nominated by the Member States appears in Table 3. The nominated bodies must be able to:

- assess the fitness for use of new products,
- be impartial in their decisions,
- collate the contributions of interested parties to form balanced assessments.

Collectively, the approvals bodies form a single organization, the European Organization for Technical Approvals, which coordinates their work. It will have common procedural rules for all approvals bodies and a constitution approved by the Commission(15). The procedural rules will probably be published as a regulation. They will cover issues such as applications by manufacturers, and the preparation, granting, refusal, withdrawal, and publication of ETAs. The rules must be approved by the Standing Committee for Construction. A Member State can designate more than one approvals body, in which case one is to be nominated as the national spokesman with EOTA. The approvals bodies are expected to provide mutual support. A manufacturer can only apply to one body who acts, in effect, as the agent for the whole EOTA.

As there are common rules, the assessment should be equally rigorous irrespective of which approvals body is applied to.

Table 3 European Organization for Technical Approvals

Belgium	Union Belge pour L'Agrément Technique dans la Construction *
Denmark	Staten Byggeforskningsinstitut (SBI) *
France	Centre Scientifique et Technique du Bâtiment (CSTB)* Service d'Etudes Techniques des Routes et Autoroutes (SETRA)
Germany	Institut für Bautechnik (IfBt)
Greece	Hellenic Organization for Standardization (ELOT)
Ireland	Irish Agrément Board (IAB)
Italy	Servizio Technico Centrale del Consiglio Superiore dei Lavori Pubblici Centro Studi ed Esperienze Anticendi del Ministero dell'Interno Instituto Centrale per l'Industrializzazione e la Tecnologia Edilisia (ICITE) *
Luxembourg	Laboratoire des Ponts et Chaussées
Netherlands	Stichting Bouwkwaliteit (SBK) * Bureau Keurings-en Certificeringsinstituut BV (BDA) BV Kwaliteitsverklaringen Bouw (BKB) Stichting Betonmortel Controle (BMC) Stichting Instituut voor Keuring en Onderzoek van Bouwmaterialen (IKOB) BV Instituut voor Materiaalen Milieu-onderzoek (INTRON) Keuringsinstituut voor Waterleidingsartikelen (KIWA) Stichting Kwaliteitscentrum Gevelelementen (SKG) Stichting Keuringsbureau Hout (SKH)
Portugal	Laboratorio Nacional de Engenharia Civil (LNEC) *
Spain	Instituto Eduardo Torroja de Ciencias de la Construcción (IETCC) * Union Española para la Inoneidad Tecnia en la Construcción (UEltc)
UK	British Board of Agrément (BBA) *

The first-named organization for each Member State acts as the spokesman within EOTA.

* *denotes a member of the European Union of Agrément (UEAtc)*

Source: Euronews Construction (May 1990)

3.7.4 The financing of ETA work has still to be determined. The Commission has agreed to meet 80% of the cost of EOTA for the first year, but long-term funding has still to be resolved. The British Board of Agrément (BBA) is self-financing but many of the other members of EOTA are financed by their governments. Some 75% of BBA's income comes from assessment and testing and only 10% from publications(16). Its experience suggests that funds are not likely to be generated commercially for financing guidelines, though the assessment of individual products appears to be self-financing.

3.7.5 Several EC countries, such as Denmark and Greece, have only recently introduced a technical approval procedure, while others, such as France and the UK, have had long-standing arrangements(17). The European Union of Agrément (UEAtc) has existed since 1960. Its members include all the EC states except Greece and Luxembourg, as well as Austria. Three EFTA countries, Norway, Sweden, and Finland, have observer status. It has drafted technical guides (formerly known as directives) to serve as common frameworks for assessing fitness for purpose of new products. These are issued in the UK as Methods of Assessment and Test (MOATS). Certificates issued by one member are accepted by others, though Germany does not currently have a body that is either issuing or confirming agrément certificates. The UK member of UEAtc is the

British Board of Agrément. The UEAtc provides a basis for the development of ETAs just as CEN offers one for standards. The difference is that the Directive created a new organization for ETAs rather than adopting an existing one. This raises the question of what is the future for a body such as UEAtc. EOTA should, in principle, be concerned only with regulatory work under the Directive. It has no function in relation to testing products against characteristics other than the essential requirements. However, demand is likely to continue for technical approvals assessed against additional criteria and the coordination and mutual recognition of this work could still be undertaken by UEAtc unless EOTA absorbed it. At issue is a similar question to that raised in relation to standards in Section 3.6.1, namely, should ETAs be concerned only with the essential requirements or should they also include wider aspects of fitness for purpose?

3.7.6 The UK is proposing to adopt a two-stage approach towards ETAs in the UK[18]:

- *Stage 1.* The British Board of Agrément is to be the sole UK body authorized to issue ETA certificates until such time as the EC agrees on the detailed requirements to apply to bodies eligible for designation as technical approvals bodies. It will act as the UK spokesbody within EOTA. Other organizations may be recognized by the government as being able to carry out assessment of fitness for use for ETAs but will not have the authority to issue certificates. The BBA Council will set up an ETA Technical Advisory Committee comprising representatives of interested parties, such as users, specifiers, and manufacturers. This Committee will advise the BBA Council on the technical content of individual certificates and the Council will be responsible for the issuing of ETA certificates. Other organizations may be recognized for assessment purposes if they are able to demonstrate their ability to take impartial decisions and their technical competence. A precondition is accreditation by the National Accreditation Council for Certification Bodies under EN 45011 (see Section 3.11). They will also need to carry adequate professional indemnity insurance in view of their exposure to product liability claims. They will be limited for ETA work to those product groups which are covered by NACCB accreditation. Manufacturers will be able to determine which recognized organization they wish to contract with for the execution of product assessment work.

- *Stage 2.* Once the EC has reached agreement on the detailed operational and performance criteria to be applied to bodies to be considered eligible for designation to issue ETA certificates, the government will consider designating other organizations in addition to the BBA to carry out ETA work in their own right. They will be required to become members of EOTA. The government considers that only once EC criteria for ETA bodies have been agreed can the commercial acceptability of private sector ETA certification be assured.

The BBA has been assessed to EN 45011 by NACCB with unlimited scope for product approvals. In principle, an ETA body could also be an approved certification or inspection body or a testing laboratory (see Section 3.11). It could offer manufacturers a one-stop service of product approvals and attestation of conformity. The BBA has various NAMAS accreditations, carries out surveillance of manufacturers who obtain its certificates, and is drawing up a quality management system. It would be well placed to offer such a service to manufacturers.

3.8 ATTESTATION OF CONFORMITY

3.8.1 It is one thing for a producer to claim that a product conforms to a technical specification but quite another to demonstrate that the product supplied actually complies in all cases. The Directive cannot meet its stated aim of ensuring that products are placed on the market only if they enable construction works to satisfy essential safety requirements unless it also contains a means for verifying that products conform to technical specifications. This is the function of a set of procedures known as *attestation of conformity.* They are intended to confirm that construction products comply with technical specifications, that is, harmonized European standards, European technical approvals, or national standards accepted by the Commission as complying with the essential requirements.

3.8.2 The Directive and the Standing Committee for Construction distinguish between two types of product, with a different approach to the attestation of conformity being taken in each case:

- *'Minor part' products.* Article 4(5) recognizes that there are certain products that play only a minor part with respect to health and safety. They may be placed on the market providing that the manufacturer declares that they comply with the 'acknowledged rule of technology'. The UK Regulations define this as 'technical provision acknowledged by a majority of representative experts as reflecting the developed stage of technical capability at a given time as regards products, processes and services, based on relevant consolidated findings of science, technology and experience'. The Commission, after consultation with the Standing Committee, will draw up and maintain a list of such products. They will not follow any of the procedures that result in the award of the CE mark and, therefore, will not enjoy automatic access to the markets of other Member States. The device has been used in other New Approach directives. For example, the Simple Pressure Vessels Directive permits low-pressure vessels to be manufactured in accordance with the sound engineering practice of a Member State[(19)]. 'Minor part' products do not carry the CE mark.

- *Other products.* These are the remaining products and must follow one of the approaches to the attestation of conformity. They carry the CE mark to demonstrate attestation of compliance with the technical specifications.

Article 6(2) creates a transitional arrangement under which products can be placed on the market in a Member State, if they satisfy national provisions, until such time as European technical specifications provide otherwise. However, such products do not carry the CE mark. There has also been some discussion of whether there could be products with local characteristics that could be permitted to be placed on the market in certain local markets[(20)].

3.8.3 The Directive identifies two main approaches to the attestation of conformity:

- *Certificate of conformity issued by a certification body.* The manufacturer has a system of *factory production control* and takes samples in accordance with a prescribed test plan. The approved *certification body* assesses and maintains surveillance of the production control and carries out initial type-testing of the product. There is an option for the approved body to carry out audit sampling at the factory, in the market or at the construction site[(21)].

- *A declaration of conformity by the manufacturer.* There are three main approaches to a *manufacturer's declaration of conformity*, referred to in the Directive as the first, second, and third possibilities:

  - *First possibility.* An approved body certifies the factory production control, either by initial inspection only or by initial inspection and continuous surveillance. The manufacturer carries out factory production control and initial type-testing, and may also carry out sample tests in accordance with a prescribed test plan.

  - *Second possibility.* The manufacturer is responsible for factory production control and an approved body carries out initial type-testing[(22)].

  - *Third possibility.* The manufacturer is responsible for both initial type-testing and factory production control.

These routes to conformity attestation tend to be referred to as Levels 1, 2, 3, and 4 respectively and are illustrated in Figure 9. The Council's decision to adopt a modular approach to the attestation of conformity (see Section 2.3.1) does not affect the functioning of the Directive, though it may cause changes to be made when it comes up for revision in 1993.

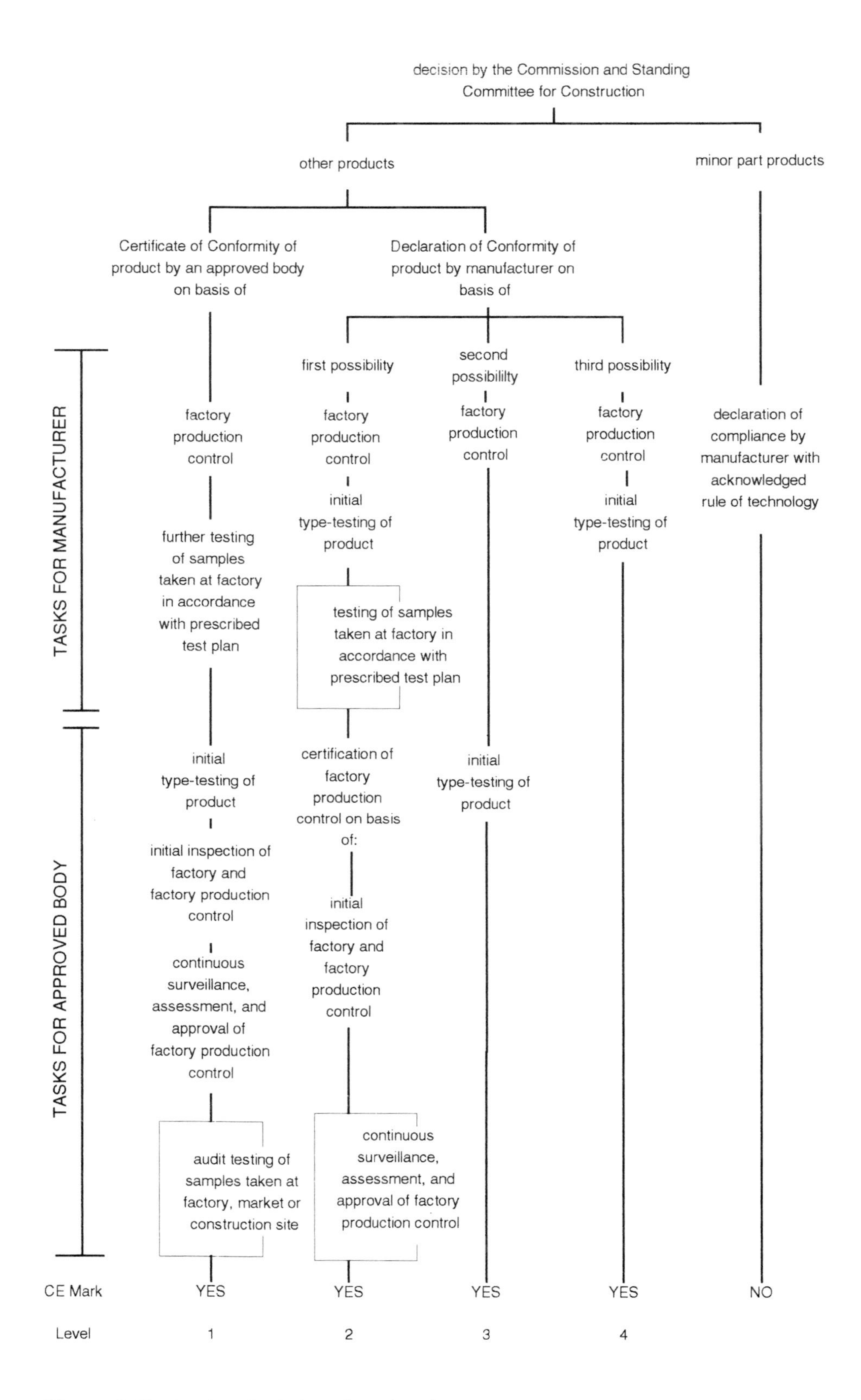

Figure 9 *Routes to attestation of conformity*

Source: For attestation of conformity procedures – Council Directive of 21 December 1988 on the approximation of the laws, regulations and administrative provisions of Member States relating to construction products (89/106/EEC), *Official Journal*, L 40, 11 February 1989, annex III.2; for attestation levels – Commission of the European Communities, Standing Committee for Construction (1991) *Guidance Paper No 8: Choice of Conformity Attestation Procedure*, CONSTRUCT 91/68.

3.8.4 Each of these routes results in the award of a CE mark and, with it, a passport for the product to move freely within the EC. However, the level of assurance given to the purchaser clearly varies, yet neither the purchaser nor the manufacturer has any control over the minimum level of assurance stipulated. As the Standing Committee for Construction has stated, 'the minimum requirements to be met by the construction product cannot be voluntarily agreed between manufacturer and purchaser, but are definitely fixed by the European technical specification'[(23)].

The CE mark is primarily aimed at enabling the regulator to police the market rather than providing information for the consumer.

3.9 ATTESTATION OF CONFORMITY TECHNIQUES

3.9.1 The Directive recognizes seven methods that can be used to control conformity of products:

- Initial type testing of the product,
- The testing of samples taken at the factory in accordance with a prescribed test plan,
- Audit testing of samples taken at the factory, on the open market, or on a construction site,
- The testing of samples from a batch that is ready for delivery or has been delivered,
- Factory production control,
- Initial inspection of the factory and of factory production control,
- Continuous surveillance, judgement, and assessment of factory production control.

The first four of these may be undertaken either by the manufacturer or by an approved body, but the latter two are the function of an approved body. Approved bodies are designated by Member States (see Section 3.11). Factory production control is the responsibility solely of the manufacturer. The seven methods can be assembled in combination to provide procedures for the attestation of conformity that meet the requirements of particular products.

3.9.2 *Factory production control* is defined by the Directive as meaning the permanent internal control of production exercised by the manufacturer. All its elements are to be systematically documented in the form of written policies and procedures. This is to ensure that those involved understand quality assurance and to enable the achievement of the product characteristics and the effective operation of the control system to be checked. The Standing Committee for Construction has endorsed guidelines for factory production control that closely follow the requirements of EN 29002 (BS 5750: Part 2) and a manufacturer who applies EN 29002 is deemed to satisfy the requirements for factory production control in the Directive[(21)]. The guidelines are intended for use in the assessment and certification of factory production control and of construction products by approved bodies and for incorporation into technical specifications such as harmonized European standards and European technical approvals. It is recognized, though, that writers of technical specifications need not take over every requirement in the guidelines. The specifications will need to go beyond the guidelines in areas such as the testing and inspection of raw materials and components and the finished product, in the control of production processes, and in the control of test equipment. Table 4 sets out the main elements of factory production control recognized by the Standing Committee for Construction.

3.9.3 An approved body may be required to carry out an *initial inspection* of the factory production control system and *continuous surveillance*. Guidance from the Standing Committee indicates that the initial inspection is to determine whether a manufacturer has the prerequisites for factory production control in the form of appropriate staff and equipment[(21)]. This will involve assessing the attitudes of top management to quality control, the suitability of the manufacturer's quality manual, and the capacity of the manufacturer to ensure that the product conforms to technical specifications. If continuous surveillance of the system is required, this will necessitate the annual

Table 4 Elements of factory production control

1 Organization

1.1 *Responsibility and authority.* Definition of responsibility, authority, and interrelation of personnel so that action can be initiated to prevent the occurrence of non-conformity and to identify and record product quality problems.

1.2 *Management representative for factory production control.* Manufacturer must appoint person with authority and knowledge to be responsible for supervising factory production control.

1.3 *Management review.* The production control system shall be reviewed at intervals by the management to ensure its continuing suitability and effectiveness and records of reviews are to be maintained.

---

2 Quality system

Manufacturer must establish and maintain an effective documented factory production control system. The quality manual is to include:

- the quality aims and organizational structure,
- procedures for specifying and verifying raw materials and components,
- manufacturing and production control techniques, processes and systematic actions that will be used,
- inspections and tests that will be carried out before, during, and after manufacture and their frequency.

---

3 Inspection and testing

3.1 *General.* All necessary facilities, equipment and personnel shall be available to carry out necessary tests and inspections. Subcontractors may be used under the control of the manufacturer.

3.2 *Inspection and test status.* The status of the product shall be identified by suitable means so as to indicate conformance or non-conformance throughout production. The inspection authority responsible for the release of the conforming product shall be recorded.

3.3 *Testing.* Testing is to be performed according to the test methods given in the technical specification. This can include indirect testing and sampling.

3.4 *Inspection and test records.* Records include a description of the product, date of manufacture, testing method, test results, limits used, and person carrying out the test. Non-conforming items are to be identified. Records are to be kept for at least 10 years.

---

4 Control of non-conforming products

If the result of a test or inspection is unsatisfactory, steps must be taken to rectify the shortcoming and to set aside and mark non-conforming products. Retesting and inspection must follow after rectification to provide evidence that the defects have been overcome. Notification shall be made to customers if products have been delivered before test results are available.

---

5 Handling, storage, packaging, and delivery of the product

5.1 *General.* Manufacturer shall establish, document, and maintain procedures for handling, storage, packaging, and delivery of product.

5.2 *Handling.* Manufacturer shall provide methods of handling that prevent damage or deterioration.

5.3 *Storage.* Manufacturer shall provide secure storage area to prevent damage or deterioration of product pending use or delivery.

5.4 *Packaging and marking.* Manufacturer shall control packing and marking so as to comply with technical specifications and attestation of conformity requirements.

5.5 *Traceability.* Delivered products must be identifiable and traceable with regard to their production data. The manufacturer must maintain records required in technical specifications and mark products or delivery documents accordingly.

---

6 Training of personnel

The manufacturer shall establish and maintain procedures for the training of personnel and maintain records of training. Personnel performing specific tasks shall be qualified by appropriate training and experience.

Source: Commission of the European Communities, Standing Committee for Construction, *Guidance Paper No 7: Guidelines for the performance of the factory production control for construction products*, CONSTRUCT 91/067

confirmation of a favourable assessment of the system. This should involve two routine inspections a year. During these, test results should be examined to ensure that the required testing has been carried out. The approved body should ensure that the prerequisites still exist and that the factory production control system has been maintained. The manufacturer should notify the approved body of any changes to the factory production control system or quality manual and these may necessitate a reinspection.

3.9.4 A manufacturer may already possess voluntary certification of his quality assurance system and this can be taken into account in the assessment of the factory production control system, providing that the certified system contains the same elements and the certification is by an approved body. Where this results in two certification bodies becoming involved, it is clearly necessary for them to cooperate.

3.9.5 An *extraordinary inspection* will have to be undertaken after failure of a routine inspection, or after a period of at least six months without production. Extraordinary inspections may be requested by the manufacturer or a responsible authority or, with justification, when an approved body thinks it necessary. The failure of an extraordinary inspection will normally result in the withdrawal of the approved body's certificate.

3.9.6 *Type-testing* may be undertaken by the manufacturer or by an approved body. Where an approved body is involved, it selects the sample at random, usually during the initial inspection of the plant[22]. Samples will be taken from factory-inspected production during subsequent routine inspections. In special cases samples are taken from the open market or at the construction site. The frequency of *audit samples* is determined by the technical specifications. Where applicable, there may be comparison between the manufacturer's routine test results, the results of witness testing using the manufacturer's test facilities, and the tests by approved bodies. Inspections with the purpose of carrying out sampling are unannounced. If the tests reveal non-compliance with the technical specifications, the approved body should require the manufacturer to rectify the defect within a short period (less than a month). If the defect results in danger, the competent authorities are to be informed by the approved body. After major faults, there will be an extraordinary inspection and follow-up tests and, if failure occurs, the withdrawal of the certificate. In the event of minor faults, the manufacturer may produce evidence of rectification, which is to be confirmed during the next routine inspection.

3.10 CHOICE OF ATTESTATION OF CONFORMITY PROCEDURES

3.10.1 The Directive grants the Commission the power, in most instances, to determine the method of attestation an individual product must follow. This is to be done after consultation with the Standing Committee for Construction. A manufacturer can opt voluntarily for a more onerous method of attestation if he so chooses.

3.10.2 In a few limited cases, the method of attestation is prescribed by the Directive:

- *Individual non-series items.* A declaration of conformity by the manufacturer in accordance with the third possibility will suffice unless technical specifications provide otherwise.

- *Where attestation has been set at Level 3 or 4 and the manufacturer has failed to, or does not wish to, apply the technical specifications that would require a manufacturer's declaration of conformity by the second or third possibility.* The fitness for purpose must be established using the second possibility, i.e. type-testing by an approved body. If a manufacturer, whose product conformity should be attested to by the second or third possibilities, wishes to deviate from an existing technical specification, this method must be used.

3.10.3 The choice between the methods for attesting conformity depends upon four factors:

- The importance of the part played by the product with respect to the achievement of the essential requirements by the building or works into which it is incorporated,

- The nature of the product,
- The effect of variability in the product's characteristics on its serviceability,
- The product's susceptibility to defects during manufacture.

Thus, the choice of procedures depends in part on the role the product fulfils in construction works and partly on the nature of the product. The Commission is obliged to select the least onerous procedure consistent with safety. The Directive does not make it clear whether the procedure is to be the least onerous for the regulator, manufacturer, or purchaser. It is also not entirely clear what is meant by the term 'safety'. The interpretation implied by the methodology discussed in Sections 3.10.4 to 3.10.6 is that it should be regarded as enabling construction works in which the construction products have been incorporated to satisfy the essential requirements. However, the Council Resolution of 1985 on the New Approach to Technical Harmonization and Standards could also be interpreted to include health and consumer and environmental protection (see Section 2.1.2.3).

3.10.4 The Standing Committee for Construction has put forward a methodology that would enable the appropriate method of attestation to be determined[(24)]. All the essential requirements should be regarded as equally important so that attestation should confirm that all are being satisfied. Products can have a number of different uses. If there is no indication as to the precise use to which the product is to be put in the packaging or labelling, then the most stringent attestation procedure associated with the most demanding use should be applied. There can be different attestation procedures used for a single specification if it permits different levels or classes of performance. Four questions are posed:

- *Is the part played by the product with respect to each essential requirement important, medium, or little?* The question must be applied to a clearly defined use. If there is more than one intended use, then it is to be answered for the most demanding. In considering the use, attention must be paid to fitness for purpose and durability.
- *Will small variations in the product's characteristics or properties be likely to endanger significantly the serviceability or working life of the work? Yes or No?* Small variations may be taken to mean a decrease in performance of less than one level or class. If such variations are difficult to verify on site, the likelihood of there being a significant effect on serviceability or working life is increased.
- *Are the characteristics or properties likely to vary significantly as a result of small variations in the manufacturing process or in manufacturing parameters? Yes or No?* Again, significant variations may be taken to mean a variation of at least a level or class in performance.
- *Are such variations in manufacturing parameters difficult to control? Yes or No?*

3.10.5 The four questions produce a decision tree of the form found in Figure 10. The answers to the first two questions are likely to be given by the Standing Committee for Construction and the last two by the specification writers. The decision tree has been applied experimentally to cement, fly ash for concrete, glass in building, ready-mix concrete, admixtures, and steels for reinforcing and prestressing. Figure 11 shows the decision tree for cement to illustrate how the process may operate.

3.10.6 A decision tree of this form has the advantage of assigning products to risk classes on the basis of objective criteria and on a consistent basis. The questions use classificational rather than quantitative data so that the risk classes must be, to some extent, an arbitrary division of a continuous variable. It implies that each of the four questions should be given equal weighting for each product, which will result in different risk classes than would be the case with differential weighting. The questions posed do not directly answer by how much persons or property are put at risk by the failure of a product to make its contribution to the achievement of the essential requirements by a building. Nor do they consider the cost of the risk that results, or by how much can the risk be moderated by any given method of attestation of conformity. They do not directly answer the questions: what is the danger, is it cost-effective to do something about it, and is it feasible to control the danger through better control of production? The result could be too low a level of assurance in situations in which there is a low probability of a catastrophic event or else a high cost of attestation in situations in which a lower level of assurance is acceptable.

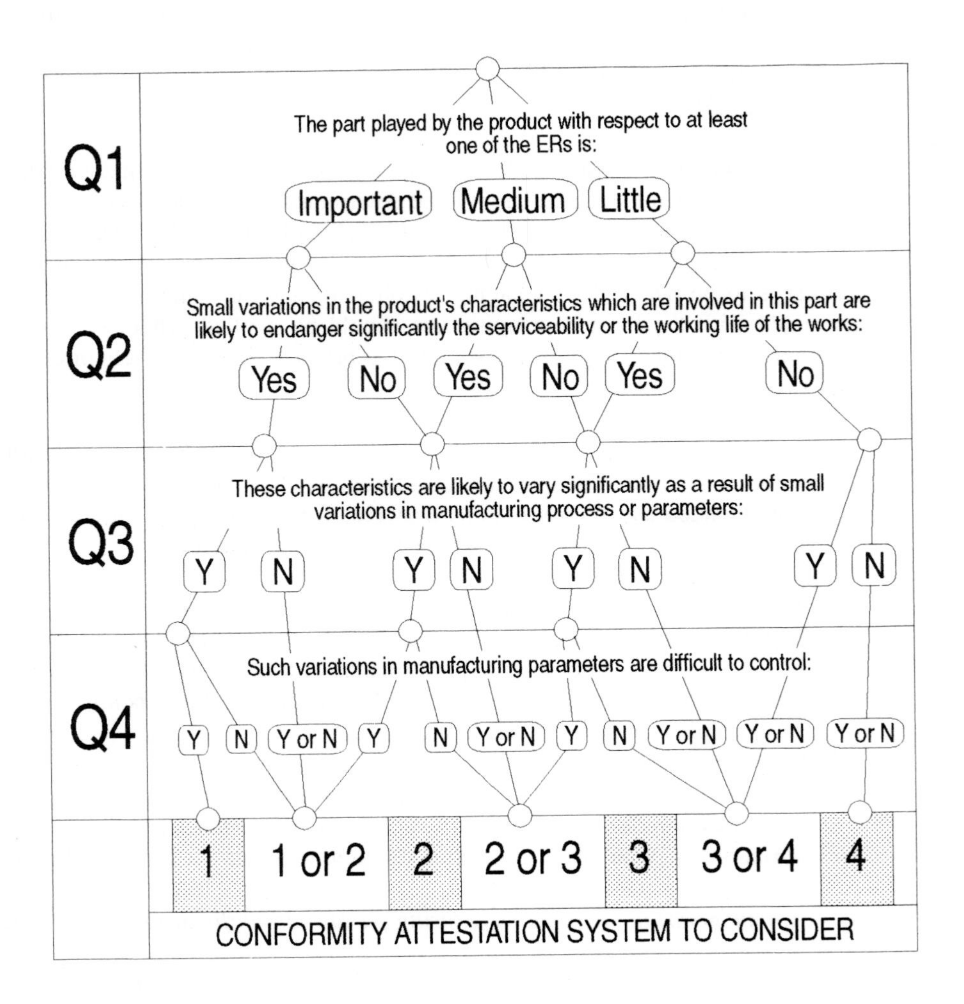

Figure 10 *Attestation of Conformity Decision Tree*

Source: Commission of the European Communities, Standing Committee for Construction (1991) *Guidance Paper No 8: Choice of Conformity Attestation Procedure*, CONSTRUCT 91/68.

3.11 APPROVED BODIES

3.11.1 The Directive identifies three types of body that are to be involved in the attestation of conformity:

- *Certification body.* This is an impartial body which carries out conformity certification to ensure that given rules of procedure and management are followed and that the product conforms to the appropriate technical specifications.

- *Inspection body*. This is an impartial body which can assess and audit manufacturers' quality control operations to ensure that they meet specified criteria and to select and evaluate products on site or in factories against specific criteria.

- *Testing laboratory*. This is a laboratory that measures, tests, or calibrates so as to determine the characteristics or performance of a product.

The same organization could carry out all the functions assigned to each type of body. In the UK, the distinction between a certification body and an inspection body is not clear-cut.

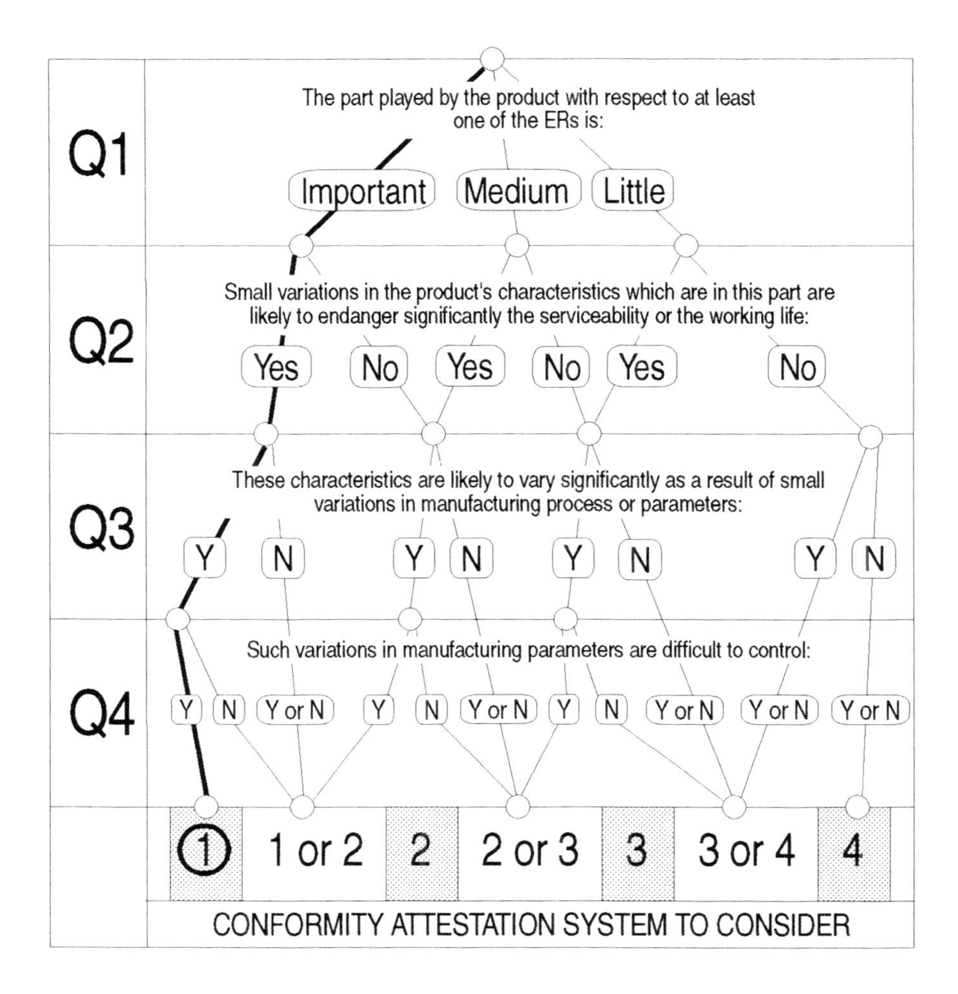

Figure 11 *Decision Tree for Cement*

Source: Commission of the European Communities, Standing Committee for Construction (1991) *Guidance Paper No 8: Choice of Conformity Attestation Procedure*, CONSTRUCT 91/68.

3.11.2 Approved bodies are designated by Member States, who are to notify the Commission of their identity, the products that fall within their competence, and the tasks that have been assigned to them. As Member States have certain responsibilities for the bodies they designate, this has been interpreted to mean that they can designate only those established in their territory[25]. Annex IV of the Directive follows the Toy Safety Directive in setting out the minimum conditions that approved bodies must meet (see Section 2.3.3.2). These are:

- having available personnel, means, and equipment to carry out their tasks,
- having personnel with the necessary technical competence and professional integrity,
- being impartial,
- being able to maintain professional secrecy,
- having civil liability insurance or having their liability guaranteed by the state, which is interpreted in the UK to mean having professional indemnity insurance.

Although Member States are only obliged to verify periodically that approved bodies have the necessary resources and personnel to accomplish their tasks, the Standing Committee for Construction has suggested that, in practice, they will have to verify that all the conditions have been met. It has further suggested that, in the interests of promoting mutual confidence and in order to ensure transparency, Member States should be prepared to justify their designations to the Commission.

3.11.3 The conditions set out in Annex IV of the Directive are imprecise. Earlier drafts of the Directive[5] suggested that the designated bodies would need to comply with the relevant ISO Guides, but this was dropped from later versions. However, since the enactment of the Directive, the EC has adopted as a guiding principle the use of the EN 45000 series for the designation and notification of approved bodies and these substantially incorporate the requirements of the ISO Guides (see Section 2.3.3.3). The EN 45000 series of standards was produced by CEN under mandate from the Commission and EFTA. They are therefore harmonized European standards. The Standing Committee for Construction has determined that testing laboratories should be assessed against EN 45001, *General criteria for the operation of testing laboratories*, certification bodies against EN 45011, *General criteria for certification bodies operating product certification*, and EN 45012, *General criteria for certification bodies operating quality system certification* and inspection bodies against EN 45011 until CEN has adopted a specific standard for inspection bodies. EN 45011 and EN 45012 define an inspection body as one that 'performs inspection services on behalf of a certification body'.

3.11.4 The EN 45000 series is not an exact equivalent to the criteria in Annex IV. The Standing Committee for Construction has interpreted 'supplier's quality system' in EN 45012 as being the equivalent of 'factory production control'. There is no requirement in the EN 45000 series for bodies to have civil liability or professional indemnity insurance and, as yet, there has been no guidance issued as to the minimum level of cover that approved bodies should have. In other respects, the EN 45000 series goes further than the legal requirements of the Directive. The Standing Committee has produced an analysis of the requirements set out in Annex IV and the relevant clauses of EN 45001, EN 45011, and EN 45012 and this is shown in Table 5.

3.11.5 In the letter of designation to approved bodies, the Standing Committee has suggested that Member States should set out:

- the legal basis for designation,
- the tasks, products, and tests for which the body is designated,
- the period for which designation is valid,
- details of how compliance with Annex IV is to be demonstrated (such as compliance with the EN 45000 series) and the evidence of civil liability insurance that is to be produced,
- the requirement to keep full records and to take part in proficiency testing,

- the requirement to make available records to the Member State and to grant it access to carry out inspections,
- the conditions under which designation may be withdrawn and for the transfer of records to another body.

Table 5 Correspondence between Annex IV of the Construction Products Directive and the clauses in the EN 45000 series of standards

Annex IV Criteria	EN 45001 (BS 7501)	EN 45011 (BS 7511)	EN 45012 (BS 7512)
1. Availability of:			
personnel	5.2	4(b),7	4(b),7
means	5.3	11	11
2. Technical competence	5	6,8,9,10,12	6,8,9,10,12
Professional integrity	4	3	3
3. Impartiality	4	4(a),6(b),15	4(a),6(b),15
4. Professional secrecy	5.4	13	13
5. Civil liability insurance	—	—	—

Source: Commission of the European Communities, Standing Committee for Construction (1991) *Guidance Paper No 6: Guidelines for the designation of approved bodies in the field of council directive 89/106/EEC on construction products*, CONSTRUCT 90/065.

3.11.6 It is particularly important that the precise tasks for which a body has been approved be made clear. This will include the methods of attestation of conformity for which it is to be responsible, e.g. type-testing, certification of factory production control, the products for which it may act, and the tests that it may carry out. There has been an attempt to look at the implications of this through an examination of glass products[26]. This involved seeking to identify the products and their uses. The number of products multiplied by the number of uses provides the potential number of attestation routes and the scope of the required certification and inspection bodies. It would advantageous if one testing laboratory could carry out the range of tests for a particular product and for certification and inspection bodies to be able to deal with a family of products.

NAMAS
The National Measurement Accreditation Service was set up in 1985 through amalgamation of the National Laboratory Testing Accreditation Service (NATLAS) and the British Calibration Service. It is managed by the National Physical Laboratory on behalf of the DTI. It accredits site and mobile testing and calibration laboratories as well as conventional ones. Approximately 1300 of the UK's estimated 8000-10 000 laboratories are accredited. Reassessment is at intervals of 3-4 years, with 6-monthly surveillance visits.

3.11.7 The UK's approach to designation has been to state that a prerequisite of approval of testing laboratories is for them to meet the requirements of EN 45001. This can be demonstrated by accreditation under the National Measurement and Accreditation Service (NAMAS). For certification and inspection bodies the prerequisite is compliance with EN 45011 and/or EN 45012, which can be demonstrated by accreditation by the National Accreditation Council for Certification Bodies (NACCB). Although these are prerequisites, there is no obligation on the government to designate every body that meets them, nor to designate a body as being competent for each activity for which it is accredited. There is no scheme for inspection bodies that is distinct from that for certification bodies.

NACCB
The National Accreditation Council for Certification Bodies was set up in 1984 under the charter of the British Standards Institution. It functions separately from the BSI and is responsible to the DTI. It accredits four categories of certification body: those involved in the certification of quality management systems; product conformity assessment; product approval; and the certification of personnel engaged in quality verification.

3.11.8 The Directive, when fully functioning, will probably make substantial demands for testing, certification and inspection facilities. It is not certain that there will be adequate capacity to meet these demands from bodies that comply with the EN 45000 series. A report by IMES identified a number of shortages in facilities in the UK[27]. Among the testing facilities which may be in short supply are fire testing, architectural ironmongery, chimney flues, air admittance valves, backsiphonage protection devices, gas boilers, oil-fired boilers, and building energy management systems. Test facilities could be under pressure from manufacturers' requirements under the Directive as well as from approved bodies. Similarly, the report pointed to wide discrepancies in the coverage of certification schemes, with products such as bricks, drains and sewage pipes having almost the entire output of an industry covered by a scheme, while in fencing, for example, schemes were estimated to cover only 5-10% of firms, and no schemes were found for piling. The shortage of qualified auditors was identified as a potential bottleneck.

3.11.9 Several responses to a possible shortfall of facilities are feasible. Bodies that do not comply with the EN 45000 series could be designated as an interim measure. The demand for testing and certification should raise fees and encourage the provision of facilities. The Commission has considered the issues of subcontracting of work by approved bodies and the use that may be made of manufacturers' laboratories. It has taken the view that a limited amount of subcontracting would be possible by approved bodies, providing it was done under clearly defined terms of reference, for specific tasks, and with transparency in the contracts. However, excessive subcontracting would negate the point of having approved bodies. While Member States would not need to be notified of subcontracting, only designated bodies should be subcontractors. Registers would have to be kept of subcontract work[28]. The UK's response has been that the approach adopted by the Commission is unnecessarily complex and legalistic, particularly in view of the requirements in the EN 45000 series concerning the use of subcontractors.

3.11.10 The use of manufacturers' laboratories would extend the range of potential facilities. IMES[27] estimate that only 1500 of the UK's 8000-10 000 laboratories are independent of both government and manufacturers. However, the use of manufacturers, laboratories raises the question of how impartial they are likely to be. Manufacturers' laboratories can vary between in-house facilities under the control of the production department to independently owned and run facilities that are mainly financed by manufacturers. Where a manufacturer's laboratory undertakes testing on a subcontract basis from an approved body, there seem few potential problems since the approved body is responsible for granting approvals and not the laboratory. The issue of impartiality arises where a manufacturer's laboratory is carrying out type-testing as in the declaration of conformity second possibility. It has been suggested that the key issue is not the ownership of the testing facility but whether it can conduct itself in an independent and objective manner[29]. Manufacturers' laboratories could be designated as approved bodies providing that their impartiality is verified and policed and NAMAS accreditation could be argued to provide an adequate guarantee of impartiality and confidentiality. As they represent a substantial part of the total testing resources available, to exclude them could place a significant barrier in the way of the implementation of the Directive.

3.12 CE MARK

3.12.1 Products that bear the CE mark are presumed to be in conformance with the Directive and enjoy freedom of mobility within the EC. The UK Regulations do not make the CE mark a mandatory requirement as the UK government believes that the Directive permits manufacturers to satisfy its requirements without complying with the technical specifications and the attestation of conformity associated with them. Instead, there could be direct compliance with the obligations of the essential requirements without the product having to follow one of the routes to the attestation of conformity. Therefore, the product would not bear the CE mark. The Commission is believed to disagree with this interpretation. Other Member States could make the CE mark mandatory, which would mean that construction products not bearing it could not be imported into them. In practice, the alternative means of satisfying the Directive may not be cost-effective, so the point may be of theoretical interest only.

3.12.2 It must be emphasized that the CE mark does not convey any information about whether a product is fit for *all* its claimed purposes but merely that, if incorporated and maintained in accordance with the instructions, the works into which it is incorporated should satisfy the essential requirements. A product could fail tests concerned with attributes that are not among the essential requirements and still receive a CE mark. In consequence, quality marks are likely to continue so that manufacturers can demonstrate that their products do more than meet the minimum legal requirements. The CE mark, as was discussed earlier, is an area in which different New Approach directives have produced different requirements, leading to the Commission promising legislation to resolve the resulting discrepancies (see Section 2.3.2). Such legislation would be binding on all existing directives and would automatically change those requirements of the Construction Products Directive which were in conflict with it.

3.12.3 The CE mark should be accompanied by sufficient information to ensure that the authorities are able to police the market effectively and to enable the purchaser to know the purposes for which the product is fit. Relevant information should appear either on the product itself or a label attached to it, its packaging, or on the delivery documentation. This should be in the language of the Member State in which it has been supplied. The Standing Committee for Construction has advocated the use of symbols and codes in order to overcome language problems. The information the UK Regulations require to accompany the CE mark includes, where appropriate:

- characteristics of the product given by reference to relevant technical specifications,
- the last two digits of the year of manufacture,
- identification of the approved body involved in the attestation of conformity,
- the number of the EC certificate of conformity,
- the identity of the manufacturer.

The third and fourth items will not apply in every case but depend upon the approach taken to the attestation of conformity. In addition, the manufacturer may choose to include additional information, such as a factory code. In the case of products imported from outside the EC, the UK Regulations make the CE mark the responsibility of the importer.

3.12.4 Table 6 sets out the information that should accompany certificates and declarations of conformity. The Directive requires them to be presented in the official language(s) of the Member State in which the product is to be used. The UK Regulations require them to be kept by the issuer for at least 10 years. Suggested formats for the certificate and declaration of conformity are being developed by the Standing Committee for Construction.

Table 6 Certificates and declarations of conformity

	EC Certificate of Conformity	EC Declaration of Conformity
Issuing body	*Approved certification body*	*Manufacturer or his agent in the EC*
Name and address of certification body	*	
Name and address of manufacturer or agent in EC	*	*
Name and address of approved body		if applicable
Description of product	*	*
Provisions to which product conforms	*	*
Particular conditions applicable to use of product	*	*
Certificate number	*	
Conditions and period of validity of certificate	if applicable	
Name and position of person empowered to sign	*	*

Source: Council Directive of 21 December 1988 on the approximation of laws, regulations and administrative provisions of the Member States relating to construction products (89/106/EEC), *Official Journal*, L 40, 22 February 1989

3.12.5 A number of construction products will not bear the CE mark. These include:

- products supplied for the first time before implementation date,
- products with no relevant essential requirements with which the works into which they are incorporated must comply,
- products for which there are not relevant technical specifications,
- minor part products,
- products for which the manufacturer has chosen to comply directly with the Directive rather than with technical specifications.

The first category should diminish over time. The second and fourth categories are products that do not need to go through attestation of conformity and so do not obtain a CE mark. The third category will, initially, contain all construction products that play a major role with respect to the essential requirements, but the numbers will gradually fall over time as technical specifications are drafted.

3.13 STANDING COMMITTEE FOR CONSTRUCTION

The Directive is unusual among the New Approach directives in setting up a separate Standing Committee distinct from that established under 83/189/EEC (see Section 2.2.2.2). The Standing Committee comprises two representatives from each Member State and is chaired by a representative of the Commission. Its remit is to examine questions on the implementation and application of the Directive referred to it by the Commission or a Member State. The Standing Committee has regulatory powers concerning the following issues:

- the drawing up and acceptance of interpretative documents,
- the compliance of national technical specifications, harmonized standards, and European technical approvals with the essential requirements,
- determining which products have a minor role to play with respect to health and safety,
- approving mandates for standards and guidelines for European technical approvals,
- the functioning of the European Organization for Technical Approvals,
- the procedures to be adopted for the attestation of conformity for specific products,
- the practicability of the procedures set out in the Directive and appropriate amendments to them.

It is able to determine these issues by means of qualified majority voting (see Section 2.1.1.2). Where the Commission and the Standing Committee are in disagreement, the Council of Ministers will determine the matter.

3.14 POWERS AND RESPONSIBILITIES OF MEMBER STATES

3.14.1 A Member State can take appropriate measures to have withdrawn from the market those products declared to be in conformity with the technical specifications which do not actually comply, even though such products may bear the CE mark. The Commission must be notified of such action. In particular, the Commission is to be notified if the failure to conform is the result of failure to meet technical specifications, the incorrect application of technical specifications, or shortcomings in the technical specifications. Member States can take action against those within their territories who make an inaccurate declaration of conformity.

3.14.2 In the UK responsibility for ensuring that products comply with the Directive falls primarily upon the trading standards officers and, for imported goods, customs officers. The Regulations ensure that the appropriate officers have the necessary powers to fulfil their responsibilities, including the powers to prohibit products being placed on the market, to obtain information, to make test purchases, to seize or detain goods, to search, to require the placing of warning notices, and to recover the expenses of enforcement. Manufacturers are protected from the wrongful exercise of powers by rights of appeal against suspension notices, compensation for wrongful seizure and detention, and against the disclosure of information by the authorities. These are discussed in more detail in Section 10.3.

3.14.3 A Member State can question whether a harmonized standard or European technical approval complies with the essential requirements by seeking its review by the Standing Committee for Construction. In the light of this, the Commission can order its withdrawal.

3.14.4 Member States are under the obligation, under Article 6 (1) of the Directive, to ensure that public bodies, private bodies acting as public undertakings, and private bodies acting as public ones by virtue of their monopoly position do not impede free trade in products bearing the CE mark by their rules or conditions. The effect of this obligation would appear to be to extend the provisions in the Public Works Directive on the use of technical specifications to all public works contracts, including those that fall below the threshold for the activation of the rules for advertising and the award of contracts (see Section 7.3).

3.15 INTERIM AND TRANSITIONAL ARRANGEMENTS

3.15.1 The Directive, unlike some other New Approach directives, does not have a formal transitional period during which products approved under previous national arrangements can be traded alongside those approved by European systems. Yet, for some time after the coming into force of the Directive, there will be gaps in the technical specifications. Until these are filled, the provisions for attestation of conformity for products cannot come into effect, so that products will be unable to obtain the CE mark. National systems for technical specifications and the attestation of conformity will remain in place until superseded by European ones, though the products that meet national specifications cannot bear the CE mark.

3.15.2 Article 16 addresses the issue of the acceptance by one Member State of another's tests and certificates as equivalent to its own until such time as European technical specifications exist. It requires Member States to presume conformity with their national specifications where a product has satisfied tests and inspections carried out in accordance with the specifications of the Member State of destination by an approved body in the producing Member State. Producing Member States approve bodies for this purpose. The reports and attestations of conformity that are produced must be accorded the same value by the importing Member State as it would grant to its own corresponding national documents. The importing Member State can make representations to the Commission if it can substantiate any misgivings it may have about the designated body in the producing Member State. If there is evidence that the tests and inspections are not being carried out properly in conformance with its specifications, the importing Member State can request that action is taken by the producing Member State. If the action is inadequate, the importing Member State may prohibit the product being placed on its market or make it subject to special conditions.

3.15.3 Article 16 could be used to enable Member States to reach bilateral agreements on the recognition of approved bodies or the equivalence of national attestation provisions. Some agreements already exist, for example, between NAMAS in the UK and RNE (France) and Sterlab (Netherlands). Interim measures of this nature could become, in effect, transitional ones so that a quality infrastructure may be created before the Directive comes into effective operation. It should be emphasized that the agreements referred to here are between Member States and are not the voluntary agreements for mutual recognition by testing and certification bodies that are the responsibility of the European Organization for Testing and Certification.

3.16 INTERFACE WITH HEALTH AND SAFETY AT WORK DIRECTIVES

3.16.1 Since 1989 the EC has adopted a series of directives concerning minimum health and safety requirements for workers at work under a Framework Directive (see Section 5.1.1). One of these, concerned with the minimum safety and health requirements for the workplace[30], interfaces with the Construction Products Directive. Its provisions include ones that affect the application to workplaces of certain of the essential requirements, in particular those concerning safety in use, safety in the case of fire, and hygiene, health, and the environment. The Directive is to be brought into force in the UK principally by means of the Workplace (Health, Safety and Welfare) Regulations, supported by an Approved Code of Practice. Drafts of these were issued for consultation by the Health and Safety Commission in January 1992[31]. Draft proposals for new Fire Precaution Regulations have been issued by the Home Office[32].

3.16.2 The Workplace Directive applies to buildings and their ancillary areas used as workplaces. It does not apply to other types of workplaces such as means of transport or construction sites. It applies, from 1 January 1993, to new workplaces used for the first time and to those that have undergone modifications, extensions or conversions. It applies to workplaces in existence on 31 December 1992 from 1 January 1996. This means that workplaces being designed or built which were not in use by 31 December 1992 must satisfy the requirements for new workplaces. It is not clear from either the Directive or the proposed UK Regulations what is meant by the term 'modification' and, therefore, how extensive an alteration will have to be before the workplace is to be regarded as having been modified.

3.16.3 The Directive's provisions fall into three main groups:

- The initial structure of the building as it affects the user, e.g. the design of windows so as to allow their safe cleaning,
- The interaction between the building and its layout and those using it for work, e.g. the provision of safe traffic routes,
- The facilities to be provided for employees within the workplace, e.g. sanitary facilities.

The requirements for both new and existing workplaces are set out in Table 7.

Table 7 Requirements of the Workplace Directive for new and existing workplaces

Stability and solidity of the structure	Ventilation
Electrical installations	Temperature
Emergency routes and exits	Lighting
Fire detection and firefighting	Doors and gates
Movement of pedestrians and vehicles	Sanitary equipment
Rest rooms and rest areas	First aid equipment
Access for handicapped workers	Danger areas
Special provisions for outdoor workplaces, e.g. protection against inclement weather and from falling objects	

Source: Council Directive of 30 November 1989 concerning the minimum safety and health requirements of the workplace (89/654/EEC), *Official Journal*, L 393, 30 December 1989

Employers must ensure that there is proper maintenance and cleansing of the workplace. The detailed requirements for new workplaces are more onerous in certain respects than those for existing ones. In addition, new workplaces are subject to provisions concerning escalators and travolators, loading bays, and room dimensions.

3.16.4 Existing UK legislation substantially covers the Directive's requirements but is not comprehensive or codified. Some 35 pre-1974 acts and regulations will be repealed by the proposed Regulations. Certain workplaces, such as schools and hospitals, which have not been subject to specific health and safety requirements, are covered by the proposed Regulations. An obligation is placed on employers to ensure that workplaces under their control comply with the requirements of the Regulations. Moreover, any person who has control over a workplace must ensure that it complies with the Regulations. This extends the Regulations to cover common parts of buildings and facilities used by employees of other persons and the self-employed. The person in control may be the owner or landlord of the building. The proposed Regulations generally do not distinguish between the requirements for new and existing workplaces other than in the date of compliance. The exceptions to this rule concern openable windows, escalators and travolators, the ability to clean windows, and, in certain respects, traffic routes and glazing. This is generally either because existing requirements already meet those of the Directive or because a distinction cannot sensibly be drawn between those for existing and new workplaces.

3.16.5 The Directive has implications for the design of workplaces if new ones are to meet its requirements. Some of these necessitate changes in the Building Regulations, for example, concerning glazing and swing doors. There are also implications for the use of construction products. For example, Regulation 9 requires that the surfaces of floors, walls, and ceilings shall be capable of being cleaned or redecorated to a suitable standard. The draft Approved Code of Practice states that absorbent floor surfaces, such as untreated concrete, should not be used where they are likely to be contaminated by substances which will be absorbed. There are requirements with respect to maintenance. The Regulations require there to be suitable maintenance of items a fault in which would cause a breach of their requirements, including specific provisions concerning plant such as ventilation equipment and emergency lighting. The draft Approved Code of Practice provides guidance as to what constitutes suitable maintenance, laying particular emphasis on a systematic and documented approach being adopted.

3.16.6 The proposed Fire Precautions Regulations apply the principles found in the health and safety at work directives to risks from fire. Employers must undertake formal assessment of the risks to persons from a fire in the workplace, with new assessments being made after a change of use. An emergency plan must be prepared which includes the means of firefighting provided, the action to be taken by employees, and the evacuation of the premises. The plan must be regularly tested and the results recorded. Records must be kept of fire drills, maintenance work on fire detection and fire fighting equipment, and of training. The fire precautions to be taken depend upon whether the risk situation is classified as high, normal or low. High-risk situations include those where the workplace is used for sleeping accommodation (e.g. hospitals), whether easily ignitable materials are present, whether there are unsatisfactory structural features, and whether there are likely to be members of the public present in a workplace with which they are unfamiliar (e.g. a shopping centre). Workplaces must be provided with adequate means of escape, appropriate means of fire fighting, and adequate means of fire warning and detection. In high-risk areas fixed fire fighting installations, such as sprinklers, may be necessary. Maintenance and construction work carried out by persons who do not normally work in a place should be supervised by a designated person so as to reduce the risk of fire from this source. This has obvious implications for the planning of building work, including maintenance operations.

3.17 CONCLUSIONS

3.17.1 The Construction Products Directive came into force in the UK on 27 December 1991, six months after the intended implementation date. Administrative action is proposed at a later date to give effect to the sections of the Directive dealing with the transposition into national standards of harmonized European standards and the designation of approved bodies. First, however, harmonized standards must be drafted and the tasks for the approved bodies identified. The Standing Committee for Construction must also approve the interpretative documents, mandates for harmonized standards, and the standards themselves, and determine which products are to follow which attestation of conformity procedure.

3.17.2 The Directive applies to construction products, which are defined as being any product produced for incorporation in a permanent manner in construction works. Construction products may be placed on the market only if they enable the works in which they are to be incorporated to satisfy six essential requirements – mechanical resistance and stability, safety in the case of fire, hygiene, health and environment, safety in use, protection against noise, and energy economy and heat retention. The essential requirements are given concrete form in interpretative documents.

3.17.3 In most cases, products will demonstrate their conformity with the Directive by complying with a harmonized European standard or a European technical approval (or, if this is permitted by the Commission, a national specification that satisfies the essential requirements). Harmonized standards are to be drafted by CEN under mandate from the Commission once the interpretative documents have been adopted. Standards can be for products (category B standards) or for design or workmanship (category A standards). European technical approvals will be issued by bodies designated for this purpose by Member States, who collectively form the European Organization for Technical Approvals.

3.17.4 Products designated by the Standing Committee for Construction as 'minor part' products may be placed on the market subject to a declaration of conformity by the manufacturer that they comply with the acknowledged rule of technology. They will not, however, carry the CE mark. Most other products will eventually have to have their compliance with the technical specifications verified by means of attestation of conformity procedures. The precise procedures to be followed will vary according to the importance of the product with respect to the works satisfying the essential requirements and the variability of the product's characteristics. Each approach leads to the CE mark. In each case, the manufacturer must exercise factory production control. Where this is to be subject to third-party certification and surveillance and there is third-party type-testing, in both cases by an approved body, the approved body issues a certificate of conformity. In other cases, the manufacturer makes a declaration of conformity. There are three routes to the declaration of conformity, including one in which there is self-certification by the manufacturer of his factory production control, with type-testing by the manufacturer. Member States designate approved certification and inspection bodies and testing laboratories to carry out certain attestation of conformity functions. The CE mark must not be

confused with a quality mark. It merely shows that the product has met the minimum legal requirements to be placed on the market. It offers no guidance as to whether construction works that incorporate a product bearing the CE mark are capable of attaining an attribute other than those related to the essential requirements.

3.17.5 Until technical specifications are available, products can continue to be placed on the market if they comply with the specifications of a Member State. There are provisions for Member States to recognise each other's tests and certificates. Products that bear the CE mark will enjoy free mobility within the EC without hindrance by Member States. Member States are required to take action to preserve the integrity of the CE mark but can act against products that bear the mark if they have evidence that these do not comply with the essential requirements.

References: 3 Construction Products Directive

1. Council Directive of 21 December 1988 on the approximation of laws, regulations and administrative provisions of the Member States relating to construction products (89/106/EEC), *Official Journal*, L 40, 11 February 1989.

2. The Construction Products Regulations 1991, SI 1991, No. 1620.

3. United Nations Economic Commission for Europe (1985), *Building Regulations in the ECE Countries: Second Report*, New York.

4. Bureau d'Informations et de Prévisions Economiques and its partners in Euroconstruct (1988), *The 'Cost of Non-Europe' in Building Products*, Commission of the European Communities. English-language version published by National Economic Development Office (1989).

5. Proposal for a Council Directive on the approximation of the laws, regulations and administrative provisions of the Member States relating to construction products (submitted to the Council by the Commission), COM(86) 756/3 final.

6. Department of the Environment Circular 13/91, *European Economic Community: Directive 89/106/EEC Construction Products.*

7. Amended proposal for a Council Directive on the implementation of minimum safety and health requirements at temporary or mobile work sites (91/C 112/04), *Official Journal*, C 112, 27 April 1991.

8. Department of the Environment (1991), Construction Products Directive: Information for Manufacturers and Suppliers, *Euronews Construction*, No. 15, September.

9. Courtier, R. H. (1990), Harmonized design – a view of quality assurance in the EEC, *Quality Assurance in Construction*, Thomas Telford.

10. Commission of the European Communities, *Council Directive 89/106/EEC on the approximation of the laws, regulations and administrative provisions of the Member States relating to construction products: Interpretative Document for the Essential Requirement: Mechanical Resistance and Stability*, Document TC1/018-rev 1, July 1991; *Safety in the Case of Fire*, Document TC2/021, 20 September 1991; *Hygiene, Health and the Environment*, Document TC3/023, 20 June 1991; *Safety in Use*, Document TC4/014-rev 1, 14 August 1991; *Protection Against Noise*, Document TC5/016, 12 July 1991; *Energy Economy and Heat Retention*, Document TC6/013, May 1992.

11. Commission of the European Communities Standing Committee for Construction (1990), *Guidelines for the preparation of standardization mandates relating to the Council Directive 89/106/EEC of 21 December 1988 on Construction Products*, CONSTRUCT 90/049.

12. Chemillier, P. (1992), EOTA – Structure and progress to date, *BBA Monthly Datafile News*, Issue 10, January.

13. British Board of Agrément (1992), *EC Standing Committee gives green light for ETAs*, Press Release, 6 January.

14. European Organization for Technical Approvals (1991), *EOTA*, No. 1, September.

15. European Organization for Technical Approvals (1990), *Working Arrangements*, ACTC (90) P49, P50.

16. British Board of Agrément (1990), *Annual Report.*

17. Atkinson, G. (1987), *A Guide through Construction Quality Standards*, Van Nostrand Reinhold.

18. Department of the Environment (1991) *The Structure and Organization of ETA Resources in the UK*, ACTC(19)P8 rev 2.

19. Council Directive of 25 June 1987 on the harmonization of the laws of the Member States relating to simple pressure vessels (87/404/EEC), *Official Journal*, L 220, 8 August 1987.

20. Commission of the European Communities, Standing Committee for Construction (1990), *Draft Guidance Paper No. 1: Treatment of so-called 'LOCAL PRODUCTS' within the scope of Council Directive 89/106/EEC*, CONSTRUCT 90/038-rev 2.

21. Commission of the European Communities, Standing Committee for Construction (1991), *Draft Guidance Paper No. 10: Guidelines for the assessment and certification of the factory production control by an approved body*, CONSTRUCT 91/073.

22. Commission of the European Communities, Standing Committee for Construction (1991), *Draft Guidance Paper No. 9: Guidelines for the certification of construction products by an approved certification body*, CONSTRUCT 91/072.

23. Commission of the European Communities, Standing Committee for Construction (1991), *Guidance Paper No. 7: Guidelines for the performance of the factory production control for construction products*, CONSTRUCT 91/067.

24. Commission of the European Communities, Standing Committee for Construction (1991), *Guidance Paper No. 8: Choice of Conformity Attestation Procedure*, CONSTRUCT 91/068.

25. Commission of the European Communities, Standing Committee for Construction (1991), *Guidance Paper No. 6: Guidelines for the designation of approved bodies in the field of the council directive 89/106/EEC on construction products*, CONSTRUCT 90/065.

26. Department of the Environment (1991), *Conformity attestation levels for glass products and their intended uses*, ACTC(91)P7.

27. International Marketing and Economic Services (UK) Ltd (1990), *A Study of UK Testing and Certification Resources for Construction Products*, Department of the Environment.

28. Commission of the European Communities (1990), *Guiding principles for subcontracting by 'notified bodies' pursuant to the Council Decision of 13 December 1990 concerning the modules for the various phases of the conformity assessment procedures*, Certif 90/5.

29. Department of the Environment (1991), *Guidance Paper No. 6: Annex E – The role of manufacturers' test laboratories*, ACTC(90)P56.

30. Council Directive of 30 November 1989 concerning the minimum safety and health requirements for the workplace (89/654/EEC), *Official Journal*, L 393, 30 December 1989.

31. Health and Safety Commission (1992), *Proposals for Workplace (Health, Safety and Welfare) Regulations and Approved Code of Practice: Consultative Document.*

32. Home Office (1992), *Proposals for Fire Precautions (Places of Work) Regulations 1992 and Associated Guidance: Consultative Document.*

4 Technical harmonization of building services

4.0 OVERVIEW

4.0.1 Building services are products produced for incorporation in a permanent manner in construction works. As such, they are subject to the Construction Products Directive. They are also subject to other New Approach directives and can only bear the CE mark if they satisfy the requirements of all relevant directives. The principal New Approach directives adopted to date to affect building services are those concerned with Gas Appliances, Electromagnetic Compatibility, and Machinery. They are not just concerned with construction products but with a wider range of items, many of which have no connection with construction. The Gas Appliances Directive is concerned with gas appliances and fittings other than those used in industrial processes. Thus, appliances, such as domestic gas central heating boilers, are subject to both the Construction Products and Gas Appliances Directives. The Electromagnetic Compatibility Directive is concerned with any electrical and electronic apparatus that is liable to cause electromagnetic disturbance or whose performance may be affected by electromagnetic disturbance. The apparatus covered by the Directive includes any appliance, equipment, or installations that contain electrical or electronic components and so includes electrical engineering in construction works. The Machinery Directive is concerned with any assembly of linked parts or components, at least one of which moves. It also covers assemblies of machines that function as an integrated whole. It thus applies to mechanical engineering in construction works.

4.0.2 As these three Directives, like the Construction Products Directive, have been produced under the New Approach to Technical Harmonization and Standards (see Section 2.1.2), they have a number of points in common. The principal points of similarity are:

- *The setting out of harmonization requirements in the form of essential requirements necessary for the achievement of safety of persons and domestic animals and for the protection of property and the absence of detailed technical specifications,*

- *The use of harmonized European standards, drafted by CEN and CENELEC under mandate from the Commission, as the primary means by which it may be demonstrated that a product complies with the essential requirements,*

- *The bearing of the CE mark by products that satisfy the Directives, and a prohibition on Member States from impeding the free mobility of those products that carry it,*

- *The right of Member States to challenge standards and products, where they have reason to believe that they do not satisfy the essential requirements, and an obligation on them to take steps to protect the integrity of the CE mark,*

- *The use of approved or notified bodies designated by Member States for the purpose of carrying out tests on products, designs, and production systems as part of the process by which a product is attested as conforming to the essential requirements.*

4.0.3 There are also some important differences between these Directives and the Construction Products Directive.

- *The absence of dedicated Standing Committees to manage these Directives. The Commission receives technical advice on each of these three Directives from the Committee set up under the directive 83/198/EEC, which lays down a procedure for Member States to provide information on technical standards and regulations (see Section 2.2.2). For the Machinery Directive, the Commission is also advised on implementation by a Standing Committee of representatives of the Member States, but none of the Directives is, in this sense, as closely managed as the Construction Products Directive.*

- *The absence of interpretative documents.* ***The essential requirements are set out in much greater detail than in the Construction Products Directive, both in terms of the areas with which they are concerned and the aspirations that they contain. However, they are not as detailed as the interpretative documents produced under the Construction Products Directive.***

- *The absence of an equivalent procedure to that of the European technical approval to handle the approval of innovatory products or the innovatory use of products.* ***Instead, use tends to be made of type-testing by approved bodies in circumstances in which there are no appropriate standards or the manufacturer has not fully complied with the available standards.***

- *Differences in the procedures adopted for the attestation of conformity.* ***In some cases the terminology employed or the procedures used have no direct equivalents either with the Construction Products Directive or other New Approach directives. This illustrates the problem that, while the New Approach directives are supposed to follow a common pattern, there are, in practice, wide variations in approach, particularly to the attestation of conformity (see Section 2.3.1). This can lead to incompatibility between the approaches of different directives and can present problems for manufacturers, who may have to satisfy more than one directive in order to place a product on the market. For this reason, the decision 90/683/EEC has sought to reduce the variations to choices from within a common set of modules. However, these cannot apply to existing directives until they come up for review.***

- *The UK regulations bringing these Directives into force are likely to take the form of safety regulations made under Section 11 of the Consumer Protection Act 1987.*

4.1 GAS APPLIANCES DIRECTIVE

4.1.1 Introduction

4.1.1.1 In June 1990, the EC adopted a directive for the approximation of the laws of Member States relating to appliances burning gaseous fuels[1]. This was due to come into force on 1 January 1992, with Member States being required to have adopted and published their implementing provisions by 1 July 1991. It repeals and replaces two previous directives dealing with gas appliances and gas water heaters, namely 84/530/EEC (as amended by 86/312/EEC) and 84/531/EEC (as amended by 88/665/EEC), though neither of these had been formally activated. The UK Regulations to implement the Directive came into force on 6 April 1992[2]. The Regulations are safety regulations made under section 11 of the Consumer Protection Act 1987 (see Section 9.3.8). Until 31 December 1995, appliances that comply with a Member State's regulations in force on 1 January 1992 can continue to be supplied. This will provide manufacturers with a transition period in which to redesign products and obtain the necessary attestations of conformity. The UK Regulations in force on 1 January 1992 were the Gas Cooking Appliances (Safety) Regulations 1989 and the Heating Appliances (Fireguards) Regulations 1991, the general safety requirements of Section 10 of the Consumer Protection Act 1987, and the duties of manufacturers with regard to articles for use at work under the Health and Safety at Work Act 1974.

4.1.1.2 The Directive requires gas appliances and fittings sold in the EC to satisfy essential safety requirements so as not to endanger persons, animals, or property. Failure to comply with these is a criminal offence. Appliances that meet the essential requirements carry the CE mark as well as certain specified information on installation, servicing, and use, in the language of the country of destination. The CE mark is awarded only after a type-examination and one of several alternative methods of supervision of production by a body approved for this purpose by one of the Member States. Member States are not permitted to impede free trade in, and the installation of, gas appliances and fittings that comply with the Directive. However, it will not wholly overcome barriers to trade as these also result from Member States supplying gas with different combustion properties and at different pressures[3].

4.1.2 Scope

4.1.2.1 The Directive applies to two types of product.

- *Appliances*. These are appliances that burn gaseous fuels that are used for cooking, heating, hot water production, refrigeration, lighting, or washing and have a normal water temperature not exceeding 105°C. Gaseous fuels are defined as being any fuel which is in a gaseous state at a temperature of 15°C under a pressure of 1 bar. Forced-draught burners and heating bodies to be equipped with such burners are defined as being appliances.

- *Fittings*. These are safety devices, controlling devices, regulating devices, and sub-assemblies (other than forced-draught burners and heating bodies), which are separately marketed for trade use and designed to be incorporated into an appliance or assembled so as to constitute an appliance.

The distinction between appliances and fittings has implications for the way in which different products are treated with respect to attestation of conformity.

4.1.2.2 The Directive excludes appliances specifically designed for use in industrial processes carried out on industrial premises. Issues concerning their safety fall within the remit of the health and safety at work directives (see Section 5.1.1). It must be emphasized that the exclusion only covers industrial processes so that gas appliances used in other contexts on industrial premises are covered by the Directive, for example, those in use in commercial catering equipment, building heating systems, and factory heating and washing facilities.

Gas appliances installed into construction works, such as domestic central heating units, are subject to the Gas Appliances Directive as well as to the Construction Products Directive.

4.1.2.3 The drafts of the UK Regulations proposed to extend the scope of the Directive so that second-hand appliances supplied must also satisfy the essential requirements[(4)]. However, the Regulations adopted exclude second-hand appliances even if they have been repaired or reconditioned.

4.1.3 Essential requirements

4.1.3.1 The Directive provides that gas appliances may be placed on the market and put into service only if, when normally used, they do not compromise the safety of persons, domestic animals, and property. Member States are required to take all necessary steps to ensure that this is done so that the placing of an unsafe product on the market is a criminal act. Enforcement in the UK is through trading standards departments and the Health and Safety Executive.

4.1.3.2 An appliance is said to be *normally used* when it is:

- Correctly installed and regularly serviced in accordance with the manufacturer's instructions,

- Used with a normal variation in gas quality and supply pressure. Member States must communicate to the Commission the types of gas and supply pressures used on their territories,

- Used in accordance with its intended purpose or in a way which can reasonably be foreseen.

4.1.3.3 The Directive sets out essential requirements that appliances and fittings must satisfy in order to be regarded as being safe. Member States may not impede the free mobility, or the putting into service, of appliances and fittings that satisfy the essential requirements. Appliances that satisfy the essential requirements may carry the CE mark, while fittings have a certificate of conformity.

The essential requirements fall into three main groups and are relatively detailed when compared with those to be found in the Construction Products Directive. They are:

- *General conditions.* Appliances must be designed and built so as to operate safely and present no danger when normally used. When they are placed on the market, they must be accompanied by technical instructions for the installer, instructions for use and servicing, and appropriate warning notices. The latter must also appear on the packaging. These instructions and warning notices are to appear in the official languages of the Member States of destination. The technical instructions and warning notices should include the type of gas used, the gas supply pressure, the flow of fresh air required, the conditions for the dispersal of combustion products, and restrictions on use, particularly requirements for ventilation. Fittings must be provided with instructions for installation, adjustment, operation, and maintenance. They must be so designed and built as to fulfil their intended purpose when incorporated into appliances in accordance with instructions.

- *Materials.* Materials must be appropriate for their intended purpose and must withstand the technical, chemical, and thermal conditions to which they may foreseeably be subjected. Manufacturers must guarantee the properties of materials that are important for safety.

- *Design and construction.* Appliances are to be constructed so that when normally used safety will not be impaired by instability, distortion, breakage, or wear. Specifically, condensation must not affect safety; the risk of explosion resulting from external fire is to be minimized; water and inappropriate air should not penetrate the gas circuits; fluctuations or failures of auxiliary energy should not result in an unsafe situation; levers and controls should be marked and give appropriate instructions so as to prevent handling errors; and the failure of controlling and regulatory devices should not lead to an unsafe situation. There are specific requirements with respect to unburned gas release, ignition, combustion, the rational use of energy, temperatures, and appliances that may come into contact with either foodstuffs or water used for sanitary purposes. For example, the surface temperatures of external parts of appliances intended for domestic use must not present a danger for the user or a danger to surrounding areas.

4.1.3.4 Gas appliances that are to be incorporated into construction works must also satisfy the essential requirements set out in the Construction Products Directive. In particular, these include safety in the case of fire, hygiene, health and the environment, safety in use, and energy economy and heat retention (see Section 3.3.5).

4.1.4 Technical specifications

An appliance is presumed to satisfy the essential requirements if it complies with:

- *A national standard transposing a harmonized European standard.* CEN is to be mandated by the Commission to draft the latter.

- *A national standard.* This applies in circumstances in which there are no harmonized standards. Such standards must be accepted by the Commission as complying with the essential requirements. Other Member States will be notified of which standards have been accepted and their reference numbers will be published in the *Official Journal.*

The Directive does not contain any procedure equivalent to the European technical approval found in the Construction Products Directive. Both the Commission and Member States may challenge standards on the grounds that they do not satisfy the essential requirements.

4.1.5 Attestation of conformity

4.1.5.1 Attestation of conformity provides assurance that there really has been compliance with the essential requirements. Figure 12 sets out the alternative approaches permitted by the Directive and Table 8 the obligations on manufacturers and notified bodies under each approach. The approaches differ according to whether the product is defined as being an appliance or a fitting. Appliances may bear the CE mark, providing that they comply with the requirements of this Directive and any other relevant directive, such as the Construction Products Directive. They are also accompanied by either a written declaration or a written certificate of conformity. Fittings do not bear the CE mark, being component parts, but are to be accompanied by a certificate declaring conformity with the Directive, listing their characteristics, and stating how they must be incorporated into an appliance so that the appliance satisfies the essential requirements. Otherwise the approach to attestation of conformity for a fitting is identical to that for a series-produced appliance.

4.1.5.2 For appliances, attestation of conformity varies according to whether production is part of a series or is of a single unit or of a small quantity. For *series-produced* items, attestation of conformity comprises two stages. The first of these is the *EC type-examination*. Under this a prototype is examined by a *notified body*, which checks and certifies that the appliance complies with the Directive. Notified bodies are designated by Member States. The requirements that notified bodies must satisfy are set out in Annex V of the Directive and are identical to those used for approved bodies in other New Approach directives (see Section 2.3.3). Bodies which satisfy assessment criteria laid down in applicable harmonized standards (the EN 45000 series) are presumed to satisfy the requirements of Annex V. Member States notify the Commission and other Member States of the bodies responsible for carrying out attestation procedures. The UK Regulations make it clear that relevant notified bodies include ones approved by other Member States.

4.1.5.3 The UK government proposes initially to designate as notified bodies British Gas (Watson House and Midlands Research Station), the British Standards Institution, and Calor Gas Appliance Testing Laboratory[4]. Other bodies may also be designated providing they hold NAMAS accreditation to EN 45001 (for product testing) and NACCB accreditation to EN 45011 and/or EN 45012. The UK Regulations grant the Secretary of State for Trade and Industry power to approve notified bodies for unlimited or specific periods of time and to set conditions for their operations. The Regulations empower notified bodies to carry out their various functions under the Directive and oblige them to carry them out in the ways set out in it. Their powers include the issuing of notices to manufacturers that suspend EC type-examination certificates and EC verifications. They are permitted to charge appropriate fees, which are equal to the sum of their costs in carrying out their functions and a 'reasonable' profit. The latter is defined by reference to the character and extent of the work done and the commercial rate normally charged for profit for similar work. Thus the Regulations are intended to prevent notified bodies from exploiting their quasi-monopoly positions by making excess charges. They also make it clear that manufacturers must pay appropriate fees in order to obtain the necessary approvals. Thus, a product could satisfy the Directive but fail to obtain a CE mark as a result of non-payment by the manufacturer.

4.1.5.4 A manufacturer lodges an application with just one notified body. The application includes his identity, a declaration that the application has not been lodged with any other notified body, and the *design documentation*. The contents of the design documentation are specified by Annex IV of the Directive (Schedule 1 of the UK Regulations) and must include:

- A general description of the appliance,
- Conceptual designs, manufacturing drawings, and diagrams of components and sub-assemblies,
- The standards that have been applied and the solutions adopted to meet the essential requirements,
- Test reports,
- Manuals for installation and use.

Where appropriate, the design documentation must also contain:

- Attestations relating to equipment incorporated in the appliance,

- Attestations and certificates relating to the methods of manufacture, inspection, and monitoring of the appliance,

- Any other document making it possible for the notified body to improve its assessment.

The notified body examines the design documentation and verifies that the appliance has been manufactured in conformity with it and appropriate standards. Where the solutions adopted are not based upon standards, it will test whether they comply with the essential requirements. Innovations can therefore be dealt with even though there is no procedure equivalent to the European technical approval. Where the prototype satisfies the requirements of the Directive, the notified body issues an *EC type-examination certificate* and informs other notified bodies. The certificate contains any conditions for its validity, descriptions of the appliance's functioning, and data for its identification. Relevant technical elements, such as drawings and diagrams, are appended. The manufacturer must keep the notified body informed of modifications, which must also be approved.

4.1.5.5 Once the EC type-examination has been completed, the manufacturer has to choose between one of four procedures aimed at ensuring that production takes place in accordance with the type-test. This must be done prior to the appliance being placed on the market. Although the four procedures vary in the degree of assurance that they provide to the purchaser, the manufacturer is able to choose which approach to adopt. There is no equivalent to the risk- assessment exercise undertaken to determine the method of attestation of conformity for construction products. It is possible that market forces may result in appliances that follow particular routes being unmarketable as consumers may either feel that the level of assurance is insufficient or else are not prepared to pay for a higher level of assurance. Thus, the manufacturer's choice may be constrained by economic factors. The choices of attestation at the production stage are between:

- *EC Declaration of Conformity to Type*. The manufacturer takes the necessary measures to ensure that the appliances produced conform to the prototype. This is checked by the notified body carrying out random on-site tests at least once per annum. In the event of failure, the notified body takes appropriate measures to prevent the marketing of the appliance. The manufacturer affixes the CE mark and draws up a written *declaration of conformity*. The CE mark is accompanied by that of the notified body that carried out the random checks.

- *EC Declaration of Conformity to Type (guarantee of production quality)*. The manufacturer introduces a *quality system* that ensures the conformity of appliances with the prototype. An application is lodged by a notified body for the approval of the quality system. The application includes documentation of the system and of the approved type. The manufacturer must also undertake to carry out the obligations arising from the quality system and to ensure its continuing suitability and effectiveness. The documentation of the quality system includes its objectives, the organizational structure and the responsibilities and powers of management, the manufacturing processes and how quality is controlled during them, the nature and frequency of tests and examinations, how the quality objectives are monitored, and the method employed to monitor the effectiveness of tests and examinations. The notified body evaluates the system but will presume compliance where the quality system implements the 'corresponding harmonized standard'. The DTI[5] interprets this to mean EN 29002 (BS 5750: Part 2). The manufacturer must inform the notified body of changes in the system. The manufacturer is subjected to *EC surveillance*, which is aimed at ensuring that he fulfils his obligations under the quality system. The notified body checks the quality system at least every two years and can make unannounced visits. It has access to the quality system documentation, design documentation, and quality records, including test and inspection results, calibration data, and staff qualifications. It also carries out occasional testing of appliances. The manufacturer is responsible for affixing the CE mark and for drawing up a written *declaration of conformity*.

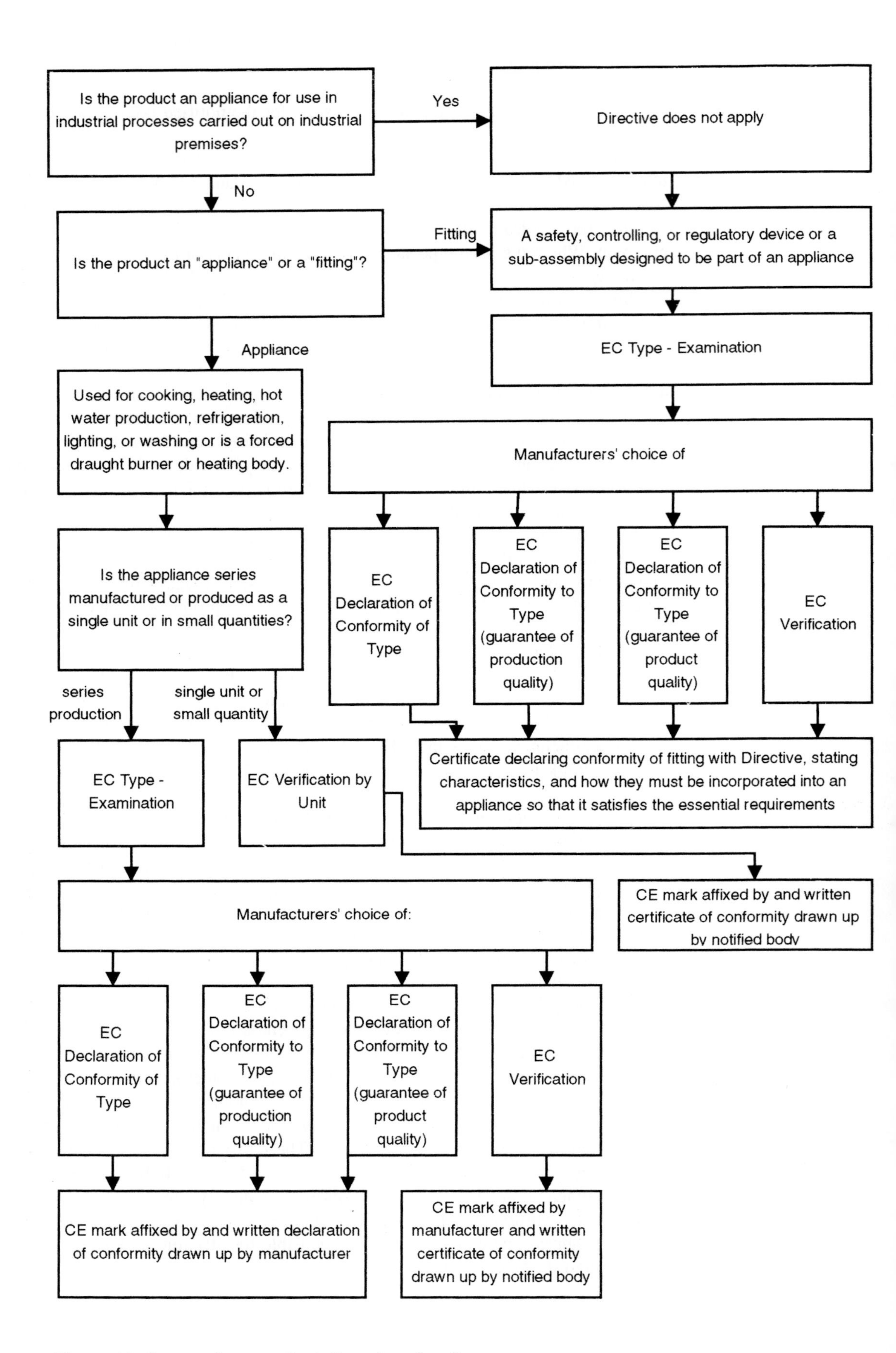

Figure 12 *Gas appliances attestation of conformity*

Source: Council Directive of 29 June 1990 on the approximation of the laws of the Member States relating to appliances burning gaseous fuels (90/396/EEC), *Official Journal*, L 196, 26 July 1990

Table 8 Gas appliances attestation of conformity responsibilities

	EC Declaration of Conformity to Type	EC Declaration of Conformity to Type (guarantee of production quality)	EC Declaration of Conformity to Type (guarantee of product quality)	EC Verification Test	EC Verification by Unit
Manufacturer	• Product design documentation • Take steps to ensure homogeneity of production • Affix CE mark • Draw up written declaration of conformity	• Produce design documentation • Install and maintain quality system • Affix CE mark • Draw up written declaration of conformity	• Produce design documentation • Install and maintain quality system • Test each appliance for conformity • Affix CE mark • Draw up written declaration of conformity	• Produce design documentation • Take steps to ensure homogeneity of production • Affix CE mark where testing by batches	• Produce design documentation
Notified body	• Test prototype • Random on-site checks of appliances	• Test prototype • Evaluate quality system • Surveillance of quality system	• Test prototype • Evaluate quality and testing systems • Surveillance of quality and testing systems	• Testing prototype • Test sample batches or each appliance produced • Affix CE mark where testing by each appliance • Draw up written certificate of conformity	• Test each appliance • Affix CE mark • Draw up written certificate of conformity

Source: Council Directive of 29 June 1990 on the approximation of the laws of the Member States relating to appliances burning gaseous fuels (90/396/EEC), *Official Journal*, L 196, 26 July 1990

- *EC Declaration of Conformity to Type (guarantee of product quality).* The manufacturer installs a quality system in line with that of the guarantee of production quality. However, as part of the quality system, each appliance is examined to check its conformity with the essential requirements. The notified body evaluates the quality system but will presume conformance with the Directive's requirements for quality systems if it implements the corresponding harmonized standard. The DTI[5] interprets this to mean EN 29003 (BS 5750: Part 3). The manufacturer is subjected to *EC surveillance* with the notified body checking the quality system at least every two years. The manufacturer is responsible for affixing the CE mark and for drawing up a written *declaration of conformity.*

- *EC Verification.* The notified body checks that appliances conform to the Directive. The manufacturer can choose whether this is done for each appliance or on a statistical basis through the sampling of batches. The acceptance criteria for batches are set as:

  - A standard quality level corresponding to a 95% probability of acceptance with a percentage of non-conformity between 0.5 and 1.5%, *and*

  - A limit quality corresponding to a 5% probability of acceptance with a percentage of non-conformity between 5 and 10%.

  If batches are rejected frequently, the notified body may suspend statistical verification. The manufacturer affixes the CE mark where testing is by batches; the notified body does so when testing is undertaken for each appliance produced. The notified body draws up a written *certificate of conformity* irrespective of whether testing is by batch or individual appliance.

4.1.5.6 Where an appliance is produced as a *single unit* or in small quantities, it may be subject to *EC Verification by Unit.* The notified body checks that each appliance is in conformity with the requirements of the Directive. There is no EC type-examination or the use of any of the four methods for assuring quality in production but the *design documentation* is made available to the notified body. The notified body affixes the CE mark to the appliance and draws up a written *certificate of conformity.*

4.1.6 CE mark

4.1.6.1 The CE mark comprises the symbol, 'CE', followed by the last two digits of the year in which the mark was affixed and the identification symbol of the notified body that has carried out the random checks, EC surveillance, or EC verification. It must be visible, easily legible, and indelible, and be either on the appliance or on a data plate attached to it. The appliance must bear the manufacturer's name, the trade name of the appliance, the type of electrical supply used, if applicable, and the appliance category. Information for installation may also be added. The UK Regulations make it an offence to supply any appliance or fitting that does not satisfy the essential requirements, an appliance that does not bear a CE mark (subject to the transitional arrangements that apply until 1996), or a fitting for which a certificate has not been issued. Therefore the CE mark will be mandatory in this area.

4.1.6.2 Member States have the responsibility of ensuring that the CE mark is not misused. These include ensuring that appliances bearing the CE mark are withdrawn if they compromise safety, and taking action against those wrongly affixing marks. The UK Regulations state that data plates are to be so designed as not to be reusable. Notified bodies can withdraw the right to affix the CE mark (or to issue the certificate of conformity for fittings) if these have been wrongly attributed due to their not conforming to prototypes, or to the essential requirements, or if the manufacturer has failed to fulfil his obligations under a quality system. The Directive's enforcement in the UK is by trading standards officers for domestic appliances and health and safety inspectors for appliances used at work, using the powers granted to them respectively by the Consumer Protection Act 1987 and the Health and Safety at Work Act 1974.

4.1.7 Hot-water Boilers Directive

4.1.7.1 In May 1992 the EC adopted a New Approach directive concerned with the efficiency of new hot-water boilers fired with liquid or gaseous fuels[6]. Its aims are to eliminate technical barriers to trade that result from the measurement of energy efficiency and to encourage energy saving. Member States are to bring the Directive into force from 1 January 1994. Until 31 December 1997 they may permit boilers to be placed on the market if they comply with national specifications in force on the date of adoption, i.e. 1 January 1993.

4.1.7.2 Member States are to take all necessary measures to ensure that boilers cannot be put into service unless they satisfy certain efficiency requirements. These are measured at rated output and at part load. Different requirements are set for standard, low-temperature, and gas-condensing boilers. Harmonized standards will in due course determine the verification methods for production and measurement. The Directive allows Member States to apply a system of labelling so as to permit recognition of the energy performance of boilers:

* Applies if the efficiency at rated output and at part load is at least equal to the relevant values for standard boilers

** Applies if the efficiency at rated output and at part load is three or more points higher than the relevant values for standard boilers.

Every extra step of efficiency of three points at rated output and part load qualifies for an extra *.

4.1.7.3 The Directive has two features of more general interest:

- It is the first construction-orientated New Approach directive to be adopted that makes use of the modular approach to conformity assessment (see Section 2.3.1). Series-produced boilers are to be assessed by:

  - an EC type-examination that follows Module B at the design phase, and

  - a declaration of conformity to the approved type at the production phase in accordance with Module C (conformity to type), D (production quality assurance), or E (product quality assurance).

  The procedures for gas boilers are to be those used to assess conformity under the Gas Appliances Directive (see Section 4.1.5.5).

- It makes use of the revised criteria for notified bodies and not those first to be found in the Toy Safety Directive (see Section 2.3.3.4). Bodies that satisfy the criteria laid down in the 'corresponding harmonized standards' (i.e. the EN 45000 series) shall be deemed to comply with the criteria.

4.2 ELECTROMAGNETIC COMPATIBILITY DIRECTIVE

4.2.1 Introduction

4.2.1.1 The Directive to approximate the laws relating to electromagnetic compatibility was adopted in May 1989[7]. It was to be applied by Member States from 1 January 1992. Originally, it was intended that there would be a transitional period to 31 December 1992, during which Member States could continue to approve products on the basis of the national arrangements in force on 1 January 1992. This was intended to provide an opportunity for manufacturers to make the necessary attestations of conformity or to redesign products. However, the transitional period has been extended to 31 December 1995 with Member States being able to approve apparatus that conforms to national regulations in force on 30 June 1992. This is to permit greater time for the drafting of harmonized European standards and for apparatus in stock to be marketed[8]. The Commission has produced an explanatory document relating to the Directive[9]. The document has not been formally endorsed by the Commission and has no formal legal status, but it does provide an insight into the

Commission's thinking. It seeks to clarify certain areas of ambiguity in the Directive. The text of this document is being debated, with the UK government having raised a number of issues concerning the points made in it[10].

4.2.1.2 The Directive requires that most electrical or electronic products made or sold in the EC must be constructed so as not to cause undue electromagnetic interference or to be unduly affected by it. Failure to comply with the Directive will be a criminal offence. For the UK, it extends the present controls over radio interference to electromagnetic phenomena in general. It repeals two other directives, 76/889/EEC and 76/890/EEC, which are concerned with approximating laws on radio interference from household appliances, portable tools, and fluorescent lighting. Thus, any electrical engineering work within a building or construction work is also subject to this Directive as well as to the Construction Products Directive.

4.2.2 Scope

4.2.2.1 The Directive applies to any apparatus which is either liable to cause electromagnetic disturbance or whose performance is liable to be affected by such disturbance. Such apparatus includes electrical and electronic appliances and equipment and installations containing electrical or electronic components. Any apparatus which is subject to specific directives, such as motor vehicle spark plugs and radio equipment used by amateurs, is excluded from its scope. Electromagnetic disturbance is defined as being any electromagnetic phenomenon that may degrade performance, including noise, an unwanted signal, or a change in the propagation medium. The essential requirements of the Construction Products Directive include protection against noise, but not against other electromagnetic phenomena.

The Electromagnetic Appliances Directive applies to any construction products that contain electrical or electronic components.

4.2.2.2 Member States are obliged to take measures to ensure that apparatus is placed on the market *or* taken into service only if it complies with the requirements of the Directive, when properly installed and maintained and used for the purposes for which it was intended. The Directive explicitly considers the issue of the taking into service of apparatus as well as its supply.

4.2.2.3 The question as to what constitutes the precise scope of the Directive has raised a number of issues[11]. The Directive applies to apparatus but does not apply to components. Components are defined as items that do not have an intrinsic function and whose only purpose is to be incorporated inside an apparatus. Manufacturers of components are to indicate to the manufacturer of the apparatus how to use and incorporate them. Apparatus, covered by the Directive, to which an additional component has been added or one has been replaced, must still conform to the Directive. There is a particular problem in determining the fitness for purpose of components that may be used in a number of applications. UK legislation is likely to be limited to those components intended for use for specific purposes. Some components are sold to the public, for example as replacement parts. These should be subject to testing in the interests of consumer protection even if those supplied to manufacturers are not.

4.2.2.4 The Commission has sought to clarify some of the issues by distinguishing in its explanatory document between the terms 'apparatus', 'system', and 'installation'. Apparatus is defined as being a finished product with an intrinsic function, the term 'equipment' being regarded as being synonymous with apparatus. A system comprises several items of apparatus intended to function as a single unit, for example, a computer workstation consisting of a screen, keyboard, and printer. An installation means several combined items of apparatus or systems put together to fulfil a specific objective, but not intended to be placed on the market as a single functional unit. The Commission argues that the Directive applies to systems, which must satisfy its requirements as a unit. Each apparatus in an installation must individually satisfy the Directive, including the requirement that there must be information to enable it to be used in accordance with its intended purpose, so as to ensure the proper operation of the installation itself.

4.2.2.5 Second-hand goods, other than those being imported from outside the EC, are regarded as being outside the scope of the Directive. The Directive applies to electromagnetic products only when they first enter the supply chain, but does not regulate subsequent transfers.

4.2.3 Protection requirements

4.2.3.1 The Directive uses the term *protection requirements* instead of the essential requirements found in other New Approach directives. There are two main protection requirements:

- That the maximum electromagnetic disturbance generated by any apparatus should not exceed a level that allows radio and telecommunications equipment or any other apparatus to operate as intended. In particular, it should not interfere with industrial manufacturing equipment, lighting, information technology equipment, or domestic appliances.

- That apparatus should be constructed in such as way as to ensure that it has an adequate level of intrinsic immunity from electromagnetic disturbance so that it can operate as intended in its usual electromagnetic compatibility environment.

The Directive also stipulates that information required to enable the use of the apparatus in accordance with the intended purpose must be contained in the instructions accompanying it.

4.2.3.2 Member States may not impede the free mobility of apparatus that complies with the Directive, but may take measures to protect specific sites or the public telecommunications network, providing that they notify the Commission.

4.2.3.3 Compliance with the protection requirements may be demonstrated by adhering to harmonized standards or national standards accepted by the Commission as meeting the protection requirements. Harmonized standards are to be produced by CENELEC under mandate from the Commission, but work on radio communications and telecommunications standards has been subcontracted to the European Telecommunications Standards Institute. CENELEC is working on generic rather than product-specific standards in order to speed up the process of producing harmonized standards. Two harmonized European standards have been approved: EN 50081-1 (generic electromagnetic compatibility) and EN 50082-1 (immunity)[12].

4.2.4 Attestation of conformity

4.2.4.1 There are three main approaches to the attestation of conformity for apparatus.

- *Where harmonized European standards or national standards accepted by the Commission as complying with the protection requirements are applied.* None of the latter are believed to have yet been submitted to the Commission for its approval. The manufacturer or his authorized representative in the EC certifies conformance with the Directive by means of an *EC declaration of conformity*. The declaration must be held at the disposal of the competent authorities for 10 years after the placing of the apparatus on the market. The manufacturer affixes the CE mark to the apparatus or its packaging, instructions, or warranty. If the manufacturer is not established in the EC, responsibility for the declaration being made available rests with the person placing the apparatus on the market. The Commission has argued that this approach is based on Module A of the Council Decision 90/683/EEC (see Section 2.3.1.4).

- *Where there has not been compliance with harmonized European or accepted national standards, or only partial compliance.* This could be because no relevant standards exist. The manufacturer must produce a *technical construction file* to be held at the disposal of the competent authorities for 10 years. This describes the apparatus, the procedures used to ensure conformity with the protection requirements, and a technical report or certification from a *competent body*. The DTI plans to publish a guidance document outlining the possible content and application of the technical construction file. Competent bodies are designated by the Member States. The criteria for these are set out in Annex II of the Directive and are the same as those laid down for what are described as approved or notified bodies in other

New Approach directives (see Section 2.3.3). Bodies which are able to provide proof of their conformity with the appropriate part of the EN 45000 series are presumed to conform to the requirements of the Directive. Manufacturers' testing facilities may be recognized as competent bodies as long as they fulfil the criteria. The Commission does not have to be notified as to the identity of competent bodies. Member States are not obliged to designate competent bodies as manufacturers can contact any notified body from another Member State. The DTI has indicated that the approval of competent bodies for the purpose of this Directive is likely to involve their accreditation by NAMAS. Where the manufacturer is not established in the EC, responsibility for the technical file passes to the person who places the apparatus on the market. The manufacturer makes an *EC declaration of conformity* and affixes the CE mark. The Commission has argued that this is based on Module A of the Council Decision 90/683/EEC (see Section 2.3.1.4).

- *Telecommunications terminal equipment and apparatus designed for the transmission of radiocommunications.* The Directive required that the manufacturer obtained an *EC type-examination certificate* from a notified body. However, this has been repealed for telecommunications terminal equipment by the Telecommunications Terminal Equipment Directive, so that these are to follow one of the two other approaches to the attestation of conformity. The Commission states that the EC type-examination is based on Module B of the Council Decision 90/683/EEC and the manufacturer declares conformity with type in accordance with Module C (see Section 2.3.1.4).

Quality management is not explicitly mentioned by the Directive, but the manufacturer is required to take all measures necessary to ensure that the output from the manufacturing process complies with the manufacturer's declaration of conformity. As discussed in Section 4.2.6, attestation of conformity would not appear to apply where a manufacturer brings into service apparatus for his own use that is not placed on the market.

4.2.4.3 The *EC declaration of conformity* must contain a description of the apparatus, the specifications under which conformity is declared, the identification of the signatory empowered to bind the manufacturer or his authorized representative, and, where appropriate, reference to any EC type-examination certificate issued by a notified body. The Commission has argued that the declaration should also indicate details regarding the application of standards and the results of tests which have been applied. The UK government considers that this goes beyond the terms of the Directive. The CE mark can only be affixed if there is compliance with any other relevant directives, such as the Construction Products Directive and its essential requirement of safety in use.

4.2.5 Draft UK Regulations

4.2.5.1 The DTI issued a consultative document in July 1992 which set out the proposed Electromagnetic Compatibility Regulations and a draft Guidance Document on the Preparation of a Technical Construction File[13]. The proposed Regulations contain many parallels to the Construction Products Regulations (see Section 10). Like these, the proposed Regulations are not made as safety regulations under the Consumer Protection Act but enact similar provisions concerning the offences that may be committed and the powers of enforcement bodies. Enforcement in areas other than in relation to wireless telegraphy will be by weights and measures authorities (district councils in Northern Ireland). The proposed Regulations are due to come into force on 28 October 1992.

4.2.5.2 The proposals clarify the items to which the Regulations are to apply. They include kits and the taking into service of apparatus made from kits. Exclusions from the scope of the proposals include spare parts, apparatus for further manufacture or for incorporation into other apparatus, second-hand goods, and apparatus covered by other directives, such as medical devices and non-automatic weighing instruments. Schedule 2 of the proposed Regulations defines what is meant by electromagnetic with a degree of rigour that is lacking in Article 1.2 of the Directive.

4.2.5.3 The proposed Regulations will prohibit the supply or taking into service of apparatus that does not comply with them. This means that the apparatus must satisfy the protection requirements, have been subject to the appropriate conformity assessment procedures, carry a CE mark, and have had a declaration of conformity issued for it. Their application to the taking into service of apparatus will have the effect of requiring those who assemble electrical or electronic apparatus to satisfy the protection requirements and the attestation of conformity provisions. This could apply to tenants or building owners who commission electrical engineering work in a building for their own use.

4.2.5.4 The Consultative Document contains guidance as to the contents of the technical construction file. This is necessary because, as the Guidance Document notes, the Directive does not make it clear how one is to describe the apparatus, set out the procedures used to ensure conformity, or specify what the relationship should be between the file and the report of the competent body. The guidance document draws on work undertaken by NAMAS. It sets out a possible contents list for the file, including how the apparatus is to be identified, a technical description of it, the technical rationale, design details, and test data. It also suggests what should be included in each of the circumstances in which a file is to be produced, for example, when there are no harmonized standards in contrast to where harmonized standards have not been applied. It indicates what might be contained in the report from a competent body.

4.3 MACHINERY DIRECTIVE

4.3.1 Introduction

4.3.1.1 The Machinery Directive[(14)] was adopted in June 1989, with a first amendment being adopted in June 1991[(15)]. Further amendments have also been proposed[(16)] (see Section 5.2.5). It provides for machinery to have to comply with extensive health and safety requirements, including ensuring that the machine is safe in normal use and has proper markings and instructions. Member States were to bring the Directive into force by 1 January 1992. They were to apply the Directive from 1 January 1993. From that date, products bearing the CE mark would enjoy freedom of mobility in the EC. With certain exceptions, a transitional period is provided until 31 December 1994, during which machinery may be placed on the market or brought into service providing it conforms with the national regulations in force within a Member State on 31 December 1992. This will provide manufacturers with a period of time in which to redesign their products, retool, and seek the necessary approvals. For three aspects of machinery, roll-over protective structures for construction plant, falling object protective structures for construction plant, and self-propelled industrial trucks, manufacturers must comply with the directives 86/295/EEC, 86/296/EEC, and 86/663/EEC (as amended by 89/240/EEC) respectively until 30 June 1995. From 1 July to 31 December 1995, they may either comply with these directives or with the Machinery Directive. Thereafter, the Machinery Directive is to apply to them.

4.3.1.2 The definition of machinery is wide-ranging so that it embraces any assembly with linked moving parts. Thus, any moving parts in a building or construction work can be classified as being a machine and be subject to the Directive. Therefore, it covers mechanical engineering work. The Directive is intended to apply to any risks from machinery that are not the subject of a specific directive. Many of the products that are subject to it are not construction products, but certain construction products fall within its definition of a machine. There are interfaces with other directives, including the Construction Products Directive on the issue of safety in use, the Electromagnetic Compatibility Directive where the power source is electrical, and the Workplace Directive over the safety of doors, gates, and escalators. This section focuses on building services that fall within the definition of a machine, for example, air conditioning equipment. The Directive also applies to machinery used on the construction site. This issue is explored in Section 5.2, which looks in particular at the amendment to the Machinery Directive which extends its application so as to include mobile machinery and lifting equipment.

4.3.2 Scope

4.3.2.1 The Directive applies to machinery. This is defined as being assemblies of linked parts or components joined together for a specific application, at least one of which moves. It also applies to assemblies of machines arranged and controlled to function as an integrated whole. It is intended to apply, in particular, to machinery used in processing, treatment, moving, or packaging, but these are not its exclusive concern. Certain types of machinery are excluded from the coverage of the Directive. These include machinery with a manual power source, steam boilers and pressure vessels, firearms, storage tanks for fuel and dangerous substances, and machinery for medical use. The first amendment has removed the initial exclusion of mobile machinery and lifting equipment other than that used in the movement of persons, and this is discussed in Section 5.2. It has also made it clear that the Directive applies to interchangeable equipment that modifies the function of a machine.

4.3.2.2 The Directive is intended to cover those risks not subject to other directives – for example, electrical risks which are the subject of the Low Voltage Directive(17). This means that there are interfaces between the Machinery Directive and other directives. For construction products the principal interfaces are with:

- *Construction Products Directive and its essential requirement of safety in use*(18). This identifies as one of its families of risk the risk of injury resulting from impact with construction works, including impact with moveable parts. The elements likely to cause injury are doors, windows, and automatic garage doors. The risk level is determined by characteristics of the elements, such as sharp or cutting surfaces, the forces applied to a body, and the element's behaviour on impact. Harmonized standards in this area are likely to be concerned with definitions, measurements, and tests.

- *Workplace Directive*(19). The minimum safety and health requirements for workplaces include ones concerning doors, gates, escalators and travolators. Those for doors and gates include the requirement that mechanical ones must function so that there is no risk of accident and have identifiable and accessible emergency shut-down devices. For escalators and travolators there must be safety devices and accessible shut-down devices as well as the general requirement that they must function safely.

4.3.2.3 Member States are to take appropriate action to ensure that machinery is not placed on the market or put into use if it endangers health and safety, when properly installed and maintained, and used for its intended purpose. However, machinery that does not comply with the Directive can be demonstrated or shown at trade fairs and exhibitions, providing that there is a sign that it is not for sale until it does conform to the Directive. The essential requirements in the Directive also apply to machinery assembled by a person for his own use. This follows logically from the requirement that machinery being put into service must comply with the Directive, even though such machinery will not have been placed on the market. Thus, the Directive has implications for replacements and refurbishment work on mechanical engineering undertaken by an owner or a tenant for his own use. An amendment makes it clear that the Directive also covers interchangeable equipment that can be assembled with a machine by an operator, for example, with a tractor.

The Machinery Directive applies to those parts of construction works which have moving parts and whose risks are not the subject of another directive, i.e. it could apply to some aspects of mechanical engineering in construction.

4.3.3 Essential requirements

4.3.3.1 The essential requirements in this Directive are relatively long and detailed. They initially ran to 12 pages, but have been extended by subsequent amendments. By contrast, those in the Construction Products Directive fit on to just one page. As well as there being requirements for machinery in general, there are also essential requirements for certain specific classes of machinery, namely agri-foodstuffs machinery, portable hand-held or hand-guided tools, and woodworking machinery. The essential requirements are mandatory, but this is qualified by the phrase 'taking into account the state of the art, it may not be possible to meet the objectives set by them'. This would appear to provide manufacturers with a state of the art defence to a charge of not complying with the essential requirements.

4.3.3.2 Not all the essential requirements apply to all types of machinery. They apply only when a hazard arises. However, three essential requirements, are applicable to all types of machinery.

- *Principles of safety integration.* Machinery must be constructed so as to be fit for its function and be capable of being adjusted and maintained without risk. Risk of accident throughout its lifetime should be eliminated, including risks encountered during assembly and dismantling. Where risks cannot be eliminated, users must be informed of residual risks and protection measures taken, including training and the provision of personal protective equipment. Instructions must cover normal uses and those that could reasonably be expected. Ergonomic principles should be used to reduce discomfort, fatigue, and stress on the operator and account taken of the constraints imposed by personal protective equipment. Machinery should be supplied with all the special equipment and accessories necessary to enable it to be adjusted, maintained, and used without risk.

- *Marking.* Machinery must be marked with the name and address of the manufacturer, the CE mark, series or type, serial number, and full information relevant to its type and essential to its safe use.

- *Instructions.* Instructions should include a repetition of the markings on the machinery, foreseen use, operator workstations, and instruction for safe use, including the putting into service, maintenance and repair, adjustment, dismantling, and training. They must be in the language of the country in which the machinery is being used and include the drawings and diagrams necessary for safe use. Sales literature must not contradict the instructions and, where machinery is to be used by non-professional operators, the instructions must take into account their level of education and acumen. Instructions should include information on the reduction of noise and vibration and on the noise levels emitted.

4.3.3.3 The essential requirements that may be applicable according to whether a hazard exists include:

- The use of safe materials in the construction of machinery.

- The design of machinery so that it can be safely handled, moved, and stored.

- Safe and reliable controls, including stopping devices, and protection against logical error by the operator, involuntary starting, and the failure of power supplies or control circuits.

- Protection against mechanical hazards, noise, electricity, vibrations, temperature, emissions, fire, and explosions.

- Guards and protection devices.

- Safe maintenance.

Amendments have required there to be warning devices on unsupervised equipment and an obligation to prevent accidents as a result of the blockage of moving parts.

4.3.3.4 Member States can make rules for the protection of persons using machinery, providing that these do not require machinery to be modified, since this would contradict the principle of freedom of mobility for machinery that complies with the essential requirements.

4.3.4 Technical specifications

4.3.4.1 Conformity with the essential requirements can be demonstrated by compliance with a harmonized European standard or a national standard that the Commission accepts as conforming with the essential requirements. CEN has proposed a plan by which three levels of standard are produced[20]. The levels are:

- A: General principles for the design of machinery.
- B: Safety devices and ergonomic aspects.
- C: Specific classes of machinery and specific requirements of them.

Enforcement in the UK will be through trading standards officers and the Health and Safety Executive.

4.3.4.2 A and B standards are being prepared by the CEN Committee TC 114 and C standards by TC 151. Work is currently proceeding on C standards in the absence of published A and B standards[21] so that there is a danger of incompatibility between standards, or of need for revision of C standards at a later date.

4.3.4.3 The Commission is to be advised on challenges to standards by Member States by the Committee set up under the Directive 83/189/EEC (see Section 2.2.2), but a Standing Committee of representatives of Member States and the Commission is established to advise on the application of the Directive.

4.3.5 Attestation of conformity

4.3.5.1 The routes to attestation of conformity are shown in Figure 13. The process by which attestation of conformity takes place differs according to whether the machinery is capable of functioning independently or not. Machinery is not capable of functioning independently when it is a component part of another machine, as, for example, is the case with a fan. Here the manufacturer makes a declaration. This declaration includes:

- the manufacturer's name and address,
- a description of the machinery,
- where appropriate, reference to harmonized standards,
- a statement that it must not be put into service until the machinery into which it is incorporated has been declared to be in conformity with the Directive,
- identification of the signatory,
- where appropriate, the identity of any notified body involved in type-examination, verification, or to whom the file was forwarded.

Such a declaration enables the machinery to be moved freely within the EC without being impeded by Member States. It is the responsibility of the person incorporating it into other machinery to ensure that the essential requirements are complied with. There is no explicit consideration given in the Directive to the issue of the sale of replacement parts to the public and the necessity that they comply with the essential requirements.

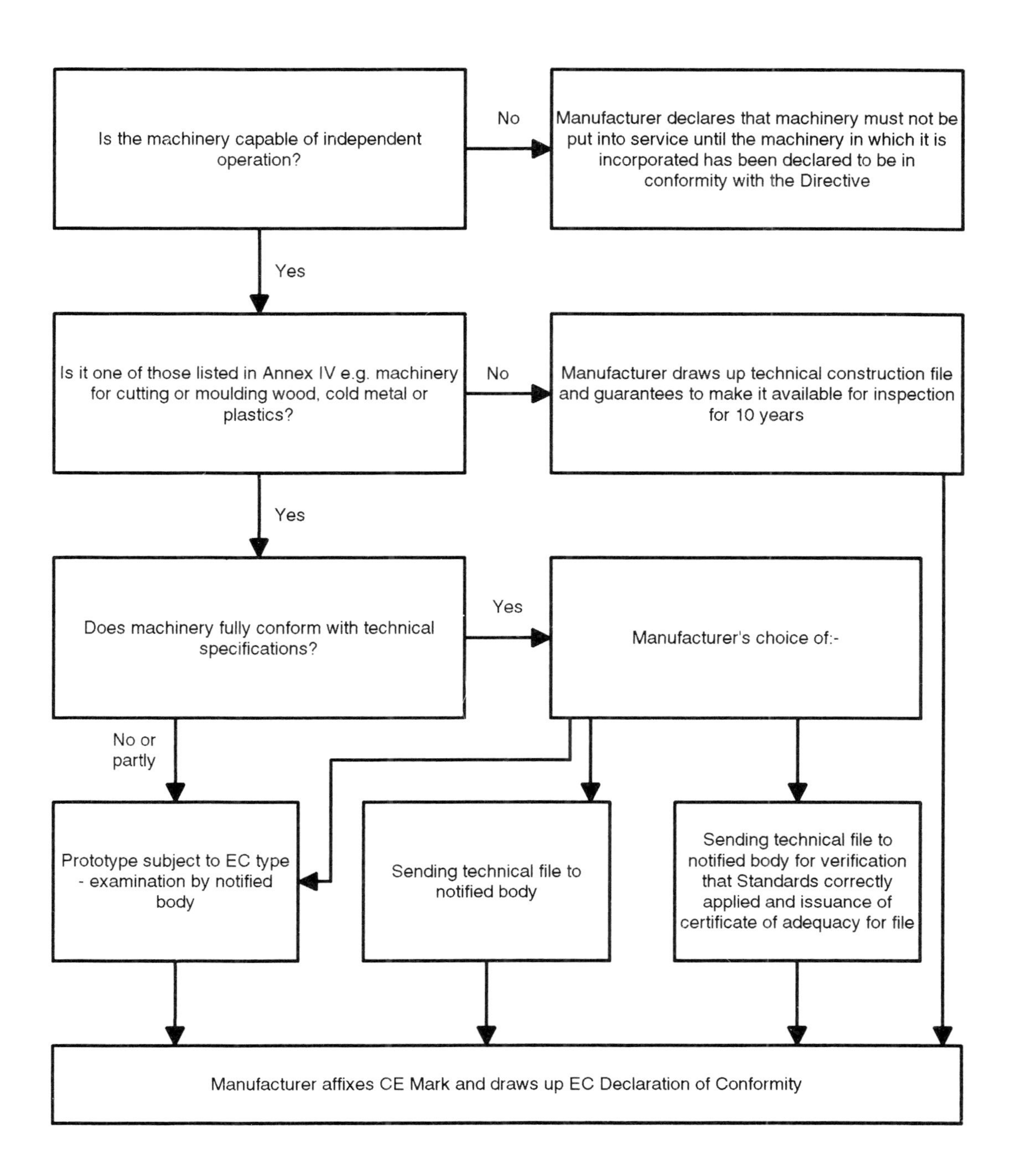

Figure 13 *Attestation of conformity for machinery*

Source: Council Directive of 14 June 1989 on the approximation of the laws of the Member States relating to machinery (89/392/EEC), *Official Journal*, L 183, 29 June 1989.

4.3.5.2 For machinery capable of *independent operation* attestation of conformity depends upon whether the machinery is of a type listed in *Annex IV* of the Directive. Annex IV lists 15 types of machinery that have particular hazards. They are principally machines for working on wood, cold metal, and plastics, certain machinery for underground working, refuse trucks and vehicle servicing lifts. They are mainly concerned with cutting or moulding or with mobile machinery. If Annex IV machinery does not conform to harmonized standards or national standards that meet the essential requirements, a prototype is subjected to an *EC type-examination* by a notified body, designated for this purpose by a Member State. Notified bodies must comply with similar requirements to those set down in other New Approach directives (see Section 2.3.3), though the wording differs in this Directive. The application by the manufacturer includes a *technical file*, which will contain drawings of the machinery and circuit controls, calculations and tests, details of the methods used to eliminate risks, a copy of the instructions, and, for series-produced items, the internal measures that will be used by the manufacturer to maintain conformity with the Directive. Where Annex IV machinery complies with standards, the manufacturer has a choice of methods of attestation:

- To draw up a technical file which is forwarded to a notified body, which keeps it,
- To submit a technical file to a notified body, which will verify that the standards have been correctly applied and draw up a certificate of adequacy for the file,
- To submit a prototype for EC type-examination.

4.3.5.3 For other types of machinery the manufacturer must draw up a *technical construction file*. This comprises drawings of the machinery and its circuit controls, tests and calculations, a list of the essential requirements, standards, and technical specifications used in the design of the machinery, descriptions of the methods adopted to eliminate hazards, a copy of the instructions, and technical reports and tests of conformity with harmonized standards. The manufacturer must guarantee that the file will remain available for inspection on his premises for at least 10 years after manufacture.

4.3.5.4 In each case the manufacturer affixes the CE mark and draws up an EC declaration of conformity. This contains his name and address, a description of the machinery, the provisions and technical specification complied with, the identity of any notified body involved in the attestation of conformity, and the identity of the person who signs on behalf of the manufacturer. If the manufacturer is not established in the EC, his obligations fall on the person placing the machinery on the market.

4.3.5.5 The attestation of conformity requirements apply to machinery that is to be placed on the market. There is also the question of whether machinery assembled by a manufacturer for his own use is also to be subject to these provisions. It is clear from the Directive that the essential requirements must be satisfied whenever machinery is bought into service, even if it is not placed upon the market. This would apply, for example, where an owner or a tenant of a building assembles, refurbishes, or modifies mechanical engineering elements of construction works for his own use. What is not altogether clear from a reading of the Directive is whether such machinery must also satisfy the attestation of conforming provisions of the Directive. In the case of the Electromagnetic Compatibility Directive, in which similar issues arise, it would appear that apparatus brought into service, but not placed upon the market, will not be subjected to the attestation of conformity procedures (see Section 4.2.2.6). However, in the case of machinery, there are indications that the government may follow the precedent set by the Simple Pressure Vessels Directive and require the attestation of conformity provisions to be followed before machinery can be brought into service[(22)].

4.3.6 Proposed Used Machinery Directive

4.3.6.1 In 1991 the Commission proposed a Used Machinery Directive[(23)]. The proposed Directive is intended to apply to machinery, as defined by the Machinery Directive and its amendments, where there is a change of use. Member States are to take appropriate measures to ensure that such machinery can be put into service only if it guarantees the safety of users or consumers. The transferor is to be responsible for the machinery's compliance with the regulations in force in the country of the user. Leasing is regarded as a transfer of machinery. Machinery temporarily made available shall be in a good state of repair and not involve any risks due to poor maintenance or wear. However, the movement of machinery between different parts of an organization, even if it involves a change in the legal situation, is not defined as being a transfer under the meaning of the proposed Directive.

4.3.6.2 The proposal draws a distinction between professional and non-professional users. It is proposed that a professional user may take machinery as it is and be responsible for bringing it into line with local regulations. Reconditioning is to comply with the essential requirements set out in the Machinery Directive. The proposal does not contain any essential requirements of its own but will adopt those set out in the Work Equipment Directive (see Section 5.1.3). It would provide for various declarations to be made on transfer, including where the transfer is being made for scrapping or reconditioning.

4.3.6.3 The proposal calls for Member States to bring it into force by 1 July 1992 and to apply its provisions from 31 December 1992. This dovetails with the timetable for implementation of the Machinery Directive. However, a number of Member States have questioned the need for such a directive and extensive amendments to the proposal have been suggested. The definitions and procedures appear to be insufficiently precise. It has been argued by the French government that safety requirements in this area are adequately covered by the Machinery and Work Equipment Directives. The potential burdens that the proposal might place on the leasing and plant hire industry could be severe. Moreover, it has been argued that, as relatively little of the trade in used machinery takes place across national boundaries, the value of a directive in this area is open to question. The Commission is currently reviewing the responses received.

4.3.6.4 The main implications of this proposal for construction concern the leasing and plant hire industry. This has an important economic function in enabling small construction firms to operate without the necessity of purchasing expensive fixed capital. There is also a market in the sale of plant at the end of contract and when firms are liquidated. There would be implications for landlords and tenants when buildings containing mechanical engineering elements are leased or sold or leases assigned.

4.4 CONCLUSIONS

4.4.1 The three principal directives discussed in this section have a number of features which are similar to each other and to the other New Approach directives. These include the definition of essential requirements for health and safety, the use of harmonized European standards as the principle technical specification, the criteria to be satisfied by notified bodies, and the bearing of the CE mark by those products that comply with them. However, they also illustrate the problems discussed in Sections 2.3.1.1 and 2.3.2.3 of differences in attestation of conformity procedures and in the application of the CE mark between directives. These could present problems as there is an interface between each of these directives and the Construction Products Directive and between certain of these directives, for example, between the Machinery and Electromagnetic Compatibility Directives. These may not be resolved until after the directives have been revised so as to conform to the modules in the Council Decision 90/683/EEC and there is a Council Regulation on the CE mark.

4.4.2 The Electromagnetic Compatibility and Machinery Directives have implications for tenants and owners of buildings as they may find themselves being regarded as manufacturers under these directives in certain circumstances. This could apply where they refurbish, modify, or assemble machinery or electrical apparatus for their own use. For electrical apparatus, it would appear that they will not need to follow the attestation of conformity provisions set out in the Directive but this may not be the case for machinery. However, the essential (or protection) requirements will still apply, though it is not clear how these will be enforced.

References: 4 Technical harmonization of building services

1. Council Directive of 29 June 1990 on the approximation of the laws of the Member States relating to appliances burning gaseous fuels (90/396/EEC), *Official Journal*, L 196, 26 July 1990.

2. The Gas Appliances (Safety) Regulations 1992, SI 1992, No. 711.

3. Building Services Research and Information Association (1990), *Technical Implications of New EC Codes, Standards and Legislation.*

4. Department of Trade and Industry (1991), *Draft Regulations Implementing the EC Directive on Gas Appliances (90/396/EEC): A Consultative Document.*

5. Department of Trade and Industry (1990), *The Single Market: Gas Appliances* (2nd edition).

6. Council Directive 92/42/EEC of 21 May 1992 on efficiency requirements for new hot-water boilers fired with liquid or gaseous fuels, *Official Journal*, L 167, 22 June 1992.

7. Council Directive of 3 May 1989 on the approximation of the laws of the Member States relating to electromagnetic compatibility (89/336/EEC), *Official Journal*, L 139, 23 May 1989.

8. Council Directive 92/31/EEC of 28 April 1992 amending Council Directive 89/336/EEC of 3 May 1989 on the approximation of the laws of Member States relating to electromagnetic compatibility, *Official Journal*, L 126, 12 May 1992.

9. Commission of the European Communities (1991), *Explanatory document on Council Directive 89/336/EEC of 3 May 1989 on the approximation of the laws of the Member States relating to electromagnetic compatibility*, III/4060/91/EN–Rev 1.

10. Department of Trade and Industry (1991), *Electromagnetic Compatibility: European Commission explanatory document on Council Directive 89/336/EEC.*

11. Department of Trade and Industry (1989), *Electrical Interference: A Consultative Document – The Implementation in the United Kingdom of Directive 89/336/EEC on Electromagnetic Compatibility.*

12. Commission Communication in the Framework of the Implementation of Council Directive No 89/336/EEC of 3 May 1989, in relation to Electromagnetic Compatibility (92/C 90/02), *Official Journal*, C 90, 10 April 1992.

13. Department of Trade and Industry (1992), *Electromagnetic Compatibility (EMC) Draft United Kingdom Regulations: A Consultative Document*, July.

14. Council Directive of 14 June 1989 on the approximation of the laws of the Member States relating to machinery (89/392/EEC), *Official Journal*, L 183, 29 June 1989.

15. Council Directive of 20 June 1991 amending Directive 89/392/EEC on the approximation of the laws of the Member States relating to machinery (91/368/EEC), *Official Journal*, L 198, 22 July 1991.

16. Department of Trade and Industry (1992), *The European Commission's Proposal for a Second Amendment to the Machinery Directive: A Consultive Document.*

17. Council Directive of 19 February 1973 on the harmonization of the laws of the Member States relating to electrical equipment designed for use within certain voltage limits, *Official Journal*, L 77, 26 March 1973.

18. Commission of the European Communities, Standing Committee for Construction, *Council Directive 89/106/EEC Construction Products: Essential Requirement Safety in Use*, Document TC4/014–rev 1, 1991.

19. Council Directive of 30 November 1989 concerning the minimum safety and health requirements for the workplace (89/654/EEC), *Official Journal*, L 393, 30 December 1989.

20. Department of Trade and Industry (1991), *The Single Market: Machinery Safety* (3rd edition).

21. Thompson, J. (1991), Moving the earth for European standards, *BSI in Europe*, Issue 14, July.

22. Council Directive of 25 June 1987 on the harmonization of the laws of the Member States relating to simple pressure vessels, *Official Journal*, L 220, 8 August 1987; The Simple Pressure Vessels (Safety) Regulations 1991, SI 1991, No. 2749.

23. Department of Trade and Industry (1991), *Proposed EC Directive on Used Machinery: Latest Developments – A Consultation Paper; Proposed EC Directive on Used Machinery: Main points to emerge from a European Commission meeting with Member States and other experts.*

5 Technical harmonization of construction site work

5.0 OVERVIEW

5.0.1 The harmonization of construction site work largely stems from the work being undertaken on health and safety of workers at work. In 1989 the EC adopted a Framework Directive on the health and safety of workers at work and this has led to individual directives on the workplace, the use of personal protective and work equipment, and to a proposed directive on construction sites. These lay obligations on employers to protect their workers from risks to their health and safety. Their fulfilment requires planning and a systematic approach, which can act as a constraint on the way in which work is undertaken. These obligations do not require construction firms to adopt quality management systems but, clearly, their adoption would help to ensure that these obligations are met. The Health and Safety Executive have argued that many organizations lack structured and well-thought-out approaches to health and safety whereas what is needed is an effective management structure into which health and safety needs can be fully integrated.

5.0.2 The construction industry is a purchaser of products from other industries that have a bearing upon site work. These include lifting equipment and mobile machinery and personal protective equipment, which are the subject of New Approach directives. If the construction firm assembles such products or machinery from components or adapts them, then it may find itself treated as the manufacturer and have to ensure that they comply with essential requirements. The health and safety directives dovetail with those on machinery and personal protective equipment in that they set out the framework for their safe use while these other directives set out the conditions for their safe design and manufacture. Safe use requires an understanding of what the manufacturer must provide by way of instructions, marking, what constitutes safe use, conditions of use and what interpretation should be placed on attestations of conformity.

5.1 SAFETY ON THE CONSTRUCTION SITE

5.1.1 The Framework Directive on health and safety at work

5.1.1.1 In June 1989 the EC adopted a Framework Directive intended to ensure the introduction of measures to encourage improvements in the safety and health of workers at work[1]. The Directive applies to all sectors of economic activity other than domestic service. It contains general principles for the prevention of occupational risks and for the elimination of accident factors. Employers are given the obligation of ensuring the safety and health of workers in every aspect of their work. The general principles include avoiding risks, evaluating the risks that cannot be avoided, combating risks at source, giving appropriate instructions to workers, adapting the work to the individual so as to reduce the effect of work on the health of workers, and developing a coherent overall prevention policy. Measures relating to safety and health at work may in no circumstances involve the workers in financial cost. Employers must designate one or more workers to carry out activities relating to the prevention of occupational risks, and they must have the necessary capabilities and the necessary means to carry out their role. Employers must take necessary measures for first aid, fire-fighting, and the evacuation of workers. They must undertake an assessment of risks, decide on protective measures, keep records of occupational accidents, and provide information on risks and preventative measures to their workers. Employers are obliged to consult their workers about safety and health at work and to ensure that each worker receives adequate training. Workers have the responsibility to take care of their own safety, which includes following instructions, making correct use of personal protective equipment, and refraining from altering safety devices.

5.1.1.2 This Framework Directive leads on to specific directives concerning particular aspects of work or the risks encountered in specific industries. That on workplaces was discussed in Section 3.6.6 above as it has implications for the design of workplaces. Also of relevance are the proposed directive concerning temporary or mobile work sites (the Construction Sites Directive) and the directives concerned with work equipment and personal protective equipment, which cover items purchased and used by the construction industry. These are discussed in Sections 5.1.2, 5.1.3, and 5.3.2 respectively.

5.1.1.3 Draft UK Regulations and a draft Approved Code of Practice to implement the Framework Directive were published by the Health and Safety Executive in October 1991[2]. The Directive will require a number of changes to the current UK regulations on health and safety at work. While the Directive's objectives are similar to the current UK regulations, its approach is more prescriptive and detailed. The Health and Safety Executive has estimated the cost of complying with the regulations to be anything between £12.5m and £50m, with continuing costs of £70m per annum. To place this in perspective, it is probably of the order of about 5% of the cost of accidents potentially preventable by tackling bad management. The costs include risk assessment, documentation of health and safety arrangements, providing information and training for employees, and appointing competent persons.

5.1.1.4 The draft UK Regulations make the following requirements:

- *Risk assessment.* This should be documented where there are five or more employees. The assessment is to aid compliance with other statutory duties, such as the Health and Safety at Work Act 1974.

- *Having adequate health and safety arrangements.* These include planning for risk avoidance or risk minimization; having an adequate organizational structure; ensuring that decisions are implemented as planned; monitoring and review.

- *Health surveillance.* This should be applied where there is an identifiable work-related risk to health, where there are techniques to indicate the presence of the disorder, and where surveillance can protect the health of employees.

- *Health and safety assistance.* Employers must appoint a competent person or persons to assist in the protective and preventative measures and provide adequate support for this task.

- *Procedures for serious and imminent danger.* These include emergency procedures covering the stopping of work and evacuation.

- *Provision of comprehensible and relevant information to employees.* Much of this should have been identified during risk assessment. Employees will need to be informed about emergency arrangements.

- *Cooperation and coordination.* This is necessary where two or more employers share a workplace, such as a construction site. There is an obligation to inform other employers of risks to their employees arising from an employer's activities both on and off site.

- *Training of employees.* This stems from risk assessment and includes refresher training as well as training when circumstances change.

- *Employees' duties.* These include using equipment in accordance with instructions, not interfering with equipment, and informing employers of risks to health and safety.

5.1.1.5 There is nothing in the Directive or in the draft UK Regulations or draft Approved Code of Practice that obliges an employer to introduce a quality management system. However, it is difficult to see how an employer could meet his obligations without an effective management system. The Health and Safety Executive argue that the absence of such a system is the root cause of many accidents. The draft Code of Practice specifically draws attention to the necessity for planning and having an adequate organizational structure, effective implementation of decisions, and monitoring and review. A total quality management system would achieve this.

5.1.2 Proposed Temporary or Mobile Construction Sites Directive

5.1.2.1 This proposed Directive applies the principles set out in the Framework Directive to temporary or mobile construction sites[3]. A Common Position was reached on the proposal on 19 December 1991. It is one of the measures that forms part of the EC's Social Action Programme, which aims to give practical effect to the Social Charter. The UK's opposition to a Social Chapter of the EC Treaty notwithstanding, the measure has been welcomed by the government. The sites referred to are sites for the carrying out of building and civil engineering work and the activities covered include excavation, construction, fitting out, renovation, maintenance, repairs, dismantling, and demolition. The proposal does not apply to drilling or extraction by the extractive industries.

The steps to be taken for the protection of health and safety occur at two stages:

- During the *project preparation* stage

- During the *project execution* stage.

5.1.2.2 If the planned duration of works is to be at least 30 days, then a *prior notice* must be sent by the client to the authorities responsible for health and safety at work before the commencement of the work. The client is defined as being the person for whom the work is to be carried out. The notice should contain the address of the site, the client's name and address, the type of project, the project supervisor's name and address, the safety coordinators for both the project preparation and project execution stages, the planned start and duration of the work, the estimated number of workers and contractors on site, and the contractors already chosen. A copy of the notice is to be displayed on the site.

5.1.2.3 At the project preparation stage, the project supervisor must take into account safety and health issues when making architectural and organizational decisions so that these are explicitly recognized in the planning of the project. During the project execution stage, the safety coordinator should ensure that employers and self-employed persons apply safety principles and adhere to the safety plan, check that procedures are working, adapt the plan as necessary, and ensure that unauthorized persons do not enter the site.

5.1.2.4 The proposed Directive sets out principles for the safe operation of construction sites. These include:

- Keeping the site in good order and in a satisfactory state of cleanliness

- Principles for the choice of workstations

- Conditions in which materials are to be handled

- Maintenance and checks on installations

- Demarcation of areas for hazardous substances and their disposal

- Conditions for the storage and disposal of wastes and surplus materials

- Adaption of the period allocated to work.

The minimum safety and health requirements for work sites found in the Workplace Directive (discussed in Section 3.3.1 above) are applicable to construction sites. They include issues such as lighting, sanitary arrangements, rest rooms, fire-fighting, and traffic routes. These principles also apply to self-employed persons. Workers must be informed of all measures taken concerning their safety and health and be consulted. If adopted, the proposed Directive should come into effect by 31 December 1993.

5.1.3 Work Equipment Directive

5.1.3.1 A further directive under the Framework Directive deals with work equipment used by workers at work[4]. It is due to come into effect from 31 December 1992. The draft UK Regulations were published in November 1991[5], though certain aspects of the Directive have already been implemented. The Directive places a number of obligations on employers with respect to the equipment workers use. Employers are obliged to take all measures necessary to ensure that work equipment is suitable for the work to be carried out or else is properly adapted for the purpose. Equipment must be able to be used by workers without impairment of their health or safety. The employer must look at the specific working conditions of his workforce, including those that may be posed by the workplace, and any hazards posed by the work equipment used. If risks cannot be eliminated, they must be minimized. The draft UK Regulations go beyond the requirements of the Directive by applying these obligations to the self-employed and to those in control when the public uses work equipment in non-domestic premises.

5.1.3.2 For work equipment provided for the first time after 31 December 1992, employers must ensure that there is compliance with the provisions of any relevant EC directive. This includes the Machinery Directive and its amendments[6]. As the employer is responsible for ensuring that work equipment is suitable for the work, this would imply that he must be familiar with the essential requirements of the relevant directives, the information, markings, and warnings that manufacturers must provide, and the meanings of the attestations of conformity. He should not make use of equipment that does not display evidence of an attestation of conformity that should have been provided and ensure that machinery that he has assembled or adapted for his own use complies with the essential requirements. All equipment, including that in use before 31 December 1992, must comply with relevant directives within four years of the implementation date.

5.1.3.3 Work equipment should be constructed or adapted so as to be suitable for its use. Where work equipment poses specific risks, its use should be restricted to those persons given the task of using it. Repairs, modifications, and maintenance should be undertaken only by specifically designated workers. Workers using such equipment should receive specific training. The employer is obliged to provide workers with adequate information on work equipment and, where appropriate, written instructions. These must be comprehensible. The information and work instructions should cover:

- The conditions of use of work equipment,
- Foreseeable abnormal situations,
- Conclusions drawn from experience in using the equipment.

Much of this information should be available if the manufacturer has complied with the essential requirements of appropriate harmonization directives. The employer is obliged to provide workers with adequate training, including training on the risks that the use of the equipment may entail, and to consult with his workers. The requirements on employers are to apply from 1 January 1993.

5.1.3.4 The Directive lays down certain minimum requirements for safety and health, though they are obligations only where the relevant risk applies. They dovetail with the essential requirements under directives such as the Machinery Directive and should serve to ensure that equipment is not only designed and constructed in such a way as to be safe when properly used, but that it is used in a proper manner. These include the requirement that equipment should have visible and identifiable control devices that can be used safely; have unambiguous warning devices and markings; be capable of being stopped completely and safely; does not start involuntarily; provides protection from falling objects, instability, disintegration or explosion, electricity, extreme temperatures, emissions, and mechanical forces; and can be maintained safely. These conditions are to apply from 1 January 1993 for equipment first provided after 31 December 1992 and from 1 January 1997 for equipment first provided before 1 January 1993. Additional annexes dealing with specific equipment may be added to the Directive later.

5.2 MOBILE MACHINERY AND LIFTING EQUIPMENT

5.2.1 Introduction

5.2.1.1 Mobile machinery and lifting equipment was originally excluded from the Machinery Directive[6]. However, the Directive has now been amended[7]. The amendments do four things.

- They alter the coverage of the Machinery Directive so that it encompasses certain lifting equipment and mobile machinery.
- They extend the range of machinery identified by Annex IV of the Directive (see Section 4.3.5.2) as requiring special processes for the attestation of conformity.
- They lay down the essential requirements that must be satisfied by mobile equipment, lifting machinery, machinery using non-manual power sources, and machinery intended for underground work.
- They repeal five directives concerned with wire ropes, chains, hooks, construction plant and industrial trucks.

5.2.1.2 This section is concerned with the amendments to the Machinery Directive that have a particularly important bearing on construction site work. Other aspects of this Directive are discussed in Section 4.3. In most cases, the amended Directive affects construction firms as purchasers rather than as manufacturers. Therefore, their interest is in what the attestation of conformity means, what assurance is being given that technical specifications have been met, and what instructions and warnings as to use are given. It is clearly up to the construction firm to ensure that machinery is being used under the conditions for which the manufacturer has declared it to be fit, and in accordance with the instructions and warnings given. However, if construction firms modify mobile machinery or lifting equipment, or assemble it from component elements for their own use, they are obliged to ensure that it complies with the essential requirements and may also be required to satisfy the requisite attestation of conformity provisions (see Section 4.3.5.5).

5.2.1.3 The amendments to the Machinery Directive were adopted on 20 June 1991. The amended Directive is due to come into effect from 1 January 1993, with a transitional period until 31 December 1994. During the transitional period manufacturers may continue to produce in accordance with the national provisions in force on 31 December 1992. Roll-over protective structures for construction plant, falling-object protective structures for construction plant and self-propelled industrial trucks must comply with directives 86/295/EEC, 86/296/EEC and 86/663/EEC (as amended by 89/240/EEC) respectively until 30 June 1995. From 1 July to 31 December 1995 they may either comply with these directives or with the Machinery Directive. Thereafter, the Machinery Directive is to apply to them.

5.2.2 Scope

The effect of the amendments is to bring within the scope of the Machinery Directive certain types of machinery excluded under the original Directive. These are principally:

- Lifting equipment, other than that designed for moving persons, i.e. passenger lifts,
- Mobile machinery, other than means of transport for passengers or goods, seagoing vessels, agricultural or forestry tractors, and machines designed for military or police use.

5.2.3 Essential requirements

5.2.3.1 The amendments introduce additional essential requirements which must be satisfied by certain classes of machinery. These are in addition to those discussed in Section 4.3.3, which must also be satisfied. They build up cumulatively so that machinery intended for use underground must also meet the requirements of the other classes as well as those specifically intended for it.

5.2.3.2 As with the original Directive, the essential requirements are set out in some detail. In outline they are:

- *Mobile equipment.* The special essential requirements for this class of machinery are concerned with the risks from mobility, including those from the operation of such machinery in a fixed position or from a series of fixed working positions. They include having:

  - Adequate lighting, if it is to be used in dark places,
  - Properly designed workstations, including the driving position and seating, so as to ensure, for example, adequate operator visibility and protection from noise,
  - Controls that enable the machinery to be safely operated, including controls over starting, moving, and travelling,
  - Protection against mechanical hazards, such as roll-over and from transmission,
  - Protection against hazards such as batteries, emissions, and fire,
  - Proper signs, warnings, and instructions.

- *Lifting operations.* The essential requirements for lifting equipment include those for machinery in general and those for mobile machinery. The hazards are mainly in the form of load falls and collisions or tipping. The essential requirements are principally concerned with protection against mechanical hazards. These include risks due to a lack of stability and from mechanical strength and stresses. There are requirements with respect to guide rails, pulleys, accessories, controls, lighting, and the ability to handle loads. Examples of essential requirements include that the driving position must be located in such a way as to ensure the widest view of trajectories and to avoid collisions; the mechanisms of machinery must be designed and constructed so that loads cannot creep dangerously or fall unexpectedly; and stability must be maintained at all stages, including transportation, assembly, and dismantling.

- *Machinery with a non-manual power source.* The essential requirements for these also include those for mobile machinery, with respect to workstations (i.e. driver position and seating), as well as those for machinery in general. In addition, requirements are laid down for:

  - Controls, including control devices and loading controls,
  - Marking, including requirements for marking chains, ropes, and lifting accessories,
  - Instructions, both for the machinery itself and for any lifting accessories, including maintenance instructions, limits of use, and normal conditions of use.

- *Machinery intended solely for underground work.* These machines must comply with the essential requirements for machinery in general as well as those for mobile machinery, lifting equipment, and machinery with a non-manual power source. In addition, there are specific essential requirements for this class of machinery. These are principally concerned with risks from lack of stability and deal with lighting, control devices, stopping, movement, fire, and emissions. Examples of specific requirements include that the braking system must not produce sparks or cause fires; exhaust gases must not be discharged upwards; and that powered roof supports must not slip before, while, or after they come under load.

5.2.4 Attestation of conformity

5.2.4.1 Attestation of conformity follows the approach set out in the Machinery Directive. Figure 13 sets this out in diagrammatic form. For machinery that is not capable of independent operation, a manufacturer's declaration is required. It must not be put into service until the machinery into which it is incorporated has been declared to be in conformity with the Directive. If the construction firm is incorporating such machinery into a final assembly of machinery for its own use, then the responsibility for ensuring that the essential requirements are satisfied lies with the construction firm and not the manufacturer of the machinery. Machinery brought into service for one's own use does not have to follow the attestation of conformity provisions.

5.2.4.2 For machinery listed in Annex IV of the Directive, there are special procedures to be followed (see Section 4.3.5.2). For other machinery the manufacturer draws up a technical construction file and guarantees to make it available for inspection for 10 years. He affixes the CE mark and draws up an EC declaration of conformity. The amendments have increased the range of machinery included in Annex IV. The additions include:

- Machinery for underground working that is either machinery on rails (including locomotives and brake vans), or hydraulic-powered roof supports, or an internal combustion engine for underground work,

- Manually-loaded trucks for the collection of household refuse that incorporate a compression mechanism,

- Guards and detached transmission shafts with universal joints,

- Vehicle servicing lifts.

5.2.4.3 Where such machinery complies fully with technical specifications like harmonized standards, the manufacturer has a choice between submitting a prototype to EC type-examination, or sending a technical file to a notified body, or sending a technical file to a notified body for verification that the standards have been correctly applied and for it to issue a *certificate of adequacy* for the file. If technical specifications have not been complied with, or only partially complied with, perhaps because there are none available, then a prototype must be subjected to EC type-examination by a notified body. In each case, the manufacturer affixes the CE mark and draws up an EC declaration of conformity.

5.2.5 Proposed second amendment to the Machinery Directive

5.2.5.1 The Commission has formally proposed a second amendment to the Machinery Directive[8]. This is likely to be negotiated during 1992. The proposal is, in part, a tidying up of the original Directive and its first amendment. Thus, the definition of 'machinery' would be extended to include roll-over protective structures, falling-object protective structures, removable guards, and lifting accessories marketed separately with the aim of being assembled into a machine by the operator. It proposes to make emergency stopping procedures more effective in certain circumstances. Users would receive instructions in the language of the country of use and also in the original language.

5.2.5.2 The proposal would also bring within scope of the Directive lifting equipment designed and constructed for raising or moving persons, including hoists and work platforms. The proposal is not intended to cover passenger lifts, which are the subject of a separate proposed directive (see Section 5.2.6). Its scope means that the proposal has potential implications for building work, building maintenance, and cleaning. The proposal includes essential requirements for the lessening of risks from lifting persons. These include the strength of the car, its control circuitry, and the control of risks to persons in the car and of persons falling from the car. It is proposed that two additions are made to the list of Annex IV machinery to include lifting machinery where there is a risk of persons falling more than five metres and speed-limiting and fall-prevention devices used in machinery for lifting persons.

5.2.5.3 The timetable for negotiating the proposal is not clear but the government considers that it is unlikely that the amendment will be adopted before the end of 1992. Ideally, the amendment should come into force at the same time as the original Directive. The Commission proposes that Member States bring the amendment into force by 1 July 1993 and apply it from 1 July 1994. Machinery that conforms with national provisions on 1 July 1993 could continue to be placed upon the market until 31 December 1995. Thus, according to this timetable, the amendment would come into effect six months after the original Directive.

5.2.6 Proposed Lifts Directive

5.2.6.1 The proposed Lifts Directive is intended to apply to lifts permanently installed in permanent buildings and to safety components for use in lifts, such as overspeed detection devices, cables, chains, and energy-accumulating shock absorbers(9). The lifts concerned can be used either to transport persons or persons and goods. It is proposed that Member States should adopt the measure by 1 January 1994 and apply its provisions from 1 January 1995. Until 31 December 1997, Member States are to allow the placing on the market and putting into service of lifts and safety components that comply with the national provisions in force on 1 January 1994.

5.2.6.2 Lifts and safety components may not be placed on the market or put into service unless they satisfy the proposed Directive. The essential requirements include ones that relate to:

- the car itself,
- cables, chains, and machinery,
- hazards to persons inside or outside of the car,
- the relationship between the manufacturer and the building works supervisor,
- marking and instructions for use.

Thus, the proposed Directive is not only concerned with the manufacture of lifts but also with their installation. The essential requirements dealing with the relationship between the manufacturer and the building works supervisor relate, for example, to liaison over the stresses the lift will place upon the building; the measures to be taken to minimize the risk of fire; ensuring that the lift shaft is not used for other services; and determining that there are appropriate emergency devices relative to the use of the building.

5.2.6.3 Attestation of conformity is to follow the modular approach to conformity assessment (see Section 2.3.1). There are two stages:

- *Design phase*. Before a lift is placed upon the market, the manufacturer must either submit a prototype for an EC type-examination (Module B) or operate a full quality assurance system, including quality assurance of design (Module H).
- *Acceptance phase*. This is to be undertaken before the lift is put into service. There are two choices:
  - Module G (unit verification), if Module B was not followed at the design phase, or
  - to follow the acceptance procedure set out in Annex VI of the proposed Directive.

  The latter can be carried out either by a competent body or by those manufacturers who have approved quality assurance systems that satisfy Module E (product quality assurance). The procedure involves verifying that a lift put into service conforms to the model. Examination is made of design documentation and the instruction manual and appropriate tests are carried out.

Notified bodies and competent bodies who carry out acceptance work are to satisfy the revised criteria for notified bodies used in the Hot-water Boilers Directive (see Section 2.3.3.4).

5.3 PERSONAL PROTECTIVE EQUIPMENT

5.3.1 Introduction

5.3.1.1 The safety and health at work directives contain the principles that risks should be eliminated wherever possible. Where this cannot be done, protective measures should be for groups of workers rather than for individuals. Therefore, personal protective equipment represents a solution to the problems posed by hazards at work that are low in the hierarchy of preferences, being neither the prevention of risks at source nor a collective solution. The Health and Safety Executive have argued that personal protective equipment rarely achieves the maximum level of protection for workers and restricts mobility. The proposed UK Regulations to implement the Personal Protective Equipment Directive make it clear that the equipment should be provided only where a risk cannot be equally or more effectively controlled by other means(10). However, circumstances do arise in which personal protection equipment has to be a part of the process of minimizing risks. The construction industry is generally recognized as exposing workers to a relatively high degree of risk of injury unless protective measures are taken. This is as a result of the environment in which the work takes place, the nature of the tasks undertaken, and the equipment and materials that are used in the work.

5.3.1.2 EC legislation covers two aspects of personal protective equipment. The Directive on the approximation of the laws relating to personal protective equipment (89/686/EEC)(11) is a New Approach directive that lays down the essential requirements that personal protective equipment must satisfy and the processes by which manufacturers can attest to the conformity of their products with those requirements. The Directive on the use by workers of personal protective equipment at the workplace (89/656/EEC)(12) is one of the individual safety directives produced under the Framework Safety Directive. Draft UK Regulations and Guidance Notes were published by the Health and Safety Executive in December 1991(10) and these may be extended in the future to cover specific types of personal protective equipment. The Directive is concerned with the use of personal protective equipment, which includes evaluating the risks to which workers are exposed and selecting equipment which is effective against them. The latter calls for the employer to be familiar with the requirements that personal protective equipment must satisfy and the processes of attestation of conformity that they have gone through. Without this, he cannot judge whether the technical specifications for the equipment are adequate for his purpose and that the attestation of conformity procedures they have gone through provides an adequate level of quality assurance. Thus, 89/686/EEC should ensure that personal protective equipment is only placed on the market if it is fit for its intended use, while 89/656/EEC should ensure that it is only used for its intended use.

5.3.2 Use of personal protective equipment

5.3.2.1 The Directive on the Use of Personal Protective Equipment by Workers at Work is due to come into effect with the other safety directives by 31 December 1992 and this should happen in the UK through the proposed Personal Protective Equipment at Work Regulations. It covers any equipment worn or held by a worker to protect himself against hazards. Ordinary working clothes or uniforms, equipment used by the emergency services, police, or military, sports equipment, self-defence equipment, personal protective equipment for use in road transport, and portable devices for detecting and signalling risks are not covered by the Directive. However, the UK Regulations are expected to be more extensive in their scope than the Directive and include personal protective equipment for the self-employed, military, and emergency services.

5.3.2.2 Personal protective equipment is to be used only when risks cannot be avoided or limited to an acceptable level by technical means or by procedures or working methods. It must comply with EC provisions, such as the Directive approximating the laws on Personal Protective

Equipment, and, therefore, bear the CE mark. It should be appropriate for the risk, without causing increased risks, and correspond to the conditions that give rise to the hazards. It must be designed so as to take into account ergonomic requirements and fit the wearer after adjustment. Member States may make regulations concerning the use of personal protective equipment, but these must not impede the free mobility of equipment that conforms to the relevant harmonization directives.

5.3.2.3 Before personal protective equipment is chosen, the employer must assess the risks and ensure that the equipment selected is effective against them. This implies familiarity with the essential requirements for such equipment, the instructions and conditions of use that apply to it, and the attestation of conformity it has been through. Annex I of the Directive provides a specimen risk survey table to assist in the assessment of risks. This is reproduced in Figure 14.

This compares the parts of the body with important risks, such as mechanical, thermal, electrical, radiation, chemical, and biological risks. The risks are further analysed by cause. For example, mechanical risks include those from falling from a height, blows, cuts, and crushing impacts, stabs and cuts, vibration, and falls from slipping. Annex III provides a non-exhaustive list of the activities that may require personal protective equipment, broken down by the parts of the body that may need protection and the nature of the protection they require. For example, building work, particularly in the vicinity of scaffolding, is identified as needing protective helmets for head protection[13], while scaffolding work is stated as needing safety shoes with puncture-proof soles and safety harnesses. The Health and Safety Executive expect that a consequence of the Directive will be to increase the use of certain types of personal protective equipment which has, up to now, only been required by a few industry-specific regulations. Examples of these are wet-weather clothing, safety footwear, and high-visibility clothing.

5.3.2.4 Employers are required to provide personal protective equipment, though workers can be obliged to contribute to its cost if it is also used outside work. Employers are also responsible for keeping it in good order and in a hygienic condition, especially if it is to be used by different workers. The draft UK Regulations propose to impose the obligation on employers to provide suitable storage facilities for personal protective equipment. It is argued that keeping the equipment in good order will not be possible without this obligation, for example, to ensure that it is stored so that deterioration can be avoided. In this respect, the proposed UK Regulations go beyond the requirements of the Directive. Workers are to be informed of the risks that the equipment is intended to protect them from and to be trained in its use. They should also be consulted. The equipment is supposed to be used in specified circumstances in accordance with instructions. Instructions have to be in a form that are understandable by workers. The draft UK Regulations propose to impose the requirements on employees to use the equipment properly, to report damage and defects, and to return it to its proper place after use.

5.3.3 Manufacture of personal protective equipment

5.3.3.1 The production of personal protective equipment is determined by the Directive approximating the laws relating to it. This was due to come into effect on 1 July 1992 with a transitional period until 31 December 1992, during which personal protective equipment manufactured in accordance with national regulations in force on the implementation date could continue to be able to be sold. The Directive is one of the New Approach directives and has a number of features which are similar to those of the Machinery Directive.

5.3.3.2 The Directive applies to personal protective equipment, which is defined as being devices or appliances worn or held by an individual for protection against health and safety risks. It covers units constituted from several devices, personal protective equipment components, and the use of personal protective equipment in conjunction with a non-protective device. It does not apply where the equipment is covered by another directive. Certain products listed in Annex I lie outside its scope. These include equipment for the armed forces, police, and for self-defence, protective equipment for private use against heat, damp and water, and adverse atmospheric conditions (i.e. clothing for domestic use), and rescue equipment.

			RISKS																				
			PHYSICAL											CHEMICAL						BIOLOGICAL			
			MECHANICAL					THERMAL			RADIATION			AEROSOLS			LIQUIDS						
			Falls from a height	Blows, cuts, impact, crush-ing	Stabs, cuts, grazes	Vibra-tion	Slip-ping, falling over	Heat, fire	Cold	ELEC-TRI-CAL	Non-ionising	Ionising	NOISE	Dust, fibres	Fumes	Va-pours	Immer-sion	Splash-es, spurts	GASES, VA-POURS	Harm-ful bacte-ria	Harmful viruses	Mycotic fungi	Non-micro-biologi-cal anti-genes
PARTS OF THE BODY	HEAD	Cranium																					
		Ears																					
		Eyes																					
		Respiratory tract																					
		Face																					
		Whole head																					
	UPPER LIMBS	Hands																					
		Arms (parts)																					
	LOWER LIMBS	Foot																					
		Legs (parts)																					
	VARIOUS	Skin																					
		Trunk/abdomen																					
		Parenteral passages																					
		Whole body																					

Figure 14 *Specimen risk survey table for the use of personal protective equipment*

Source: Council Directive of 30 November 1989 on the minimum health and safety requirements for the use of workers of personal protective equipment at the workplace (89/656/EEC), *Official Journal*, L 393, 30 December 1989

5.3.3.3 The Directive sets out the essential requirements that personal protective equipment must satisfy in order not to compromise health and safety. These are referred to in the Directive as *basic requirements*. They fall into three main groups:

- *General requirements*. These are applicable to all personal protective equipment. There is an overriding requirement that the equipment must provide adequate protection against all risks encountered. The equipment should be designed according to ergonomic principles and can provide different levels or classes of protection. It should be innocuous, comfortable, and efficient. The manufacturer is required to provide an *information notice* which shall include information on:

  – Storage, use, cleaning, maintenance, servicing, and disinfection,

  – Performance in tests,

  – The classes of protection offered,

  – Suitable accessories,

  – The obsolescence period,

  – Transportation,

  – The significance of any markings.

- *Additional requirements for certain classes of equipment*. The Directive identifies a number of different classes, including equipment that:

  – Incorporates adjustment systems,

  – Encloses parts of the body, protects faces, eyes, and respiratory tracts,

  – Is subject to ageing,

  – Can be caught up in use,

  – Is for use in an explosive atmosphere or in dangerous or emergency situations,

  – Incorporates components,

  – Protects against multiple risks.

- *Requirements for particular risks*. These include mechanical impact, compression, physical injury, drowning, noise, heat and fire, cold, electric shock, radiation, and dangerous substances.

5.3.3.4 The processes for the attestation of conformity are set out in Figure 15. In all cases the manufacturer must draw up a *technical file*, which includes plans, calculations, and details of prototypes, the basic requirements met, and the means by which quality is controlled and the equipment tested. It also includes a copy of the information notice required by the basic requirements.

5.3.3.5 If the equipment is of *simple design*, then the manufacturer draws up an EC declaration of conformity and affixes the CE mark. This is equipment where the designer can assume that the user can assess the level of protection provided against minimal risks that can be identified in good time. It is intended to cover equipment that protects against superficial mechanical action, cleaning materials of weak action, heat protection up to 50°C, non-extreme atmospheric agents, minor abrasions and vibration, and sunlight. Examples of this type of equipment could be waterproof gloves for washing up and gardening gloves.

5.3.3.6 In other cases there is to be an EC type-examination by an approved inspection body. The approved bodies must satisfy the same requirements as for other New Approach directives (see Section 2.3.3.2). The precise role of the approved body depends upon whether the product has been produced in full conformity with harmonized standards or whether there has not been compliance or only partial compliance because, for example, harmonized standards do not exist. If there is full conformance with harmonized standards, then the approved body verifies that the technical file satisfies the harmonized standards and that the prototype has been produced in accordance with the technical file and harmonized standards. If no harmonized standards have been used, or there has only been partial use of them, the approved body must also check that the technical specifications used satisfy the basic requirements. If the approved body is satisfied, it issues an EC type-examination certificate. The technical file must be held at the disposal of the competent authorities for 10 years.

5.3.3.7 If the equipment is intended to protect against mortal danger or serious harm, then its production is also subject to control. Only certain limited types of equipment fall within this category:

- Filtering respiratory devices,
- Respiratory devices providing full insulation from the atmosphere,
- Equipment providing only limited protection against chemical attack or radiation,
- Emergency equipment for use in high or low temperatures,
- Equipment to protect against falls from a height,
- Equipment to protect against electrical risks,
- Motor-cycle helmets and visors.

For these the manufacturer has a choice between two methods for controlling production:

- *The EC quality control system for final products* is intended to ensure conformity of production with the prototype. A body chosen by the manufacturer carries out random checks on production at least once a year. This body does not have to be an approved body.
- *The system for ensuring EC quality of production by means of monitoring* involves third-party approval of the quality control system. Again, the body that does this need not be an approved body. The manufacturer accepts the obligations stemming from a quality control system and agrees to maintain it. Each item of equipment is examined and tested. The chosen body examines the quality objectives, organization, tests and checks, and the monitoring of the quality control system and audits the system, including carrying out unannounced visits. It may presume compliance if the quality system complies with a harmonized standard, i.e. the appropriate part of the EN 29000 series (BS 5750).

5.3.3.8 Member States have the usual obligations laid upon them by New Approach directives. These include that of not impeding the free mobility of products that satisfy the Directive, although they can challenge the conformity of individual products and harmonized standards. They can make regulations concerning the use of personal protective equipment, providing that this does not require modification of products. The Commission is to be advised on standards by the Committee set up under the directive 83/189/EEC[14] (see Section 2.2.2.2). However, advice on the implementation of the Directive is to come from the Standing Committee established by the Machinery Directive (see Section 4.3.4.3).

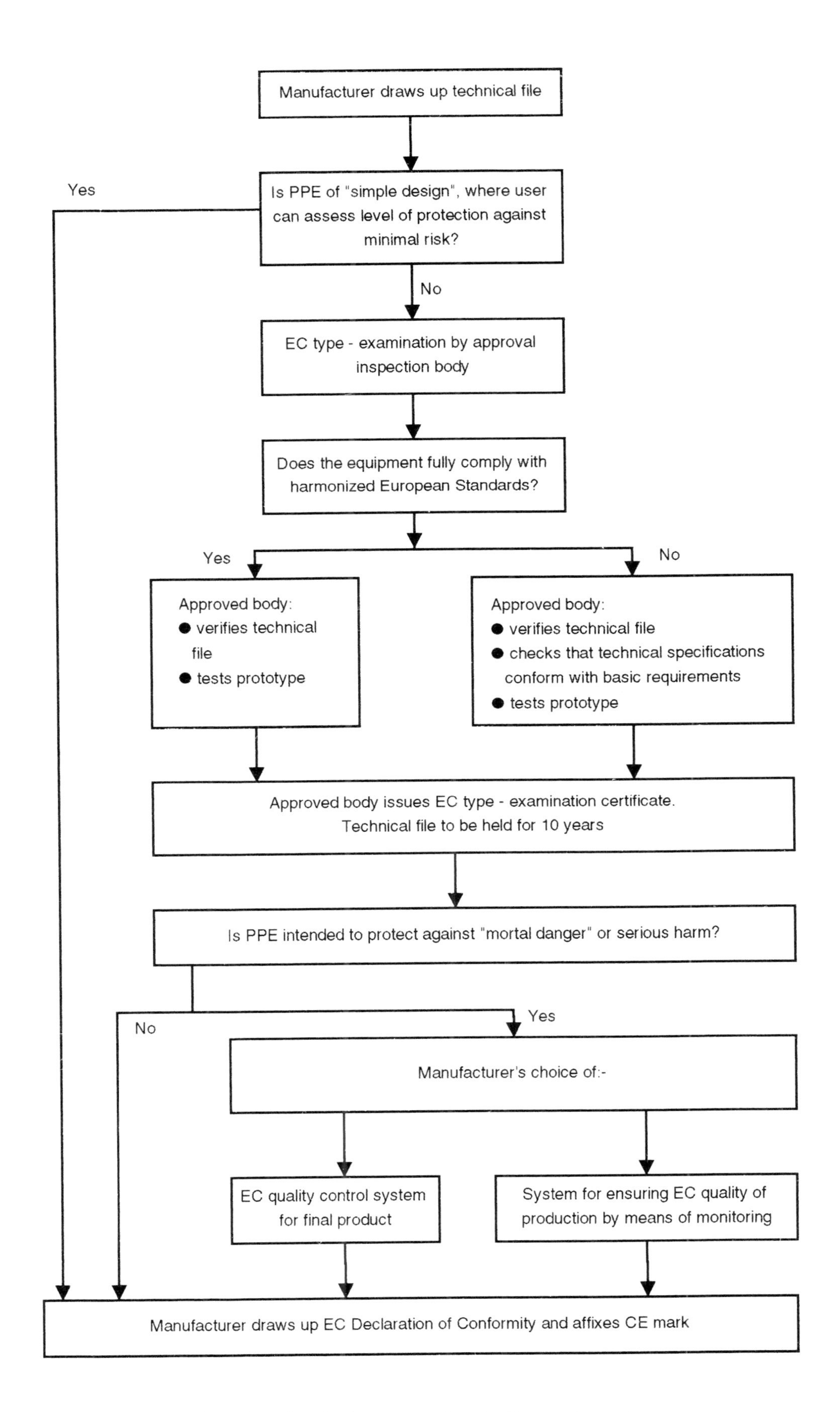

Figure 15 *Attestation of conformity for personal protective equipment*

Source: Council Directive of 21 December 1989 on the approximation of the laws of the Member States relating to personal protective equipment (89/686/EEC), *Official Journal*, L 399, 30 December 1989.

5.4 CONCLUSIONS

5.4.1 The New Approach directives for technical harmonization are concerned with the manufacture of products so that products are only placed upon the market if they do not constitute a threat to health and safety. This is to be achieved by setting down essential requirements that products must comply with. Conformity with technical specifications that reflect the essential requirements is the normal way of satisfying the directives. Attestation of conformity procedures is intended to ensure that production actually conforms to specifications. However, health and safety can only be ensured if the use of the products is regulated as well as their production. There is little point if setting up procedures to ensure that only safe products enter the market if they are abused when used.

5.4.2 The approach to this issue varies between the New Approach directives. The Construction Products Directive states that the essential requirements are to be satisfied by the construction works into which the products are incorporated rather than just the products themselves. It is left to each Member State to regulate their use through building control systems that are not harmonized by this Directive. For personal protective equipment and machinery, governments regulate their use in the workplace. Incompatible national regulations could impede free trade. The harmonization of regulations for ensuring safety in the workplace replaces national systems by a common system with a similar objective. The New Approach directives on machinery and personal protective equipment dovetail with those concerning their safe use in the workplace. Employers will be obliged to use only equipment that complies with New Approach directives. These directives require manufacturers to supply instructions and information on their safe use.

5.4.3 The safety directives impose extensive demands upon employers. These demands are likely to be fulfilled only if employers have effective management systems. These include the ability to plan, to ensure that plans are realized, and that there is a monitoring and review of arrangements. There is no obligation on employers to adopt quality management systems but an effective quality management system would provide the structure for fulfilling the obligations under the safety directives.

References: 5 Technical harmonization of construction site work

1. Council Directive of 12 June 1989 on the introduction of measures to encourage improvements in the safety and health of workers at work (89/391/EEC), *Official Journal*, L 183, 29 June 1989.

2. Health and Safety Executive (1991), *Proposals for Health and Safety (General Provisions) Regulations and Approved Code of Practice – Consultative Document*. This document also contains the text of the Framework Directive (89/391/EEC).

3. Amended proposal for a Council Directive on the implementation of minimum safety and health requirements at temporary or mobile work sites (91/C 112/04), *Official Journal*, C 112, 27 April 1991.

4. Council Directive of 30 November 1989 concerning the minimum safety and health requirements for the use of work equipment by workers at work (89/391/EEC), *Official Journal*, L 393, 30 December 1989.

5. Health and Safety Executive (1992), *Provision and Use of Work Equipment: Draft Proposals for Regulations – Consultative Document*. This document also contains the text of the Work Equipment Directive (89/391/EEC).

6. Council Directive of 14 June 1989 on the approximation of the laws of the Member States relating to machinery (89/392/EEC), *Official Journal*, L 183, 29 June 1989.

7. Council Directive of 20 June 1991 amending Directive 89/392/EEC on the approximation of the laws of the Member States relating to machinery, *Official Journal*, L 198, 22 July 1991.

8. Department of Trade and Industry (1992), *The European Commission's Proposal for a Second Amendment to the Machinery Directive;* Proposal for a Council Directive amending 89/392/EEC on the approximation of the laws of the Member States relating to machinery (92/C 25/07), *Official Journal*, C 25, 1 February 1992.

9. Proposal for a Council Directive on the approximation of the laws of the Member States relating to lifts (92/C 62/05), *Official Journal*, C 62, 11 March 1992.

10. Health and Safety Executive (1991), *Personal Protective Equipment at Work: Proposals for Regulations and Guidance – Consultative Document*. This document also contains the text of the Use of Personal Protective Equipment Directive (89/656/EEC).

11. Council Directive of 21 December 1989 on the approximation of the laws of the Member States relating to personal protective equipment (89/686/EEC), *Official Journal*, L 399, 30 December 1989.

12. Council Directive of 30 November 1989 on the minimum health and safety requirements for the use by workers of personal protective equipment at the workplace (89/656/EEC), *Official Journal*, L 393, 30 December 1989.

13. This is already covered by the Construction (Head Protection) Regulations 1989.

14. Council Directive of 28 March 1983 laying down a procedure for the provision of information in the field of technical standards and regulations (83/189/EEC), *Official Journal*, L 109, 26 April 1983.

Part C Public procurement

6 Public procurement policy in the EC

6.0 OVERVIEW

***6.0.1** The EC has long been concerned that government purchasing may operate as a non-tariff barrier by discriminating against firms from elsewhere in the Community. In view of the scale of public purchasing, such discriminatory behaviour could have significant consequences for the achievement of the Single Internal Market. The EC has sought to limit discriminatory purchasing by Member States since the early 1970s through the use of public procurement directives. They provided for the advertising of contracts of above a minimum value, the methods of tendering to be employed, and criteria to be used in the selection of tenders. Faced with evidence that few contracts were being awarded to non-domestic suppliers and of the flouting of the legislation by public bodies, the EC has responded by introducing a range of new public procurement directives. These seek to:*

- *Remedy deficiencies in the 1970s directives,*
- *Extend the principles of public procurement to the purchase of services,*
- *Extend the principles of public procurement to purchases by utilities undertakings,*
- *Provide more effective remedies for those suppliers who have been wrongly discriminated against.*

***6.0.2** These measures are likely to have important implications for quality management in construction. They provide for the use of European standards or technical approvals wherever possible. They determine the information that may be sought and used in the pre-qualification of contractors, including that concerning their technical competence and quality management. Since 1982 the UK government has used its purchasing power to encourage firms to adopt quality management by discriminating against those that fail to do so. It remains to be seen whether the detailed outcome of these measures has an effect on this policy and whether the UK government can continue to discriminate in this way.*

6.1 COST OF DISCRIMINATION IN PUBLIC PROCUREMENT

6.1.1 Public procurement can be used as a device to assist domestic industries in their competition with goods and services from overseas. Favouring domestic firms has the effect of reducing imports in a similar fashion to a quota. Importers find themselves excluded from part of a country's market as those responsible for purchasing refuse to buy their products. The consequences can be far-reaching. Importers lose potential income. Domestic producers may become less efficient as a result of protection from foreign competition and may direct their energies towards selling to the protected public sector market. The public sector pays higher prices for goods and services as a result of limited competition. Taxes are higher in consequence. The losses are on-going since an inefficient industrial structure means the loss of economies of scale and the discouragement of innovation.

6.1.2 The EC sees discriminatory public procurement as a breach of the EEC Treaty. It replaces the previously used tariffs and quotas by covert devices that achieve similar results. Such behaviour can be regarded as an infringement of the rights granted in the Treaty for nationals of one Member State to provide services for sale in another Member State and of their rights to establish businesses in other Member States.

6.1.3 The size of the public sector makes it difficult to ignore the impact of discriminatory purchasing. In 1986, the public sector accounted for 15% of the GDP of the EC. Public procurement (i.e. that part of public expenditure put out to contract) amounted to 7–10% of the

GDP. Purchases are concentrated in certain industries so that the impact on them is particularly marked. Construction accounts for 29% of public purchasing, and 85% of capital expenditure by the public sector was on transport and construction[1]. Public procurement is largely closed to intra-EC competition. Only 2% of public supplies contracts and 2% of public works contracts are awarded to firms from other EC Member States. US firms secure ten times the value of public work contracts that construction firms from other EC countries obtain[2]. However, a cautionary note should be injected. The figures may overstate the extent of discrimination since firms are classified by country of registration rather than that of beneficial ownership. Thus, an overseas subsidiary may be classified as a domestic firm. However, the general trend is clear – that few public works contracts are awarded to firms from elsewhere in the EC.

6.1.4 W S Atkins[1] has suggested that if public purchasers (outside of defence procurement) selected the most competitive supplier, savings amounting to 0.5% of the EC's GDP would be possible. Of this, 32% would come from cost savings, 17% from the benefits of increased competition, and the remaining 51% from the benefits of a restructuring of industry. However, the benefits from removing discrimination in public works procurement are likely to be small due to the low profit margins earned by contractors.

6.1.5 Although the losses from discriminatory purchasing in construction appear to be small in total, the effect may be significant for particular producers. Table 9 gives some examples of products claimed to be affected by discriminatory purchasing. The examples indicate that discriminatory behaviour is not the preserve of any one country. If sufficiently widespread, it may have an effect on business perceptions that outweighs its quantitative impact.

Table 9 Examples of barriers to trade resulting from public purchasing

Destination Country	Product	Complainant Country
Germany	Plumbing fittings	Italy
Italy	Sanitary ware	UK
France	Ceramic tiles	Italy
	Sanitary ware	UK, Spain
	Insulating glazing	Belgium
UK	Concrete pipes	France
	Roofing components and assembly systems	Denmark
Spain	Sanitary ware	UK
Ireland	Aluminium windows	UK
	Polyurethane foam	Belgium

Source: Bureau d'Informations et de Prévisions Économiques, *The 'Cost of Non-Europe' in Building Products*, Commission of the European Communities, Luxembourg, 1988. English-language version published by National Economic Development Office, 1989

6.2 EC CONTROL OF PUBLIC PROCUREMENT

6.2.1 The response of the EC to the problems caused by discriminatory public procurement practices has been to legislate to seek to ensure that public procurement takes place in an open, competitive, and transparent environment. This resulted in the Public Works Directive of 1971[3] and the Public Supplies Directive of 1977[4]. However, there is evidence that these directives have not always been followed in practice[5]. Departures include:

- Failure to advertise all the contracts that should have been advertised,
- Abuse of exceptions to the tendering and awards procedures,
- Wrongful exclusion of bidders,
- Wrongful splitting of contracts so that lots fall below the threshold for advertisement,

- Use of technical specifications so as to favour domestic producers,
- Decentralization of purchasing so that abuses are more difficult to monitor.

The evidence led the Cecchini Report to conclude that there was

> a gap between liberal appearance and protectionist reality. . . . In public procurement, the divide between economic reality and political appearances is so deep as to be almost hallucinatory. . . . EC rules-awarding procedures have had very little effect in the areas of procurement actually within their scope. The stark fact is that the Community legislator has up to now proved no match for national and local purchasing bureaucracies.[6]

6.2.2 The EC's response has been to extend its public procurement legislation to try to remedy perceived deficiencies in the 1970s legislation. This has resulted in the adoption or proposal of five main groups of directives.

- The adoption of a revised Public Supplies Directive intended to remedy the deficiencies in the 1978 Directive,
- The adoption of a revised Public Works Directive intended to remedy the deficiencies in the 1971 Directive,
- The adoption of a so-called Utilities Directive, which extends the principles of the public procurement directives to procurement by entities operating in the water, energy, transport, and telecommunications sectors,
- A proposed Public Services Directive and a parallel proposed Public Utilities Services Directive, which are intended to extend the principles of the public procurement directives to the purchase of services,
- A family of compliance or remedies directives, which are intended to provide more effective means of redress for suppliers who have been wrongfully excluded from the award of contracts. Each procurement directive will have a corresponding remedies directive.

6.2.3 The policies seek to:

- *Tighten up on the enforcement of the public procurement principles laid down in the 1970s so as to ensure that the system is fair and transparent.* This has involved, for example, providing a means by which non-discriminatory technical specifications are used, restricting the proportion of contracts for which there is single firm tendering, and improving the system for advertising contracts.
- *Extend the principles of public procurement to previously excluded areas.* These are principally the purchase of services and purchases by utilities entities in the water, transport, energy, and telecommunications sectors.
- *Provide better means of securing redress for an aggrieved contractor than the pursuit of a case before the European Court of Justice and to provide alternative means of compensation to the rerun of the contract award.*
- *Ensure that all bodies, including private ones, which undertake public functions, are bound by similar procurement rules.*

The policy measures do not cover all aspects of public procurement. This has led to suggestions that other directives should be proposed, for example, to cover defence procurement[7].

6.2.4 A cautionary note should be injected into the discussion as to the likely effectiveness of the new directives. Not all discriminatory procurement practices have been for protectionist reasons. There are other economic and social objectives that have been pursued using discrimination in procurement. These include:

- Regional policy aimed at directing public procurement towards areas of high unemployment,
- Support and encouragement of small and medium-sized enterprises,

- Ensuring a degree of self-sufficiency for strategic reasons,
- Supporting the adoption of quality management by suppliers,
- Supporting and encouraging infant industries,
- Political and electoral factors.

Member States are likely to want to continue to pursue many of these objectives and are likely to seek ways of doing so even under the new directives. The Commission also finds itself advocating measures to aid small and medium-sized enterprises, such as the splitting of contracts, which are similar to those of which it has accused Member States[8]. If the EC fails to agree common policies to achieve these, the new directives could be undermined by governmental actions.

6.2.5 There are also good economic reasons why contractors do not actively pursue many of the public contracts on offer in other Member States[9]. New legislation on public procurement will have little effect on these yet they may prevent the legislation from achieving its objectives. They include:

- Low profit margins earned from contracting, especially in relation to housebuilding and property development[10],
- Small size of contracts that have to be advertised to comply with the directives so that the profits from them are not worth pursuing,
- Localized market within which much of the construction industry operates,
- Need for local knowledge in areas such as procedures and employment practices before a contractor can successfully compete with local competitors,
- Cost of failing to win a high proportion of bids in open tendering situations.

6.2.6 For these reasons, therefore, it seems unlikely that the public procurement directives will revolutionize public procurement but are to be welcomed in so far as they open it up further to competition. However, there are likely to be costs in achieving this. These include increased delays between the procurement decision and the conclusion of the contract, reduced flexibility in contractual procedures, and the extra administrative burden. Digings[11] has concluded:

> If it looks doubtful that the new directives and enforcement measures will produce the breakthrough the Commission is seeking, the likely consequences for local authorities are equally plain to see: more bureaucracy without any tangible benefits.

6.3 PUBLIC PROCUREMENT DIRECTIVES AND THE MEMBER STATES

Different Member States have different traditions and practices with respect to the procurement of construction works. The UK and Germany have systems that make a clear distinction between the design and construction stages. The contracting authority or the design team it employs produce detailed drawings and tender documents. Construction contractors tender for construction alone and do not generally offer alternative designs. By contrast, in Italy, Spain, and Portugal contractors typically have design teams. They tend to put in a design input after tender and the offering of alternative tenders is a feature of their systems[12]. In the former system, contracting authorities are likely to set detailed design specifications and in the latter the contractor could determine these through offering alternative tenders. It will only become clear how the directives cope with these differences as Member States gain experience of their use. However, it is already apparent that bringing the directives into force poses significant issues for a number of Member States[13].

References: 6 Public procurement policy in the EC

1. W.S. Atkins Management Consultants in association with Eurequip SA – Roland Berger & Partner – Eurequip Italia (1988), *The 'Cost of Non-Europe' in Public Sector Procurement*, Commission of the European Communities, Luxembourg.

2. Directorate-General for Economic and Financial Affairs (1988), The Economics of 1992: An assessment of the potential economic effects of completing the internal market of the European Community, *European Economy*, No. 35, March.

3. Council Directive of 26 July 1971 concerning the coordination of procedures for the award of public works contracts (71/305/EEC), *Official Journal*, L 185, 16 August 1971.

4. Council Directive of 21 December 1976 coordinating procedures for the award of public supply contracts (77/62/EEC), *Official Journal*, L 13, 15 January 1977.

5. Economic and Social Committee, Opinion of the proposal for a Council Directive amending Directive 77/62/EEC relating to the coordination of procedures on the award of public supply contracts and deleting provisions of Directive 80/767/EEC, *Official Journal*, C 68, 16 March 1987.

6. Cecchini, P. with Catinat, M. and Jacquemin, A. (1988), *The European Challenge: 1992 – The benefits of a single market*, Gower.

7. National Economic Development Office (1990), *Selling to Europe: A country-by-country guide to public sector purchasing.*

8. Commission of the European Communities (1991), *The Large Market of 1993 and Opening Up of Public Procurement*, Luxembourg.

9. Wanstall, M. (1990), The Public Procurement Directives – a procurer's view, *Building Technical File*, No. 29, April.

10. Grover, R.J. (1991), The Development of a European Housebuilding Industry, in Bezelga, A. and Brandon, P. (Eds), *Management, Quality and Economics in Building*, E & F N Spon.

11. Digings, L. (1991), *Competitive Tendering and the European Communities: Public Procurement, CCT and Local Authorities*, Association of Metropolitan Authorities.

12. The Reinforced Earth Co. Ltd (1989), *Summary of Design, Tender and Construction Practices in Public Works Contracts in EEC Countries*, unpublished briefing paper, 19 May.

13. Heierman, W. (1990), The EC Directive concerning coordination of procedures for the award of public works contracts, *International Construction Law Review*, Vol. 7, No. 1, January; Adriaansens, C.A. and Nijholt, H. (1989), Dutch tender policies under the new EC directives on public works, *International Construction Law Review*, Vol. 6, No. 4, October; Nanni, A. (1992), Brief overview of EEC regulations on public procurement contracts and their implementation in Italy, *International Construction Law Review*, Vol. 9, No. 2, April.

7 Public Works Directive

7.0 OVERVIEW

7.0.1 The Public Works Directive of 1989[1] came into effect on 18 July 1990. It substantially amends the original Public Works Directive of 1971[2] which has governed the public procurement of building and construction works in the UK since July 1973. Implementation in the UK was initially by administrative action, such as directions to government departments and local authority circulars[3]. This led to criticism by the Commission that such action did not produce readily enforceable legal rights. This has now been remedied by the Award of Public Works Contracts Regulations 1991[4], which came into force on 21 December 1991.

7.0.2 The new Directive aims to improve opportunities for firms from other Member States to compete for building and construction contracts awarded by the government and public bodies. This is to be achieved by:

- *The publication of opportunities to tender for public contracts throughout the EC so that all interested parties have the chance to participate,*
- *The use of European technical specifications so as to avoid specifications that discriminate against firms from other Member States of the EC,*
- *The use of objective published criteria in the selection of contractors.*

7.0.3 The 1989 Directive substantially amends that of 1971 in a number of respects, principally by:

- *Redefining and extending the contracts and contracting authorities to which the Directive applies,*
- *Increasing the threshold above which information on contracts must be published from 1 million ECU to 5 million ECU (£3.5 million[5]),*
- *Restricting the use of single tendering and of invitations to a limited number of contractors to participate in negotiations of contracts,*
- *Requiring the use of European technical specifications, wherever possible,*
- *Extending the information about contracts to be published so as to include prior indications that a contract is to be put out to tender, the criteria by which a contract is to be awarded, and details of the award of a contract,*
- *Requiring that reasons be given for the rejection of contractors,*
- *Requiring more extensive reports from contracting authorities on the award of contracts, including improved statistical returns,*
- *Extending certain time-limits for the submission of requests to participate in and for the return of tenders.*

7.1 COVERAGE

7.1.1 Definition of public works

7.1.1.1 The Directive applies to public works contracts. These are defined as being contracts for pecuniary interest, concluded in writing, between a contractor and a contracting authority. The contracts affected by the Directive are those for which the potential contractor is a national of and established in a Member State. Non-nationals and non-residents of the EC are not to be treated more favourably than EC ones. The contracts must have as their object the execution, or execution and design, of building or civil engineering works. They can be contracts for these purposes or for engagement of a person to procure the carrying out of design and construction. Thus, the Directive also applies to management contracts, where the contractor is responsible for procuring the execution, or execution and design of, works in his own name. The Directive covers contracts let on behalf of a contracting authority by an agent as, for example, under a construction management contract. This means that the agent should be placed under a contractual obligation to comply with the Directive on behalf of the contracting authority[3]. Consultancy contracts are not covered by this Directive but are subject to the Public Services Directive (see Section 8.2). It should be noted that the contracts covered by this Directive do not have to take place within the EC, providing that they are of the type covered by the Directive and placed by an appropriate contracting authority.

7.1.1.2 Annex II of the Directive, which is Schedule 1 of the UK Regulations (see Table 10), defines what is meant by building and civil engineering works. These fall into five main categories.

- General building and civil engineering works,
- Construction of flats, office blocks, hospitals and other buildings, both residential and non-residential,
- Civil engineering,
- Installation of fittings and fixtures,
- Building completion work.

The categories should not be regarded as being exclusive, as the Directive applies to any outcome of building or civil engineering works that fulfils an economic and technical function. In addition, it applies to any works that meet the requirement of a contracting authority, irrespective of how this was achieved. If a contract is for works that fulfil an economic and technical function and the contract includes a significant proportion of goods, the Public Works and not the Public Supplies Directive applies, providing that the goods are needed for the execution of works[3].

7.1.2 Contracting authorities

7.1.2.1 The contracting authorities to whom the Directive applies are:

- *The state*: that is, Ministers of the Crown and government departments,
- *Regional and local authorities*: The Treasury expects the European Court of Justice to interpret this to include bodies other than elected councils, such as trust hospitals and universities,
- *Bodies governed by public law*,
- *Associations formed by one or more contracting authority*: These include joint authorities that have non-contracting authorities among their members.

The Directive, and its subsequent amendment[6], identify a number of bodies for each Member State that fall within the definition of a contracting authority. Those for the UK are listed in Table 11. Member States are obliged to review these lists periodically and to notify the Commission of amendments. Therefore, it is likely that additional bodies will be added over time and existing ones dropped as they are wound up. There may also be other bodies which meet the criteria, but which are not listed, so that the lists should not be treated as being exclusive.

7.1.2.2 The Directive defines *bodies governed by public law* as being those that satisfy three conditions:

- Having a legal personality. In the UK this is interpreted to mean being a corporation or being a group of persons who have not been incorporated but who act together, for example, the Monopolies and Mergers Commission,
- Being established for the purpose of meeting needs in the general interest, but not being industrial or commercial in character,
- Drawing the majority of their finance from public sources, *or* having the majority of their board of management, or equivalent body, appointed by a public body, *or* being subject to management supervision by a contracting authority.

Table 10 Categories of building and civil engineering work

Groups	Subgroups	Descriptions
500		*General building and civil engineering work (without any particular specialization) and demolition work*
	500.1	General building and civil engineering work (without any particular specialization)
	500.2	Demolition work
501		*Construction of flats, office blocks, hospitals and other buildings, both residential and non-residential*
	501.1	General building contractors
	501.2	Roofing
	501.3	Construction of chimneys, kilns and furnaces
	501.4	Waterproofing and damp-proofing
	501.5	Restoration and maintenance of outside walls (repainting, cleaning, etc.)
	501.6	Erection and dismantlement of scaffolding
	501.7	Other specialized activities relating to construction work (including carpentry)
502		*Civil engineering: construction of roads, bridges, railways, etc.*
	502.1	General civil engineering work
	502.2	Earth-moving (navvying)
	502.3	Construction of bridges, tunnels and shafts, drilling
	502.4	Hydraulic engineering (rivers, canals, harbours, flows, locks and dams)
	502.5	Road-building (including specialized construction of airports and runways)
	502.6	Specialized construction work relating to water (i.e. to irrigation, land drainage, water supply, sewage disposal, sewerage, etc.)
	502.7	Specialized activities in other areas of civil engineering
503		*Installation (fittings and fixtures)*
	503.1	General installation work
	503.2	Gas fitting and plumbing, and the installation of sanitary equipment
	503.3	Installation of heating and ventilating apparatus (central heating, air-conditioning, ventilation)
	503.4	Sound and heat insulation, insulation against vibration
	503.5	Electrical fittings
	503.6	Installation of aerials, lightning conductors, telephones, etc.
504		*Building completion work*
	504.1	General building completion work
	504.2	Plastering
	504.3	Joinery, primarily engaged in on the site assembly and/or installation (including the laying of parquet flooring)
	504.4	Painting, glazing, paper hanging
	504.5	Tiling and otherwise covering floors and walls
	504.6	Other building completion work (putting in fireplaces, etc.)

Source: The Public Works Contracts Regulations 1991, SI 1991 No 2680, Schedule 1

The definition of what constitutes a public body is more problematic in the UK than in some other Member States. Table 11 lists the bodies recognized as being governed by public law. However, it is not an exclusive list.

7.1.2.3 Certain private bodies are also subject to the Directive in circumstances in which they derive funding for specific building and construction works from public sources. Member States are required to take measures to ensure that private contracting authorities comply with the Directive where public bodies subsidise one of their works contracts by more than 50%. This is achieved in the UK by requiring contracting authorities to make it a condition of the contribution that the subsidised body complies with the Directive. However, this only applies to certain types of public works, namely to those in group 502 of Annex II (i.e. civil engineering work), and to building work for hospitals, sports and leisure facilities, school and university buildings, and buildings used for administrative purposes. This would indicate that publicly subsidised private housing projects do not fall within the scope of the Directive. It is a condition of EC finance, for example from the Regional Development Fund or the European Investment Bank, that the recipients shall comply with the Directive.

Table 11 Bodies governed by public law in the UK

Categories:
Fire authorities
Education authorities
National Health Service authorities
Police authorities
New town corporations
Research councils
Urban Development Corporations
Bodies:
Commission for the New Towns
Northern Ireland Housing Executive
National Rivers Authority
National Research Development Corporation
University Funding Council
Polytechnics and Colleges Funding Council
Central Blood Laboratory Service
Health and Safety Executive
Public Health Laboratory Service
Scottish Homes
Design Council
Arbitration, Conciliation and Advisory Service
Cardiff Bay Development Corporation
Development Board for Rural Wales
London Docklands Development Corporation
Merseyside Development Corporation
English Industrial Estates Corporation
Scottish Development Agency
Welsh Development Agency

Source: Commission Decision of 13 July 1990 concerning the updating of Annex I to the Council Directive 89/440/EEC, 90/380/EEC, *Official Journal*, L 187, 19 July 1990

7.1.3 Financial thresholds

7.1.3.1 The Directive applies to those public works contracts which have an estimated value net of VAT of at least **5 million ECU (£3.5 million)**. The exchange rate for a currency against the ECU for this purpose is set for a two-year period and is based upon the average daily rate over the preceding two years. The 1971 Public Works Directive set a threshold of 1 million ECU. The current threshold has been increased in line with inflation. In estimating the value of a contract, any supplies made available to the contractor by the contracting authority must also be included.

7.1.3.2 Where a contract is divided into lots, or where the contract is one of a number to be entered into for carrying out a work, the Directive applies where the aggregate of the lots or the total cost of the works amounts to at least 5 million ECU. Exemption is provided for lots with a value net of VAT of less than 1 million ECU, providing that the value of all the exempting lots does not exceed 20% of the total estimated value of all the lots. Contracts must not be split up with the intention of evading the Directive.

7.1.4 Exclusions from the Directive

Certain types of public works contracts are excluded from the scope of the Directive.

- Contracts awarded by carriers by land, air, sea, or inland waterway and those concerning the production, transport, and distribution of drinking water and the production and distribution of energy. These are subject to the Utilities Directive (see Section 8.3),
- Contracts which are declared secret and which must be accompanied by special security measures,

- Contracts awarded under an international agreement between a Member State and a third-party country covering works intended for a joint project. These agreements must be in conformity with the EEC Treaty and be communicated to the Commission,
- Undertakings in pursuance of an international agreement relating to the stationing of troops,
- Contracts awarded under the procedure of an international organization to which only states can be members, e.g. NATO, World Bank.

7.1.5 Public works concessions

7.1.5.1 The Directive also applies to *public works concessions*. These are defined as being public works contracts in which consideration consists wholly or partly of the right to exploit the works constructed. This could arise, for example, where a company is given a contract to build a road in return for receiving tolls.

7.1.5.2 Public works concessions are subject to the advertising provisions of the Directive where the contract value is at least 5 million ECU. In addition, the contracting authority may also *either*

- require the concessionaire to award contracts amounting to at least 30% of the value of the concession contract to third parties; *or*
- request candidates to specify in their tenders the percentage of the work they intend to assign to third parties.

Undertakings forming part of a consortium to obtain a concession contract are not regarded as being third parties, nor are any affiliated undertakings they control. A list of the latter has to be submitted with the candidature for the concession. If the concessionaire is a contracting authority, it must abide by the terms of the Directive in the award of works contracts to third parties. Concessionaires must apply the advertising rules when awarding contracts to third parties which are at least 5 million ECU in value. The sole exception to this is where the contract is for research and development.

Figure 16 sets out in the form of a flow chart the issues with respect to whether the Directive applies to a particular project.

7.2 PROCEDURES

7.2.1 Definitions

7.2.1.1 The Directive sets out three procedures for the award of public contracts:

- *Open procedures*. These are procedures whereby all interested contractors may submit tenders. The contracting authority publicises its intention to award a contract and selects the contractor from among those submitting tenders,
- *Restricted procedures*. These permit only those contractors invited by the contracting authority to submit tenders. The procedures include situations in which contractors must pre-qualify for a contract. The contracting authority publicises its intention to award a contract and invites requests from contractors to be selected to tender. Those selected must be invited to tender simultaneously,
- *Negotiated procedures*. Under these procedures, contracting authorities negotiate terms with the contractors of their choice. They can be used only under certain prescribed circumstances (see Section 7.2.2).

A contractor who submits a tender under open procedures is known as a *tenderer*, whereas one who has sought an invitation to take part in restricted or negotiated procedures is known as a *candidate*.

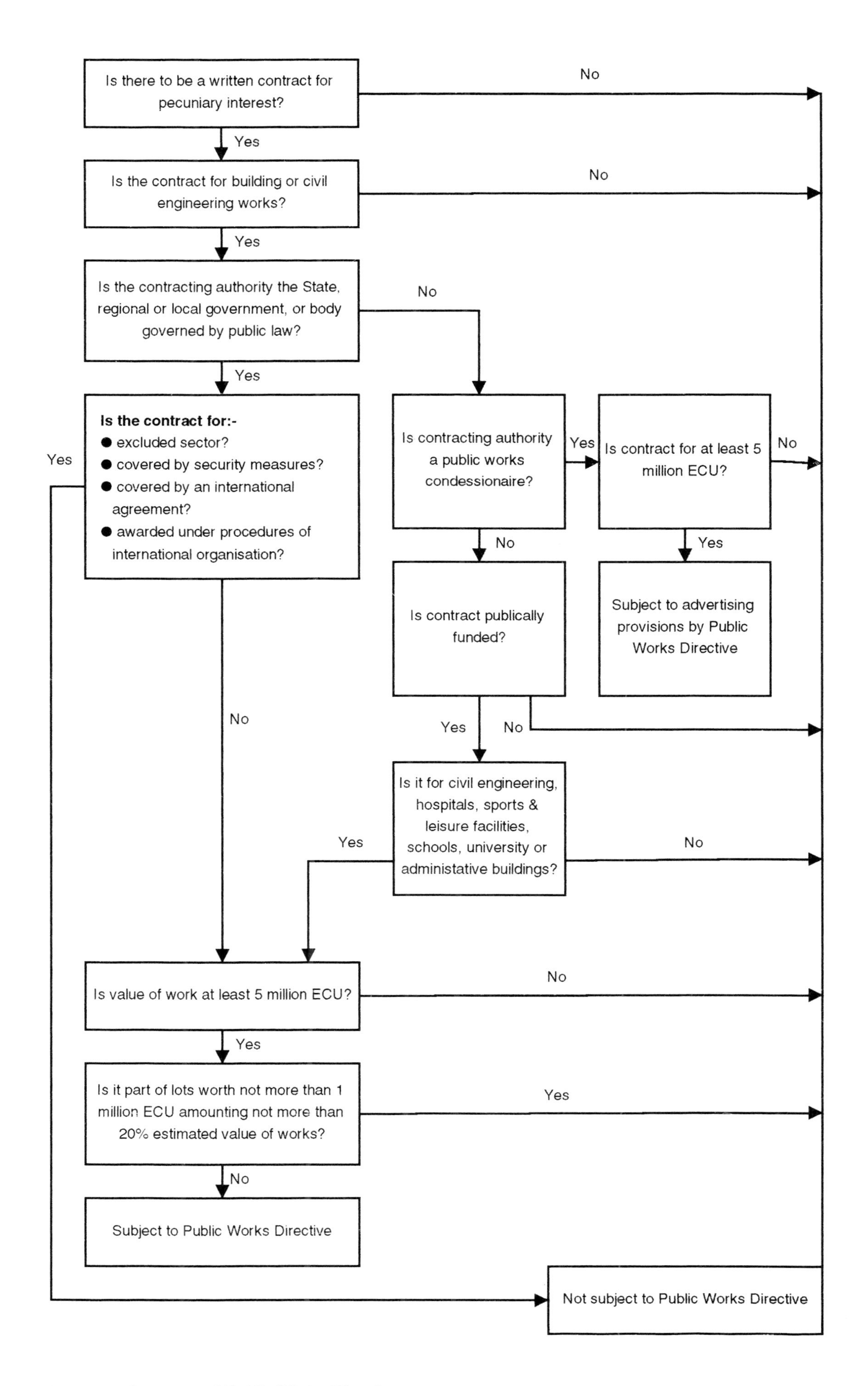

Figure 16 *Coverage of Public Works Directive*

The Directive does not abolish separate national procedures for the award of contracts. National procedures can remain providing that they do not conflict with the requirements of the Directive. In the UK these principally concern compulsory competitive tendering.

7.2.1.2 In addition to the three main procedures, a *special award procedure* may be used for certain public housing schemes. These schemes, as a result of their size, complexity, and duration, require the contractor to be part of a team together with the contracting authority and its advisers. This procedure is designed to select the contractor most suitable for integration into the team. The contract notice should, in this case, contain as accurate a job description as possible so that interested contractors can form a valid idea of what the work entails. Restricted procedures are followed in the advertising of such contracts.

7.2.2 Negotiated procedures

7.2.2.1 A contracting authority must, in general, award contracts by means of open or restricted procedures. In certain limited circumstances, contracts can be awarded using negotiated procedures. In issuing invitations to negotiate, the contracting authority must not discriminate between contractors on the grounds of their nationality or the Member State in which they are established. The Directive provides for the publication of a tender notice in certain circumstances and for other situations in which the prior publication of a tender notice is not necessary.

7.2.2.2 Negotiated procedures can be used only after the prior publication of a tender notice in the following circumstances.

- In the event of a high proportion of the tenders received in response to open or restricted procedures being irregular or unacceptable. This could occur, for example, because contractors have failed to meet the requirements specified in the contract documents or the work that is offered fails to meet the required technical specifications,
- When the works are purely for research and not to recover their costs or establish viability,
- In exceptional cases, when the nature of the works or risks attaching to them do not permit overall pricing.

In each of these circumstances, the candidate is selected according to *qualitative public criteria.* These are discussed below in Sections 7.5.1 and 7.5.3.

7.2.2.2 In the following circumstances, negotiated procedures may be used without the prior publication of a tender notice.

- When there is an absence of tenders, or of appropriate tenders, in response to open or restricted procedures,
- When the works may only be carried out by a particular contractor for artistic or technical reasons, or due to exclusive rights,
- For reasons of extreme urgency brought about by unforeseen events so that the time-limits for open, restricted, or negotiated procedures with the publication of a tender notice cannot be met. The unforeseen events that justify the use of this procedure must not be attributable to the contracting authority. The Treasury suggests that 'unforeseen' should be interpreted as 'unforeseeable' as this more closely aligns the English text with that found in other Community languages[(3)]. In consequence, the Commission and the European Court of Justice can be expected to interpret this provision more narrowly than the English text might indicate. However, this provision should enable emergency work to be carried out, say, after storm or flood damage, without the necessity for a tender notice,
- For additional works not in the original contract, which have become necessary through unforeseen circumstances. Such works should not be technically or economically separable from the main contract, or exceed 50% of the amount of the main contract. This would appear to cover most of the variations that are likely to become necessary in a construction contract,

- For repetitions of similar works by a successful contractor. Notice must have been given at the time the first project was put out to tender that this procedure might be adopted. The total cost of the original works, and possible subsequent works, must have been taken into account in deciding whether the 5 million ECU threshold for activating the advertising provisions of the Directive was reached. This procedure can only be applied within three years of the date when the original contract became binding.

7.2.3 Negotiation with contractors and tenderers

Negotiated procedures clearly permit the contracting authority to negotiate terms with a contractor. The Council and Commission have stated that negotiation with candidates or tenderers in open or restricted procedures on fundamental aspects of contracts shall be ruled out. This is to prevent the distortion of competition. If the terms of a contract are to be varied, other contractors may have been in a position to have been able to have matched or bettered the offer that was accepted. If there are to be significant changes to the contract, the contracting authority should cancel the award procedure and start again. Discussions can be held for the purpose of clarifying the requirements of the contracting authorities or to elaborate on tenders, providing that these do not involve discriminatory behaviour.

Figure 17 sets out in the form of a flow chart the options open to contracting authorities as to which procedure to use.

7.3 TECHNICAL SPECIFICATIONS

7.3.1 Definition of European specifications

7.3.1.1 Contract documents should contain the technical specifications relating to the contract. These define in an objective fashion the characteristics of the work, material, or product so as to identify when they fulfil the use for which they are intended. Clearly, there cannot be open competition for a contract unless the technical criteria for its award are made explicit to potential contractors. The characteristics concern levels of quality, performance, safety, and dimensions. They can include quality assurance, testing, packaging, terminology, symbols, and marking, and the rules relating to design, costing, inspection, acceptance of works, and methods of construction.

7.3.1.2 Technical specifications are to be defined by contracting authorities by reference to one of the following European specifications:

- National standards implementing European standards, including both design and product standards,
- European technical approvals,
- Common technical specifications drawn up in accordance with procedures recognized by, and applied uniformly in, all Member States and which have been published in the *Official Journal*.

7.3.1.3 A terminological problem has arisen as a result of this Directive referring to *European standards* whereas the standards produced under New Approach directives under mandate from the Commission are *harmonized European standards*. The former include voluntary standards drawn up by the European standards bodies whereas the latter play an important role in determining whether a product is fit to be placed upon the market. The UK Regulations follow the Directive in referring to European standards. It is not yet clear whether harmonized standards will be comprehensive ones or whether they will just contain references to attributes that relate to essential requirements (see Section 3.6.1). If harmonized standards narrowly follow the essential requirements, then it is difficult to see how public bodies could accurately specify their requirements using them or secure value for money in their purchases. For example, a harmonized European standard on floor tiles would certainly deal with the issue of the safety of pedestrians walking on them but would not necessarily be concerned with colour fastness as this is not an essential requirement. The issue of whether a public body may use European standards or only harmonized European standards would not arise but for Article 6 (1) of the Construction Products Directive[7]. This states that public bodies shall not by their rules or conditions impede the use of products that satisfy this Directive. Products that comply with a harmonized European standard satisfy it. The question is whether a public body that specifies by means of a European standard, rather than a harmonized European standard, is impeding the use of products that satisfy the Directive.

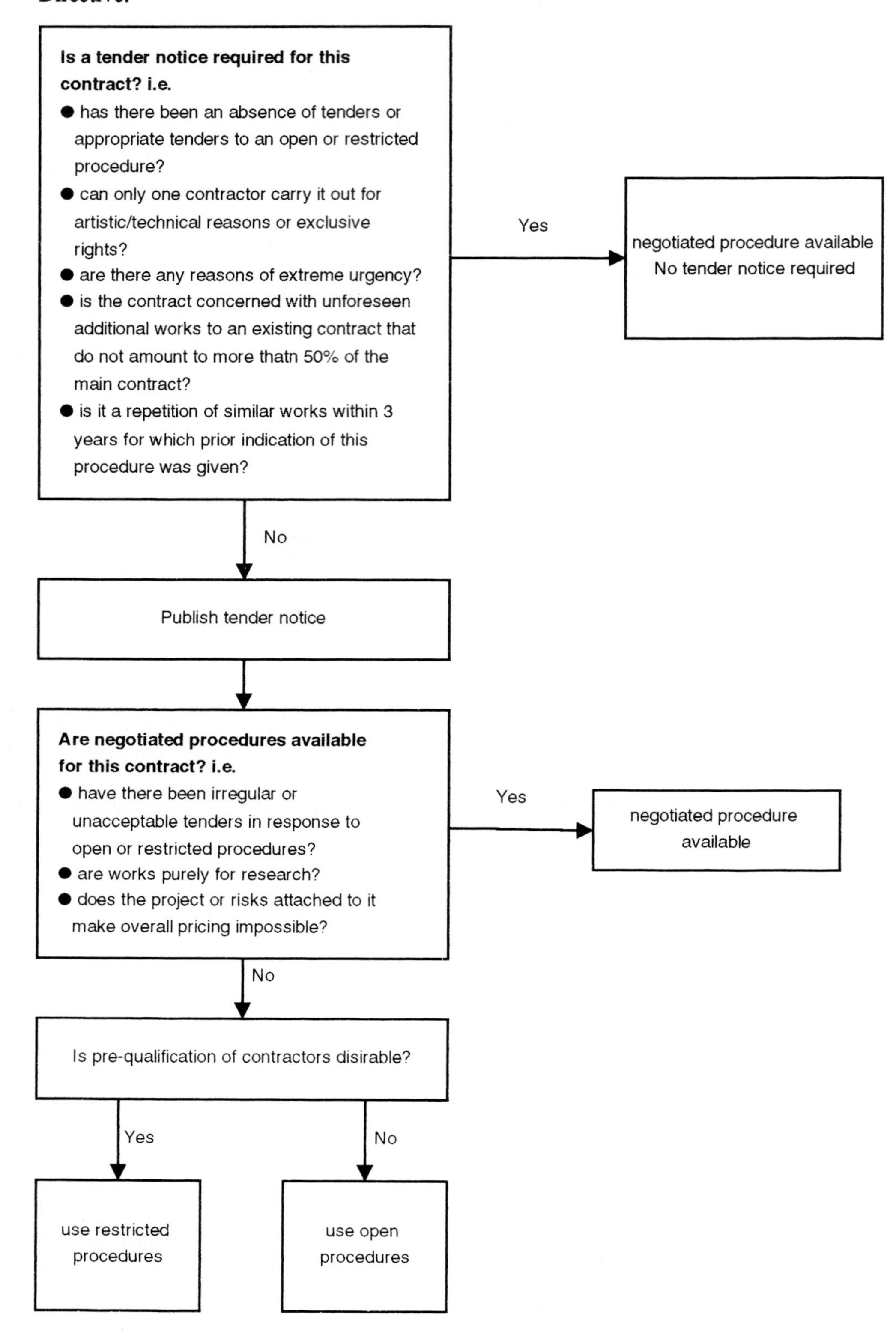

Figure 17 *Choice of award procedures*

7.3.2 Derogation from the use of European specifications

A contracting authority may depart from the use of European specifications in certain limited circumstances.

- Where a contracting authority is under an obligation to define technical specifications by reference to technical requirements which are mandatory in the UK, but only to the extent to which such an obligation is compatible with EC obligations,
- If European specifications do not include provisions for establishing conformity of a product with them, or the technical means for satisfactorily establishing conformity do not exist,
- Their use would oblige a contracting authority to acquire products or materials incompatible with those already in use, or would involve disproportionate costs or technical difficulties in making them compatible. However, derogation in this case must be part of a clearly defined and documented strategy for changing to the use of European specifications in order that this situation is brought to an end,
- They are inappropriate due to the innovatory nature of the project.

Unless it is impracticable, the reasons for not using European specifications should be recorded in the tender notice or contract documents as well as in internal documentation. Information on the reasons for not using them has to be supplied to the Commission on request and so must be recorded.

7.3.3 Absence of European specifications

7.3.3.1 In the immediate future, there will be relatively few European specifications compared with national ones, but this situation will change as CEN and CENELEC are mandated by the Commission to draft harmonized European standards and European technical approvals are awarded (see Sections 3.6 and 3.7). Where there is no European specification, use can be made of the following:

- National technical specifications that meet the essential requirements of technical harmonization directives, such as the Construction Products Directive. However, there is no indication that approval that these meet the essential requirements is likely to be given,
- National technical specifications for design, execution of works, and use of materials,
- Other documents.

7.3.3.2 If reference is to be made to 'other documents', the order of preference for making reference to them is:

- National standards incorporating international standards,
- Other national standards or technical approvals,
- Any other standard.

Contracts must not mention products of a specific make, or source, or from a particular process in order not to favour or exclude particular contractors. The use of trade marks, patents, or products of specific origin or production is prohibited unless qualified by the words 'or equivalent'. This form may only be used in circumstances in which the product could not otherwise be specified with sufficient precision.

7.3.3.3 Where a contract is to be awarded on the basis of the *most economically advantageous tender*, contractors can submit variants providing they meet the minimum technical specifications. Thus, a contractor can offer an alternative design that meets the technical specifications. Providing that this is in accordance with European specifications or with a national standard that meets the essential requirements of a technical harmonization directive, it cannot be rejected on these grounds alone. This is particularly important for ensuring that there is competition in circumstances in which the use of a technical specification, in effect, excludes certain contractors. For example, a technical approval may be closely linked to a proprietary system that other contractors cannot use, even though they may be able to offer equivalent performance through their own systems. The Directive should enable them to offer their own alternative solutions.

7.3.3.4 The ruling in the *Dundalk* case, in which an Irish local authority was found to have contravened Article 30 of the EEC Treaty, indicates that contracting authorities must be willing to consider works or products that are fit for the required purpose, even if they do not conform to the particular standards specified[8]. This requirement applies generally and not merely to those covered by the advertising rules of the public procurement directives by virtue of their size.

7.3.3.5 The Treasury states that contracting authorities may require certification that the quality management of a production process meets the requirements of the EN 29000 series (BS 5750)[3]. If certification by a third party is required, it is important that the phrase 'or equivalent' is added to any named certification body in order to avoid discrimination against firms from outside the UK, who have chosen different, but equivalent, means of demonstrating the effectiveness of their quality management. The Commission is responsible under the Construction Products Directive for determining which is the appropriate route to attestation of conformity for any particular construction product (see Section 3.8). Article 6(1) of the Construction Products Directive raises the question of whether a public body that requires a higher level of assurance for a construction product than that deemed sufficient by the Commission is through its rules and conditions impeding the use of products that satisfy this Directive. There is currently no clear answer to this question.

Figure 18 sets out in the form of a flow chart the choices between technical specifications.

7.4 TENDER NOTICES

7.4.1 Types of notice

7.4.1.1 The Directive provides for the advertising of contracts and the notification to tenderers and candidates by means of three types of notice.

- *Prior indicative notice.* Contracting authorities should make known their intention to award works contracts. The notice is intended to alert contractors to the fact that work is likely to become available rather than to provide them with detailed documentation. They are limited to 650 words. The notice is to follow the model set out in Annex IV A of the Directive and Schedule 2 of the UK Regulations (see Table 12). It should include the 'essential characteristics' of the contract and its estimated value. Indicative notices should appear as soon as possible after the contracting authority has decided to approve the planning of a contract and are published in the *Official Journal.* Similar notices are to be produced for public works concessions contracts and by public works concessionaires with respect to the contracts they are intending to award to third parties.

Table 12 Prior indicative notice

Name and address of contracting authority
Site
Nature of the services to be provided and, if available, the cost range
Estimated date for initiating award procedures and, if known, the estimated date for the start of the work and timetable for its completion
The terms of financing the work and of price revision, if known
Other information
Date of dispatch of the notice

Source: *The Public Works Contracts Regulations 1991*, SI 1991 No 2680, Schedule 2

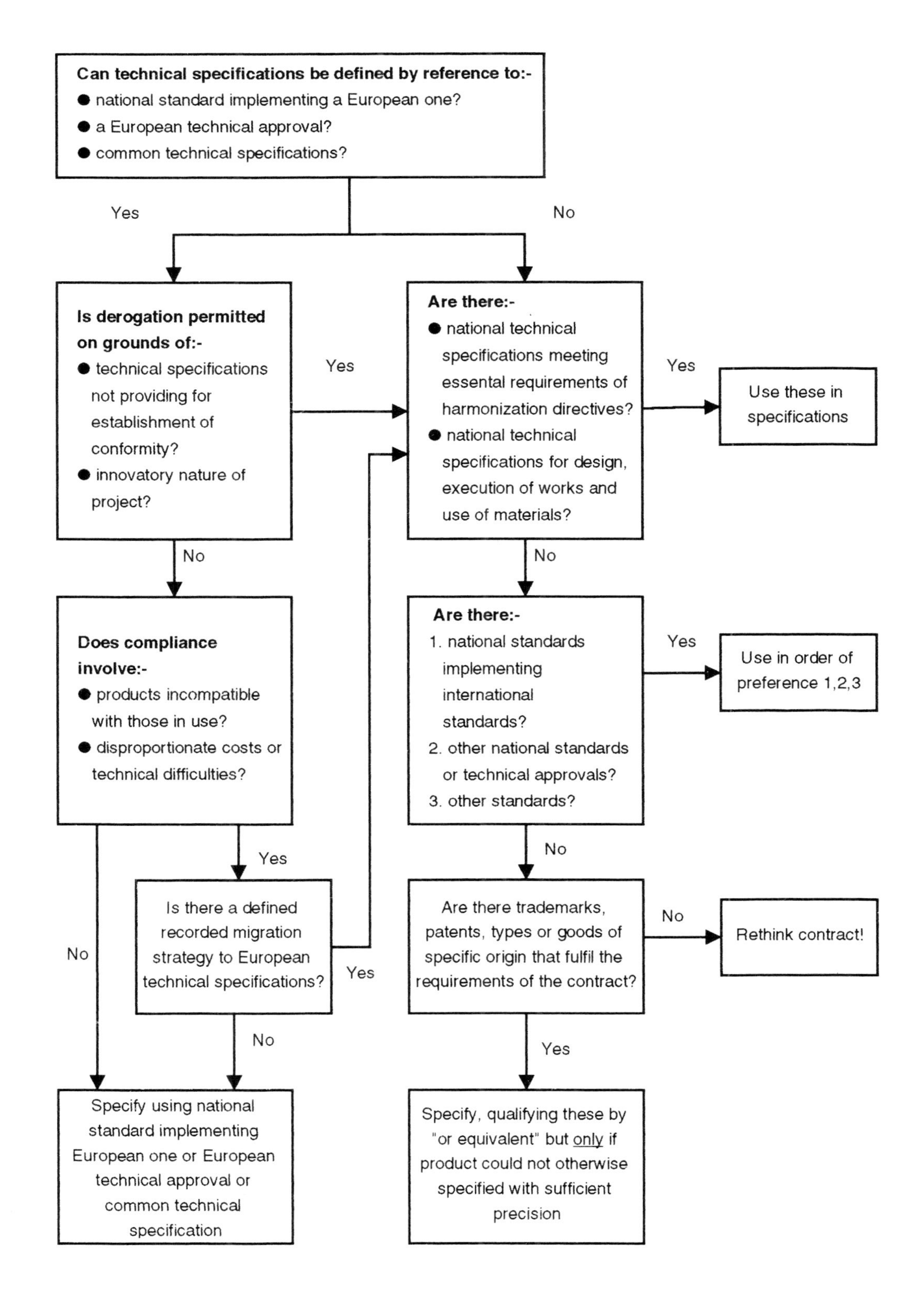

Figure 18 *Choice of technical specifications*

- *Contract or tender notice.* This is to be used in open and restricted procedures and, in certain circumstances, for negotiated procedures. Its purpose is to make known the nature of the contract which the contracting authority proposes to award. It is much more detailed than the indicative notice. There are five types of tender notice: for open, restricted, and negotiated procedures; for works concessions; and for use by works concessionaires with respect to contracts to be awarded to third parties. Model notices are set out in Annex IV B, C, and D, Annex V, and Annex VI of the Directive respectively and Schedule 2 of the UK Regulations (see Table 13). Much of the information required is the same for each notice. They identify the contracting authority, the award procedure chosen, the site, time limits for responses, any

Table 13 Contract or tender notices

	Open procedures	Restricted procedures	Negotiated procedures	Works concessions	Awarded by works concessionaires
Name and address of contracting authority		×	×	×	×
Award procedure chosen	×	×	×		
Where applicable, justification for use of accelerated procedure		×	×		
Nature of contract for which tenders are being requested	×	×	×		
Site	×	×	×	×	×
Nature and extent of the services to be provided and general nature of the work	×	×	×	×	×
Subject of the concession, nature and extent of services to be provided				×	
If applicable, size of lots and possibility of tendering for several or all	×	×	×		
Information concerning the purpose of the work or contract if latter also involves drawing up of projects	×	×	×		
Time-limit for completion	×	×	×		×
Name and address of service from which contract documents and additional documents may be requested	×				×
Where applicable, amount and terms of payments of sum to be paid to obtain contract documents	×				
Final date for receipt of tenders or for requests to participate	×	×	×	×	×
Final date for dispatch of invitations to tender		×			
Address to which tenders or request to be sent	×	×	×	×	×
Language for tenders or requests	×	×	×	×	×
Legal form to be taken by groupings of contractors to whom contract is awarded	×	×	×		
Any deposits or guarantees required	×	×	×		×
Main terms concerning financing and payment	×	×	×		
Period during which tenderer is bound to keep open his tender	×				
Minimum economic and technical standards required of contractor	×	×	×	×	×
Where applicable, prohibition on variants	×	×	×		
Criteria for the award of the contract	×	×		×	×
Date, hour, place of opening tenders and, if applicable, persons authorised to be present	×				
Where applicable, names and addresses of suppliers already selected by awarding authority			×		
Where applicable, date(s) of previous publications in *Official Journal*			×		
Where applicable, minimum percentage of works contracts to be awarded to third parties				×	
Other information	×	×	×	×	×
Date of publication of prior information notice in *Official Journal*	×	×	×		
Date of dispatch of the contract notice	×	×	×	×	×
Date of receipt of the contract notice by the Office for Official Publications	×	×	×	×	×

Source: The Public Works Contracts Regulations 1991, SI 1991 No 2680, Schedule 2

information sought concerning the contractor's economic and technical standing, and the criteria by which the contract is to be awarded. Tender notices are published in the *Official Journal*. They may also be published in journals in the contracting authority's country providing that this does not precede publication in the *Official Journal*, or provide additional information.

- *Contract award notice*. This makes known the results of an award and must be published within 48 days of the award. The model notice is set out in Annex IV E of the Directive and Schedule 2 of the UK Regulations (see Table 14). It includes the identity of the successful contractor, the number of offers received, and the range of prices. Information is not published where it would impede law enforcement, be contrary to the public interest, or be prejudicial to legitimate commercial interests or to fair competition between contractors. These notices are also to be published in the *Official Journal*.

7.4.1.2 Although notices have to be published for contracts above the financial threshold set by the Directive, similar notices may also be published in the *Official Journal*, on a voluntary basis, for contracts which are outside the scope of the Directive. The Office for Official Publications undertakes to publish notices in the *Official Journal* supplement dealing with public works within 12 days of their dispatch. There is no charge to the contracting authorities. It has been proposed that contracting authorities should use standard phrases in order to minimize delays in translation and publication. Contracting authorities need to keep a careful record of the date of dispatch of notices since this date is important for a number of the procedures in the award of a contract.

7.4.2 Time-limits for tenders

7.4.2.1 The Directive prescribes various time limits so that potential contractors, particularly those from other Member States, should not be disadvantaged by being given too limited a period of time in which to respond:

- *Open procedures*. The date for the receipt of tenders should not be less than 52 days from the date of dispatch of the tender notice to the Office for Official Publications for inclusion in the *Official Journal*. Where there has been a prior indicative notice, the time period is reduced to 36 days. A similar 52-day period also applies to the receipt of tenders for public works concessions.

- *Restricted and negotiated procedures*. At least 37 days must elapse between the despatch of the tender notice and the date set for the receipt of requests to participate. Contracting authorities must simultaneously invite selected candidates to submit their tenders. This is to be in writing. The letter of invitation must state where contract documents can be obtained and their cost, the closing date for and the language of tenders, and the address to which they should be sent, and should make reference to the contract notice. In restricted procedures, 40 days must elapse between the dispatch of the written invitations and the closing date for tenders, though this may be reduced to 26 days where a prior indicative notice has been published. The 37- and 40-day periods for request to participate and receipt of tenders also apply to contracts to be awarded by a works concessionaire and the 37-day period to requests to participate in negotiated tenders.

7.4.2.2 The Directive provides for extension of the time limits for tenders where additional information is too bulky to be supplied, thus necessitating an inspection of the documents, or where tenders can be submitted only after a site visit. Documents should be sent to contractors within 6 days of application. Additional information, requested in good time, should be supplied not later than 6 days before the date fixed for receipt of tenders. Time-limits can be reduced in circumstances in which urgency renders them impracticable. The period for requests to participate can be reduced to 15 days and the period between the invitation to tender to the receipt of tenders to 10 days. The circumstances in which this reduction applies are not defined by the Directive.

Table 14 Contract award notice

Name and address of contracting authority
Award procedure
Date of award of contract
Criteria for award
Number of offers received
Name and address of successful contractor
Nature and extent of the services provided
Price or range of prices paid
Value and proportion of contract likely to be subcontracted to third parties, where appropriate
Other information
Dates of publication of the tender notice in the *Official Journal* and of dispatch of the notice

Source: The Public Works Contracts Regulations 1991, SI 1991 No 2680, Schedule 2

This information is summarized in Table 15.

Table 15 Time-limits (days)

Procedure	Request to participate	Submission of tenders	
		with prior indicative notice	*without prior indicative notice*
Open	—	36*	52†
Restricted	37*	26†	40†
Negotiated	37*	—	—
Public works concession		52*	
Awards by public works concessionaires	37*	40*†	
In situations of extreme urgency	15*	10†	

* from date of dispatch of contract notice

† from date of dispatch of written invitation

The first day is that after the date of dispatch. The *Official Journal* must publish notices not later than 12 days after their dispatch, or 5 days in the case of accelerated procedures.

Source: Council Directive of 18 July 1989 amending Directive 71/305/EEC concerning coordination of procedures for the award of public works contracts (89/440/EEC), *Official Journal*, L 210, 21 July 1989

7.5 AWARD OF CONTRACTS

The selection of contractors involves two processes:

- Consideration of the tenderers against the *criteria for qualitative selection*,
- Consideration of tenders against the criteria for the award.

7.5.1 Economic and technical references

7.5.1.1 The contract notice specifies the economic and technical information that a contractor must supply in order that his bid can be evaluated. This information forms part of the *criteria for qualitative selection* by which a contracting authority can eliminate unsuitable contractors from consideration. In the interests of preventing contracting authorities from favouring certain contractors by virtue of the information sought, the Directive lays down what information a contracting authority can ask for and the grounds on which tenders may be treated as being ineligible or a contractor excluded from those to be invited to tender for or to negotiate a contract.

7.5.1.2 A contracting authority may require a contractor to furnish proof of his financial standing by producing four types of *economic and financial reference.*

- Evidence of enrolment on a professional or trade register under conditions laid down by the laws of the Member State in which he is established. Article 24 identifies the registers for each of the Member States (see Table 16). For the UK, the contractor should provide a certificate from the Registrar of Companies, or Registrar of Friendly Societies, or a certificate that he has declared under oath that he is engaged in the profession in question under a given business name. In effect, a contractor must prove that he is a company, friendly society, partnership, or sole trader engaged in a particular trade or profession,
- Appropriate bankers' statements,
- Statement of accounts,
- A statement of the firm's overall turnover and the turnover on construction works for the three previous financial years.

The contracting authority can decide what alternative documents to accept if a contractor is unable to supply any of these references for a valid reason. The UK's Regulations permit a contracting authority to require a contractor to provide other information to demonstrate his economic or financial standing in circumstances in which the normal requirements are not appropriate. If a contractor produces a certificate of entry for an official list of another Member State, a UK contracting authority is not permitted to ask for information on accounts or turnover if the certificate deals with these matters, though it can ask for bankers' statements.

7.5.1.3 Contracting authorities can require contractors to furnish proof of technical knowledge or ability by supplying the following *technical references.*

- The contractor's educational and professional qualifications and those of the firm's management and of the persons responsible for carrying out the work,
- A list of the works carried out over the past five years and certificates of satisfactory completion for the most important of them. The information sought can include the value of the consideration received, where and when the works were carried out, whether they were carried out in accordance with the rules of the trade or profession, and whether they were properly completed,
- A statement of the tools, plant, and technical equipment available to the contractor for carrying out the work,
- A statement of the firm's average manpower and managerial staff for the last three years,
- A statement of the technician or technical support that the contractor can call upon for carrying out the work, both from inside and outside the firm, and whether the technicians or suppliers of technical services are independent of the contractor.

It is up to the contracting authority to determine which of the economic and technical references permitted by the Directive it wishes to obtain. It may also invite contractors to supplement certificates and documents or to clarify them. Unlike the financial references, the list of technical references is to be regarded as being exclusive. It is not permissible to extend the range of references sought by seeking supplementary information. A UK contracting authority that receives a bid from a contractor with a certificate of entry on an official list of another Member State is not permitted to seek information about the contractor's past works or manpower, providing that the certificate deals with these matters.

7.5.1.4 The permissible technical references make no specific mention of quality management. However, it would be possible to identify whether a contractor employs staff with the qualifications to maintain a quality management system. The use of external testing laboratories and certification bodies could appear among the external technical support that a contractor could call upon. This interpretation is consistent with Article 23 of the Public Supplies Directive (see Section 8.1.5.1), which permits contracting authorities to ask questions about quality control, the competence of technicians responsible for quality control, and about certification bodies.

7.5.1.5 Member States who keep *official lists* of recognized contractors (i.e. Italy, Spain, Belgium, Greece) must adapt them so that they use the criteria permitted by the Directive. As was noted in Sections 7.5.1.1 and 7.5.1.2, a certificate of entry on an official list can limit the economic and technical references that a UK contracting authority can seek from a contractor. The Directive makes no reference to lists of approved contractors considered by contracting authorities to be technically and financially qualified. These are voluntary lists compiled by a contracting authority with the consent of potential contractors, and are not the official lists referred to in the Directive. The Treasury[3] considers that there is no reason why they should not continue to be used as an aid in the selection of contractors to be invited to participate in restricted or negotiated procedures, providing that selection is not discriminatory or based solely on these lists. Firms which respond to advertisements, and which meet the minimum technical and financial requirements, must also be considered on equal terms with those on the approved list. Government advice is that it is not inconsistent with the public procurement directives if, at the same time as a contract notice is placed in the *Official Journal*, firms on the approved list are sent a copy of the notice and asked if they wish to be considered[9]. Such firms would not need to provide separate evidence of their technical and financial standing. In effect, approved lists would identify those firms whose economic and technical references have already been checked, but cannot be treated as being exhaustive lists of qualified contractors.

7.5.2 Criteria for award

7.5.2.1 Contracts can be awarded on the basis of *either*

- the lowest price, *or*
- the most economically advantageous tender.

Various criteria can be used to determine the most economically advantageous tender including price, period for completion, running costs, profitability, and technical merit. However, the criteria by which this is to be determined must be recorded in either the contract documents or the contract notice, preferably in descending order of importance. The criteria employed must be objective and transparent.

7.5.2.2 The use of the most economically advantageous basis for the award of contracts enables a contracting authority to take account of variants submitted by tenderers where these meet the minimum specifications. The contract documents must contain the minimum specifications and the tender notice must indicate whether variants will be considered. Variants cannot be rejected on the sole grounds that they have been drawn up with technical specifications that either use European technical specifications or national ones that meet the essential requirements under harmonization directives.

7.5.2.3 *Abnormally low tenders* can be rejected under certain circumstances. Before rejecting a tender on these grounds, the contracting authority must seek an explanation from the contractor and may take into account reasons such as the economy of the method to be used, technical solutions, or favourable circumstances open to a contractor. If the criterion for the award of the contract is the lowest price, the Commission must be informed of the reasons for rejecting low-price tenders.

7.5.3 Selection of contractors

7.5.3.1 Contractors can be excluded from participation under certain circumstances.

- They are bankrupt, or being wound up, or under administration, or have entered into an arrangement or composition with their creditors, or are subject to proceedings that could result in any of these,

- They have been convicted of a criminal offence concerning their professional conduct or of grave professional misconduct,
- They have failed to pay taxes in the UK or social security payments in the UK or the Member State in which they are established,
- They have been guilty of serious misrepresentation in supplying information for the contract,
- They are not registered on the trade or professional register of the Member State in which they are established. These are listed in Table 16.

Contractors can establish their eligibility by an extract from the judicial record, a certificate issued by a competent authority, or a declaration under oath to the effect that none of the above conditions apply to them. A certificate of entry of a contractor on the official list of another Member State must be accepted by a UK contracting authority as evidence that none of these circumstances apply other than the non-payment of taxes or social security contributions.

Table 16 Appropriate professional or trade registers

Belgium	Registre du Commerce/Handelsregister
Denmark	Erhverus- and Selskabsstyrelsen
France	Registre du Commerce or répertoire des métiers
Germany	Handelsregister or Handswerksrolle
Greece	Certified as having declared on oath before a notary public that he exercises the profession of public works contractor
Ireland	Certified as incorporated by Register of Companies, or registered with the Registrar of Friendly Societies, or certified as having declared on oath that he is carrying on business in the trade at the place of business and under the specified trading name
Italy	Registro della Camera di commercio, industria, agricultura e artigiano
Netherlands	Handelsregister
Portugal	Commissao de Alvaras de Empresas de Obras Públicas e Particulares
Spain	Registro Oficial de Contrastistas del Ministerio de Industria y Energia
UK	Certified as incorporated by Register of Companies, or registered with the Registrar of Friendly Societies, or certified as having declared on oath that he is carrying on business in the trade at the place of business and under the specified trading name

Source: The Public Works Contracts Regulations 1991, SI 1991 No 2680

7.5.3.2 Tenderers can be obliged to confirm that they have taken account of employment protection provisions and working conditions in force in the place where the work is to be carried out. Contractors can be asked to indicate what share of the contract they intend to subcontract. Groups of contractors can submit tenders. They cannot be obliged to assume a specific legal form in order to submit a valid tender but may be required to do so if they are awarded the contract.

7.5.3.3 Under the restricted tender procedures, contracting authorities can prescribe the range within which the number of undertakings invited to submit tenders will fall and exclude candidates where an excessive number respond. The number should be indicated in the contract notice. The Directive suggests that the number should be at least 5 and up to 20 but be sufficient to ensure genuine competition. Where negotiated procedures are to be used after the publication of a tender notice, at least 3 candidates should be invited to negotiate, providing that there is a sufficient number of suitable candidates. In reducing the number of contractors to be invited to participate in these two procedures, contracting authorities must not discriminate against nationals of other Member States who satisfy the minimum requirements. Nationals from other Member States must be invited to participate on the same conditions as one's own nationals. Contracting authorities may not take into account matters other than the contractor's technical and economic references in making such decisions.

7.5.3.4 Contracting authorities can discriminate in the award of contracts for reasons of regional policy until the end of 1992, providing this is done in a manner that is compatible with the Treaty of Rome. This would permit discrimination with the objective of reducing regional disparities and for the promotion of job opportunities in areas of high unemployment. However, such discrimination would appear to be incompatible with the economic and technical criteria for the selection of contractors in the Directive. The Commission has proposed that the problem be overcome either by the progressive abolition of regional preference schemes or by permitting preference to remain for those projects that fall below the thresholds for the application of the advertising provisions, providing that this is done on a transparent basis so that discriminatory behaviour is not concealed. However, the European Court of Justice has declared the Italian regional preference scheme to be unlawful on the grounds that it breaches the requirement of the EEC Treaty for Member States to remove quantitative restrictions on imports[(10)]. Similar objections could be raised to schemes such as the UK government's General Preference, Special Preference, and Northern Ireland Preference Schemes.

7.5.3.5 In 1989 the Commission objected to certain UK advertisements which sought to identify whether a contractor proposed to use its own labour force or to rely on local recruitment. This issue is of some importance as projects are sometimes presented by a contracting authority to its local population as having the advantage of generating local employment and this may be set against any detrimental effects on the local environment. Job creation may be viewed as a form of planning gain. The Commission has taken the view that regarding more favourably a contractor who intends to recruit local labour distorts competition, and the Treasury[(3)] advises that contract notices should not require contractors to indicate whether they intend to do so or to use their own labour force. Similarly, questions about UK experience could also be regarded as being discriminatory.

7.5.3.6 The European Court of Justice ruled in a case brought by Gebroeders Beentje BV against the Netherlands government in 1987 that the principle of attaching social conditions was permissible as long as the special conditions were mentioned in the contract notice[(11)]. The Local Government Act 1988 prevents local authorities from including among qualitative selection factors certain designated 'non-commercial' matters. These include the composition of the workforce, its conditions of employment, the contractor's links with other countries, its political or sectarian affiliations, and its involvement with other aspects of government policy.

Figure 19 sets out the steps to be taken in the selection of a contractor. It should be noted that the procedures to be adopted must be planned at the same time as the decision to offer a contract is taken. This is because the contract notice must seek the necessary information on contractors' economic and technical standing and identify the criteria to be used in the award of the contract.

7.5.4 Contract reports

7.5.4.1 Eliminated candidates or tenderers can request reasons for the rejection of their bid. These must be supplied within 15 days by the contracting authorities. A rejected tenderer may also request the name of the successful one. A contract award notice must be published within 48 days of the award of a contract. If a competition is cancelled, the contracting authority shall inform candidates or tenderers of the reason on request and notify the Office for Official Publications of the cancellation.

7.5.4.2 For each contract, the contracting authority is to draw up a written report which includes its name and address, the subject and value of the contract, the names of candidates and tenderers admitted and rejected and the reasons for this, the successful tenderer and the reasons for his selection, and a justification of negotiated procedures, if used. The EC can request all or part of this report. Each Member State must provide a report to the Commission on 31 October 1993 for the calendar year 1992, and at two-yearly intervals thereafter, on the contracts awarded under the terms of the Directive. This should include the number and value of contracts above the threshold value awarded by each contracting authority or category of authority, the procedures used, the category of work, and the nationality of contractors. The Treasury will collate and submit the report on the basis of the returns from other government departments, covering both their own activities and those of the contracting authorities for which they are responsible. Contracting authorities are to supply the necessary information to the Treasury or relevant ministry by 31 July of each reporting year.

7.5.4.3 An *Advisory Committee for Public Contracts* was set up to monitor compliance with the public procurement directives and to advise the Commission. Its membership is drawn from the Member States and it is chaired by the Commission. It can act on matters initiated by the Commission or Member States.

7.6 PUBLIC WORKS COMPLIANCE DIRECTIVE

7.6.1 Introduction

7.6.1.1 The public procurement directives do not contain any provisions for their enforcement. Where funding for a project comes from EC sources, funds could be withheld in the event of a breach. Questionnaires and sample checks are used to confirm compliance and the failure to answer questions can result in the suspension of payment and steps being taken to recover the funds spent. In order to overcome the lack of enforcement provisions in the directives, the EC has enacted or proposed a series of remedies or compliance directives that should provide redress for those contractors who have been wrongly discriminated against in the making of an award and provide a procedure by which the Commission can take immediate action in the event of an apparent infringement of Community rules by a Member State. The compliance directives are intended to provide a speedy and effective means of redress for aggrieved contractors. Like all directives, it is up to each Member State to determine how it will implement them.

7.6.1.2 The Compliance Directive for Public Works and Supplies was enacted in 1989[12]. It should have been implemented by 1 December 1991 and the UK did so on 21 December 1991 under the Award of Public Works Contracts Regulations[4]. Other Member States to have brought the Directive into force are Belgium, Denmark, Ireland, Netherlands, and Spain[13]. The Directive requires Member States to set up procedures so that decisions on the awards of public contracts can be reviewed rapidly and effectively, especially any that may have infringed Community law. The procedures must be available to any person with an interest in obtaining a works or supplies contract and who has been, or risks being, harmed by an alleged infringement. They must not discriminate between undertakings claiming injury as a result of an award. The procedures can require a complainant first to notify the contracting authority of the alleged infringement and of his intention to seek review before pressing his complaint through the review procedure.

7.6.2 Review procedures

7.6.2.1 The review procedures must include the following provisions:

- The power to take interim measures to correct an alleged infringement or to prevent further damage being done to the complainant. This can include the suspension of a contract award,
- The ability to set aside unlawful decisions, including the removal of discriminatory technical, economic, or financial specifications,
- The power to award damages to persons harmed by an infringement of public procurement procedures.

The UK Regulations require contracting authorities to comply with the regulations and state that this is a duty owed to contractors. Only those firms from within the EC are able to enforce their provisions. A breach of the regulations is not a criminal offence but is actionable by contractors.

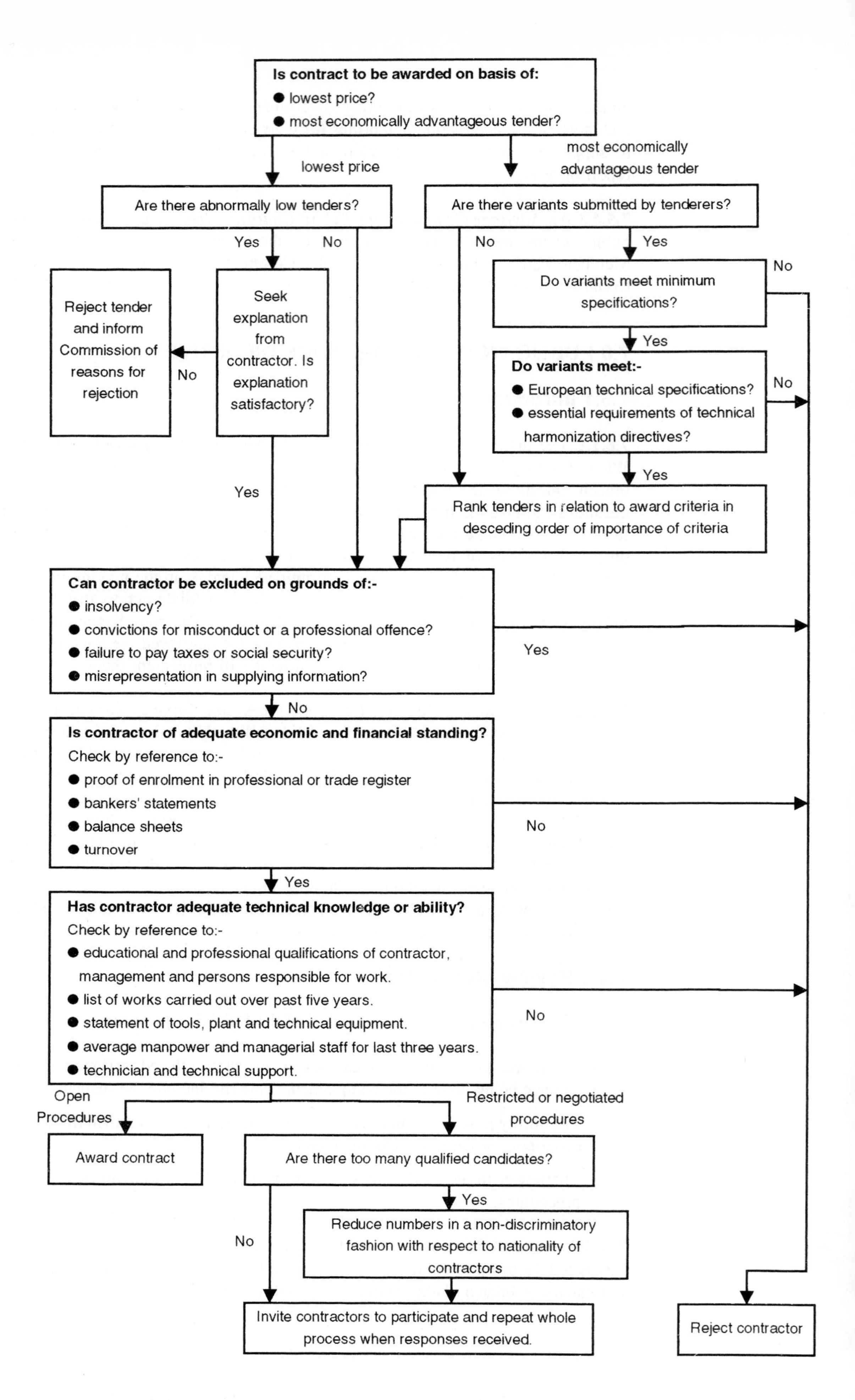

Figure 19 *Selection of contractors for award of contract or for invitation to bid*

7.6.2.2 The Directive does not require its powers to be vested in a single body. Nor do the review procedures automatically have to result in the suspension of a contract award. A Member State can provide that, when the review body considers whether to order interim measures, it may take into account the probable consequences for all interested parties, including the public interest. Thus, it may be permissible not to grant interim measures where the negative consequences could exceed their benefits. This means that a successful contractor need not be penalized by the setting aside of his award just because another applicant has suffered from an infringement of the public procurement procedures. Alternatively, a Member State can require a contested decision to be set aside before the award of damages. It is permissible for the powers of the review body to be limited to the award of damages to any person harmed and not to extend to the setting aside of the contract. Decisions by review bodies must be capable of effective enforcement. If the review body is not a judicial body, it must give decisions in writing. Its decisions and the way in which it exercises its powers must be capable of being challenged at law or of being reviewed by an independent body.

7.6.2.3 Action in the UK is to be taken by a contractor before the High Courts of England, Wales and Northern Ireland or Court of Session in Scotland. Actions cannot be brought unless the contractor has informed the contracting authority of his complaint. They must be brought promptly and, in any case, within three months. It is possible that the court may rule that an action is out of time even if it is brought within three months, where it determines that the action has not been brought with sufficient promptness(14). The court may decide to:

- suspend the contract procedure or the implementation of a decision,
- set aside an award decision,
- award damages.

If a contract has been entered into, the court can only award damages and cannot set aside the contract. Injunctions can be granted against the Crown.

7.6.3 Powers of the Commission

The Commission is empowered to intervene where it thinks there has been a clear infringement of Community provisions. It will notify the Member State and contracting authority of its reasons for believing an infringement has occurred and request correction. Within 21 days the Member State must have communicated to the Commission:

- that the infringement has been corrected, *or*
- a reasoned submission of why there has been no correction, for example, because the case is under review, *or*
- a notice that the award procedure has been suspended.

Member States are obliged to provide the Commission with an annual report on the operation of their review procedures. Where a Member State has failed to bring the Directive into force, a contractor can appeal directly to the Commission.

7.7 CONCLUSIONS

7.7.1 A body proposing to purchase construction works needs to address a number of questions as a result of the amended Public Works Directive:

- ***Is it a body to which the Directive applies?*** See Section 7.1.2
- ***Is the contract one to which the Directive applies?*** See Sections 7.1.1, 7.1.3, 7.1.4
- ***What procedures should be used to award the contract?*** See Section 7.2.5
- ***What technical specifications should be used?*** See Section 7.3

- *What notices have to be published?* See Section 7.4.1
- *What references should be sought from contractors?* See Section 7.5.1
- *How should the contractor be selected?* See Sections 7.5.2, 7.5.3
- *What reports must be produced and what records retained?* See Section 7.5.4
- *What can happen if a contractor alleges that irregularities have taken place in the award of the contract?* See Section 7.6

7.7.2 Since 1982 the UK government has had the policy of supporting the use of quality management by favouring in its procurement firms which possess independently certificated quality management systems that satisfy the requirements of BS 5750 (EN 29000 series). The revised Public Works Directive has three main implications for this policy in so far as it affects construction.

- *The EN 29000 series of quality management system standards (BS 5750) and the EN 45000 series of standards for certification bodies and testing laboratories (BS 7501-7503, BS 7511-7513) are European standards and so can be specified in contracts covered by the Directive. However, the specification of certificates issued by a particular certification body, for example, would appear to be governed by the rules concerning trademarks,*
- *Public bodies are to use European specifications where possible. They may well include quality management provisions. For example, they may specify the samples to be taken of a product for particular tests,*
- *The Directive identifies what can be asked by way of technical references. By asking questions about the qualifications of a contractor and his employees and about external technical support, it should be possible to discover whether a contractor has the human resources to operate a quality management system and whether there is third-party certification of any quality management system.*

7.7.3 There are some potentially serious problems concerning the interface between the Construction Products Directive and public procurement directives, such as the Public Works Directive. These concern Article 6 (1) of the Construction Products Directive, for which there is no equivalent in any of the other New Approach directives. This says that Member States shall ensure that the use of products that satisfy this Directive shall not be impeded by rules or conditions imposed by public bodies. Demonstration of satisfaction of the Directive by construction products will normally be by their compliance with a harmonized European standard or a European technical approval. The public procurement directives refer to the use of European standards rather than harmonized European standards drafted by the European standardization bodies under mandate from the Commission. This raises the question of whether, for construction products, the requirements of the Construction Products Directive can be met if public bodies are permitted to specify using European standards rather than harmonized European standards. Will the use of the former be regarded as impeding products that satisfy the Construction Products Directive? It is possible for such standards and technical approvals just to contain attributes relating to the six essential requirements. If this is the case, it would seem unlikely that public bodies will be able to specify in such a way as to ensure that they meet their obligations to their citizens and secure value for money in their purchasing. They are likely to need to specify by reference to a broader range of attributes than those that relate to the Construction Product Directive's essential requirements. However, at present, there have been no harmonized standards produced under the Construction Products Directive and no products that have yet satisfied it. There is therefore time to ensure that the apparent inconsistencies between the two types of directive are resolved. The public procurement directives' provisions concerning technical specifications seem adequate and it is difficult to see why a technical harmonization directive should be concerned with public procurement.

References: 7 Public Works Directive

1. Council Directive of 18 July 1989 amending Directive 71/305/EEC concerning coordination of procedures for the award of public works contracts (89/440/EEC), *Official Journal*, L 210, 21 July 1989.

2. Council Directive of 26 July 1971 concerning the coordination of procedures for the award of public works contracts (71/305/EEC), *Official Journal*, L 185, 16 August 1971.

3. The principal administrative document is *European Economic Community: Directive 89/440/EEC Public Sector Works Contracts*, Circular 16/90, Department of the Environment, 13 August 1990. Although this document is addressed to local authorities, it also contains the consolidated text of the 1971 and 1989 Public Works directives and the Treasury's *Guidance on the EC Works Directive*, 1990.

4. The Public Works Contracts Regulations 1991, SI 1991, No. 2680.

5. The sterling equivalents of the ECU thresholds are taken from Commission of the Economic Communities (1992) *Opening Up Public Procurement*, Background Report ISEC/B4/92. The sterling values of the thresholds have been increased since the adoption of the Directive.

6. Commission Decision of 13 July 1990 concerning the updating of Annex I to the Council Directive 89/440/EEC, *Official Journal*, L 187, 19 July 1990.

7. Council Directive of 21 December 1988 on the approximation of laws, regulations and administrative provisions of the Member States relating to construction products (89/106/EEC), *Official Journal*, L 40, 11 February 1989.

8. Case 45/87 Dundalk Water Supply System: EC Commission *v.* Ireland, *Common Market Law Reports*, 225 (1987) European Court Reports 1369.

9. Department of the Environment (1989), *European Economic Community Directive 88/295 Public Sector Supply Contracts*, Circular 6/89.

10. Case 21/88 Du Pont de Nemours Italiana Spa *v.* Unità Sanitaria Locale No 2 di Carrara, *The Times Law Reports*, 11 April 1990.

11. Case 31/87 Gebroeders Beentjes BV *v.* Netherlands, *Common Market Law Reports*, 287.

12. Council Directive of 21 December 1989 on the coordination of the laws, regulations and administrative provisions relating to the application of review procedures to the award of public supply and public works contracts (89/665/EEC), *Official Journal*, L 395, 30 December 1989.

13. Commission of the European Communities (1992), *Opening up public procurement*, ISEC/B4/92.

14. Duffy, P. (1992), European practice briefing, *Solicitors Journal*, 136, 6 March.

8 Public procurement of goods and services and by utilities

8.0 OVERVIEW

This section examines the public procurement directives concerned with the purchase of goods and services and the purchase of goods, services, and construction works by the utilities industries (i.e. those concerned with the supply of drinking water, gas, electricity, transport, and telecommunications). The principles involved in their purchasing are similar to those discussed in relation to the Public Works Directive. Consequently, this section is concerned with the main differences between these directives and the Public Works Directive.

8.0.1 Public Supplies Directive

8.0.1.1 The Public Supplies Directive of 1988[1] came into effect on 1 January 1989. It is concerned with the purchase of goods by public bodies, including acquisitions made under rental or leasing agreements and the purchase of construction products. It substantially amends the two previous Public Supplies directives of 1977[2] and 1980[3]. Many of its provisions are similar to those found in the Public Works Directive, particularly the procedures to be used, the contracting authorities to which it applies, advertising rules, the use of technical specifications, and the selection of contractors and the award of contracts. The Compliance Directive[4] is the same as that for the Public Works Directive. The main differences between the Public Supplies and Public Works Directives concern:

- *Contracts covered,*
- *Computation of financial thresholds to which the Directive applies,*
- *Differences in procedures, including those necessitated by GATT,*
- *Treatment of technical references.*

8.0.1.2 The Public Supplies Directive was initially brought into force in the UK by administrative action. Relevant documents include Guidance Notes issued by the Treasury in 1988 to government departments[5] and a joint circular to local authorities from the Department of the Environment and Welsh Office issued in 1989[6]. Subsequently, the Directive has given rise to the Award of Public Supply Contracts Regulations 1991, which came into effect on 21 December 1991[7]. In addition, the Institute of Purchasing and Supply has produced a guide to the Directive for local authorities[8].

8.0.2 Proposed Public Services Directive

8.0.2.1 The Commission has proposed a procurement directive on services. This reached a Common Position on 25 February 1992[9]. Such a directive is necessary if there is to be equity in procurement from the construction industry. It is feasible for there to be substitution of services for goods at the margin. For example, a fencing contractor could offer to provide security for a building, which could include the supply of fencing. The proposed Directive is similar in many respects to the Public Works and Public Supplies Directives, for example, the bodies to which it applies, the award procedures to be used, advertising rules, rules on technical specifications, the seeking of technical and financial references from contractors, and the criteria for the award of contracts.

8.0.2.2 Not all services are included in the scope of the proposal. The main exclusions are property rentals, broadcasting, and public debt management services. Services are divided into two groups with only parts of the proposed Directive to be applied to a restrictive category of services that includes transport, financial, legal, educational, health, and social services. The thresholds that determine whether the Directive is to apply vary according to the type of service but the most widely applicable one is 200 000 ECU. The proposed Directive also contains rules for the conduct of design contests. The proposal makes explicit reference to the use of certification of a contractor's quality assurance system to the EN 29000 series by a certification body conforming to the EN 45000 series. It also provides for retaliatory action to be taken against suppliers from countries who discriminate against EC undertakings. A proposed amendment to the Compliance Directive dealing with public works and public supplies would extend its remit to include public services.

8.0.3 Utilities Directive

8.0.3.1 The so-called Utilities Directive of 1990[10] extends the principles found in the public procurement directives to the purchase of goods and construction works by entities operating in the water, energy, transport, and telecommunications sectors. These tend to be bodies that enjoy a natural monopoly by virtue of the costs of the networks needed to provide their services. As a result, their activities are often publicly owned or regulated. They were excluded from the remit of the 1970s public procurement directives, although a number of them were then in public ownership. The Directive extends the principles of public procurement to utilities undertakings, irrespective of whether they are publicly or privately owned. However, it applies only to their activities in the specified areas and not to any other aspects of their business. Thus, for example, it does not apply to British Rail's property development activities or to the water companies' waste disposal operations. This could present problems when both regulated and non-regulated activities share procurement functions and purchases are made simultaneously for both types of activity.

8.0.3.2 The Directive was due to come into effect by 1 July 1992. Although it draws on many of the features found in the Public Works and Public Supplies Directives, there are a number of points of detail in which it differs. These are principally:

- *Financial thresholds applied to determine whether particular contracts fall within the provisions of the Directive,*
- *Circumstances in which negotiated procedures can be used,*
- *Notices that must be published,*
- *Procedures for the award of a contract and the exclusion of contractors.*

8.0.3.3 The Commission has proposed a Utilities Services Directive[11] which would extend to the utilities entities the procurement principles found in the proposed Public Services Directive. The Utilities Remedies Directive[12] provides redress for suppliers who have been wrongfully discriminated against.

8.1 PUBLIC SUPPLIES DIRECTIVE

8.1.1 Definition of public supplies

8.1.1.1 Public supply contracts are defined as being contracts for pecuniary interest which are concluded in writing between a contracting authority and a supplier of products. The products can be supplied by means of sale, conditional sale, lease, rental, or hire purchase, and their delivery may include siting and installation. Goods include growing crops, things attached to land, gas, and water, but not electricity. They include construction products purchased by a public body, for example, for the use of a direct labour organization. Where contracts involve the supply of both goods and construction works, the Public Works Directive takes precedence. Where a contract involves the supply of both goods and services, the Public Supplies Directive applies if the value of the goods amounts to at least half of the contract.

8.1.1.2 The contracting authorities are the same as those found in the Public Works Directive. There is no equivalent to a public works concession nor is there provision for the Directive to apply in situations in which private bodies derive their funding from public ones. However, where a public body grants a private one 'special or exclusive rights' to carry on a service for the benefit of the public, the instrument granting this right must stipulate that the private body shall observe the principle of non-discrimination by nationality when awarding public supply contracts to third parties.

8.1.1.3 Central purchasing agencies, such as HMSO and the Crown Suppliers, have traditionally acted on behalf of departments and have assumed responsibility for meeting the purchaser's obligations with respect to both GATT and the EC. Departments are now able to go out to competitive tendering and are not obliged to use the central purchasing agencies. Where they do so, departments have an obligation to observe the public procurement rules, even if a central purchasing agency wins the contract. If an agreement is made with a private body to obtain supplies for a department, this body can be made contractually liable for meeting a department's obligations. The Commission accepts that such a body can advertise in the *Official Journal*, even when it does not have a specific government client in mind, so that it can thus supply government departments under framework arrangements.

8.1.2 Financial thresholds

8.1.2.1 There are two main thresholds in the Directive that determine whether the advertising provisions apply to specific contracts. These differ according to the type of public body:

- *Public bodies covered by the GATT Agreement on Public Purchasing*. These are central government departments and related bodies, for example, the Building Research Establishment, National Economic Development Council, Property Services Agency, National Physical Laboratory. Expenditure on warlike purchases by the Ministry of Defence is excluded from GATT. The bodies affected are defined by Annex I of the 1980 Public Supplies Directive (Schedule 1 of the UK Regulations). Annex II (Schedule 2 of the UK Regulations) defines non-warlike defence expenditure. For these, the threshold is **130 000 ECU** net of VAT (**£91 000**[(13)]). An *indicative notice* must be published each year if the estimated value of procurement in any product area is at least **750 000 ECU (£525 000)**. The form must follow that in Schedule 3, Part A of the UK Regulations and includes the nature and value of the products to be supplied and the estimated dates of the commencement of award procedures. Statistical information is required on contracts that fall both above and below the threshold,
- *Other public bodies*, including regional and local authorities and bodies governed by public law. For them the threshold is **200 000 ECU** net of VAT (**£140 000**).

8.1.2.2 The Directive contains rules as to how contracts are to be valued.

- Fixed-term contracts of 12 months or less are to be valued at the contract sum,
- Fixed-term contracts of 12 months or more are valued at the annual value plus a residual value of the outstanding part,
- Indefinite contracts, or those of doubtful duration, are valued at the monthly value times 48,
- Regular or renewable contracts are valued at the aggregate cost over the previous year adjusted by anticipated changes in quantity, or their estimated value over the next year, or the estimated cost over the next year.

Where a contract contains options, it must be valued at the highest possible total, including all the optional elements.

8.1.2.3 Particular problems arise with certain types of contract organization. The Commission is understood to accept that independent procurement by separate parts of a purchasing authority can be treated in isolation for the purpose of applying the aggregation rules, but not if the purchasing officers are obliged to contract for their purchases under a central arrangement[(5)]. Without this understanding, it would be difficult to see, for example, how purchases made under the local management of schools could be treated other than as part of the aggregate expenditure of the local education authority, and this could undermine the degree of autonomy in management that the measure was intended to achieve. The UK Regulations reflect this by not requiring aggregation where purchases are made by discrete operational units, who have received the power to undertake devolved purchasing decisions and who take decisions independently of other parts of the controlling authority. With framework agreements, which allow goods to be ordered or called-off as necessary, the Commission has said that they can be treated as contracts and advertised in the usual way if they exceed the threshold. Subsequent call-offs can therefore be regarded as having fulfilled the Directive's requirements without further advertising, providing that individual call-offs are recorded in the statistical return[5].

8.1.3 Procedures

8.1.3.1 The Directive is biased towards the use of open procedures. Restricted procedures can be used, but this must be justified by the need to maintain a balance between the contract value and the procedural costs, or by reference to the specific nature of the products to be procured. A record must be kept justifying their use. The Council has said that a contracting authority, which uses restricted procedures in accordance with national provisions compatible with Community law, need not necessarily curtail its use of the procedure[5]. However, public bodies must be aware that while they may make use of restricted procedures without hindrance in the purchase of construction works, they must adhere to different rules for the purchase of construction products. Negotiated procedures may be used in similar circumstances to those that apply for public works (see Section 7.2.2), except that they may not normally be used for contracts of more than three years duration.

8.1.3.2 There is no provision in the Directive for the publication of prior indicative notices except where there is a requirement for this under GATT rules. Contract notices for contracts of between 100 000 ECUs and the appropriate threshold can be published in the *Official Journal* on a voluntary basis. This should ensure that the *Official Journal* is not overrun by unofficial notices.

8.1.4 Technical references

8.1.4.1 The technical references that may be sought under the Directive are stated in a different form to those in the Public Works Directive. These include the ability to ask for:

- Descriptions of an undertaking's technical facilities, which include its measures for ensuring quality and its research facilities,
- Indication of the technicians or technical bodies involved, 'especially those responsible for quality control', and whether they are independent of the supplier,
- Samples, descriptions, and photographs of products,
- Lists of deliveries made in the past three years of goods similar to those in the public supplies contract,
- Certificates drawn up by official quality control institutes or agencies of recognised competence attesting to conformity with specifications,
- Checks to be carried out by the contracting authority on the producer's supply capacities and quality control measures, in cases where the goods to be supplied are complex or, exceptionally, are required for a special purpose.

8.1.4.2 Public bodies are given greater explicit powers to assess a supplier's quality management system for construction products than for construction works (see Section 7.5.1.3). It is not clear how these powers can be reconciled with Article 6 (1) of the Construction Products Directive[14]. This states that public bodies shall not by their rules or conditions impede the use of products that satisfy the requirements of this Directive. Products will satisfy this Directive if they comply with harmonized European standards and the minimum attestation of conformity provisions set by the Commission. The Public Supplies Directive would appear to allow public bodies to set higher levels of quality assurance than those determined by the Commission. This could be regarded as impeding the use of products that satisfy the Construction Products Directive. The Construction Products Directive has no bearing on the use of the Public Supplies Directive for the procurement of products that are not construction products.

8.2 PUBLIC SERVICES DIRECTIVE

8.2.1 Services included

The proposed Directive does not define the services to be covered in a positive sense. A list of services is provided in Annex I (see Table 17). Certain services are stated to be excluded, namely:

- Those which fall within the scope of the Public Works or Public Supplies Directives: if a mixture of products and supplies are to be supplied, the Public Services Directive will apply if the value of services exceeds that of products,
- Contracts for the purchase, lease, or rental of real property, or rights appertaining to it,
- Acquisition of broadcasting material,
- Contracts for voice or radio telephony, telex, paging, or satellite services,
- Contracts for arbitration and conciliation services,
- Public debt management services, including the issuing of government bonds.

Table 17 Services covered by the proposed Public Services Directive

Annex 1.A : Services covered by Article 9	Annex 1.B : Services covered by Article 10
Maintenance and repair	Hotel and restaurant services
Land transport	Transport services by rail
Air transport	Water transport
Transport of mail	Supporting and auxiliary transport services
Telecommunications services	Financial services – banking and investment services
Financial services – insurance and banking services	Legal services
Computer services	Placement and supply of personnel
R & D	Investigation and security
Accounting	Education
Market research and public opinion polling	Health and social services
Management consulting	Recreational, cultural and sporting
Architectural, engineering, urban planning, and landscape architectural and related testing, analysis and consulting services	Other services
Advertising	
Building cleaning and property management	
Publishing and printing	
Sewage, refuse disposal, and sanitation	

Source: Annex 1, Amended proposal for a Council Directive relating to the coordination of procedures on the award of public service contracts, *Official Journal*, C 250, 25 September 1991

Defence services are included but exclusions on grounds of secrecy and international agreements apply to all service contracts. The proposed Directive does not apply to awards which have to be made to a contracting authority as a result of an exclusive right. In other words, this proposal does not oblige Member States to introduce compulsory competitive tendering so that in-house operations have to compete with outside contractors. However, where a Member State obliges its contracting authorities to use compulsory competitive tendering, the proposed Directive affects the way in which many of these contracts are awarded.

8.2.2 Public bodies included

The proposed Directive will apply to the same public bodies as the Public Supplies and Public Works Directives (see Section 7.1.2). In addition, it will apply to those bodies who are subsidized by more than 50% by a public body for a works contract. The proposed Directive will create a category of *public service concessionaires.* These will provide services on behalf of a public body in return for the right to receive payments. Concessionaires will be obliged to follow the advertising rules set out in the Directive when awarding service contracts for the services that are covered by Article 9 (see Table 17).

8.2.3 Thresholds

There are various thresholds that determine whether the proposed Directive is to apply to particular contracts. The general threshold at which the Directive is to apply is **200 000 ECU (£140 000)** net of VAT but is **130 000 ECU** for contracting authorities that are subject to the GATT Agreement. The thresholds also apply in determining whether public services concessionaires should follow the advertising rules for contracts concerning those services listed as covered by Article 9 which are to be put out to contract with third parties. The valuation principles to be applied to contracts follow those for the Public Supplies Directive (see Section 8.1.3). As with the other public procurement directives, there is a prohibition on the splitting of contracts to avoid the provisions of the proposed Directive and the requirement to include supplies made available by the contracting authority in the contract sum.

8.2.4 Design contests

The proposed Directive is also to apply to certain design contests in areas of architecture, town planning, area planning, civil engineering, and data processing, which offer prizes or payments of at least **200 000 ECU (£140 000)**. Such contests cannot exclude participants from other Member States. The jury should be autonomous and a majority of its members should have the same qualification that is being sought from participants. Members of the jury are to have no connections with participants. The criteria for selection is to based on the design contest notice (see Table 18).

Table 18 Design contests

Design contest notices information	Results of design contests
Name and address of authority	Name and address of authority
Project description	Project description
Nature of contest: open or restricted	Number of participants and number of foreign participants
Final date for receipt of projects for open contests	Winners and prizes
Envisaged number of participants, criteria for selection, already selected participants, and final date for receipt of requests to participate for restricted contests	Dates of dispatch of notice and receipt by Office for Official Publications
If there is restriction to a particular profession, criteria for the evaluation of projects	
Names of jury members	
Number and value of prizes and payments to participants and if prize-winners are entitled to be awarded follow-up contracts	
Dates of dispatch of notice and receipt by Office for Official Publications	

Source: Amended proposal for a Council Directive relating to the coordination of procedures on the award of public service contracts, *Official Journal*, C 250, 25 September 1991

8.2.5 Procedures

8.2.5.1 Services are divided into two categories. Those listed in Annex 1.B (see Table 17) fall into a restricted category for which there is only partial application of public procurement principles. For these, only the rules on technical specifications and contract notices need be applied. The full range of procedures in the proposed Directive apply to the services listed in Annex 1.A. If the services are a mixture of those listed in Annex 1.A and 1.B, then the procedure to be followed is determined by whichever group constitutes the majority of the contract.

8.2.5.2 Negotiated procedures with and without a prior notice may be used on similar terms to those available under the Public Works Directive (Section 7.2.2). Negotiated procedures with a prior tender notice are also available if unacceptable variants have been offered and if the contract specifications cannot be precisely established. The latter is particularly applicable in the case of intellectual services. Negotiated procedures without a tender notice also apply where there is a design contest in which a contract must be offered to the winner.

8.2.5.3 Contracting authorities must produce indicative notices at the beginning of the financial year for services in Annex 1.A, where procurement is estimated to be at least **750 000 ECU (£525 000).** As with other public procurement directives, tender notices are produced for contracts and concessions and these, broadly, follow those in Table 13. A contract award notice is produced in each case. For public service concessions, design contests, and services listed in Annex 1.A, this is for publication, but for those in Annex 1.B it is for publication with the consent of the authorities.

8.2.6 Contractor selection criteria

8.2.6.1 The rules on technical specifications, discussed in relation to the Public Works Directive, apply (Section 7.3). The criteria for qualitative selection also follow the Public Works Directive except that they also include the ability to seek the technical references available under the Public Supplies Directive (Section 8.1.5). Legal persons can be required to identify the staff who are to work on the contract and their qualifications.

8.2.6.2 Contracting authorities can require the production of certificates drawn up by independent bodies conforming to the EN 45000 series (BS 7501-7503, 7511-7513) attesting to the conformity of a contractor's quality assurance system to the EN 29000 series (BS 5750). However, they must accept other evidence of equivalent certificates from bodies in other Member States and other equivalent evidence from suppliers 'who have no access to such certificates or no possibility of obtaining them within the relevant time limits' (Article 29). The ability of suppliers to perform services may be evaluated with regard to 'their skills, efficiency, experience, and reliability' (Article 28).

8.2.7 Contract award

8.2.7.1 The principles of selection by lowest price or most economically advantageous bid apply (see Section 7.5.2). The proposed Directive lays down rules as to when recipients of state aid can have their bid rejected as being abnormally low. This can be done only if the tenderer has been consulted and if the tenderer is unable to show that the aid has been notified to the Commission. State aid can include the setting off of operating losses, provision of capital, grants or privileged loans, the foregoing of profits or returns on capital due, and compensation for burdens imposed by public authorities.

8.2.7.2 There are also provisions for retaliatory action against third-party countries which restrict access by EC undertakings to their public service contracts or which do not permit EC undertakings access to these on equal terms to their own nationals. This has been a particular problem with the USA, where legislation restricts the ability of undertakings from other countries from competing on an equal footing. Similar powers for retaliation have been written into the directives that seek to harmonize the regulation of credit institutions. The Commission can suspend or restrict the award of contracts to undertakings from such countries.

8.2.8 Compliance

The Commission has proposed that the Public Works and Public Supplies Compliance Directive should have its scope amended so as to include services contracts (see Section 7.6).

8.3 UTILITIES DIRECTIVE

8.3.1 Coverage

8.3.1.1 The Directive applies to contracting entities engaged in specified activities, which may be public undertakings or private bodies. It applies to their purchases of supplies or construction works but not to their purchase of services, which is the subject of a separate proposal. In the case of private bodies, the Directive applies only if they operate on the basis of special or exclusive rights granted by a Member State. In particular, these can be said to exist where an entity enjoys compulsory purchase powers to acquire or use property, or can place network equipment on, under, or over the public highway, or supplies drinking water, electricity, gas, or heat to a network which enjoys special or exclusive rights. However, the Directive only applies to the specified activities within the EC of private bodies and does not affect any other activity they may undertake, such as the development of surplus land or acting as a public utility outside the EC.

8.3.1.2 The activities covered by the Directive are:

- Provision of fixed networks to provide the public with drinking water, electricity, gas, or heat, or to supply such networks with these items. For a water entity, the Directive also applies to the disposal or treatment of sewage. It applies to irrigation and land drainage work, where at least 20% of the volume of water made available from the project is for drinking water. Excluded from the Directive are bodies producing gas or heat as a consequence of another activity and whose supply to the public network amounts to not more than 20% of the entity's turnover. Similarly excluded are bodies producing drinking water or electricity because its consumption is necessary for another activity and the supply to the public network does not exceed 30% of the entity's production,
- Exploring for or extracting oil, gas, coal, or other solid fuel,
- Provision of airports, ports, or terminals to carriers by air, sea, or inland waterway,
- Operation of a transport network by railway, automated system, tramway, trolley bus, bus, or cable. This does not apply to bus services in circumstances in which other entities are free to provide a service in an area;
- Provision or operation of public telecommunications networks or services.

8.3.1.3 The Directive does not apply to purchases of water nor to those of electricity, gas, oil, or coal for the production of energy. Member States can request the Commission to exclude mineral exploitation and extraction from the operation of the Directive providing that certain conditions are met. Similar exclusions on grounds such as national security and international agreements apply as with the Public Works and Public Supplies directives (see Section 7.1.4). The list of bodies to which the Directive applies appears in Annexes I to X (see Table 19).

8.3.2 Financial thresholds

Different thresholds for the advertising provisions of the Directive apply according to the type of contract:

- Supply contracts for water, electricity, gas, oil, coal exploration, ports, and railway and transport networks, **400 000 ECU**,
- Supply contracts for telecommunications, **600 000 ECU**,
- Construction works contracts, **5 million ECU**,

The calculation of the supply thresholds follows the approach discussed in Section 8.1.3, and for the works contracts, including the question of lots, that discussed in Section 7.1.3.

8.3.3 Procedures

8.3.3.1 The Directive provides for open, restricted, and negotiated procedures. The negotiated procedures operate rather differently from the Public Works and Public Supplies Directives. Negotiated procedures can be used without a prior call for competition under the same circumstances that apply in the other public procurement directives both with and without a tender notice (see Section 7.2.2). They may also be used for 'bargain purchases' and when goods may be purchased under advantageous circumstances due to the financial difficulties of the supplier. In addition, there is explicit recognition of negotiated procedures being used as part of a framework agreement.

Table 19 Bodies to whom the Utilities Directive applies

Production, transport, or distribution of drinking water
Water companies covered by the Water Acts 1945 and 1989
Central Scotland Water Development Board
Department of the Environment for Northern Ireland

Production, transport, or distribution of electricity
Successor companies to the Central Electricity Generating Board and suppliers to the National Grid
Area electricity companies
North of Scotland Hydro-Electricity Board
South of Scotland Electricity Board
Northern Ireland Electricity Service

Production or distribution of gas or heat
British Gas PLC
Local authorities supplying heat to the public
Area electricity companies

Exploration and extraction of oil or gas
Entities governed by Petroleum (Production) Act 1934 as extended by the Continental Shelf Act 1964 or the Petroleum (Production) Act (Northern Ireland) 1964

Exploration for and extraction of coal or other solid fuel
British Coal Board and entities to which it has granted a licence
Entities exploring or extracting under the Marine Development Act (Northern Ireland) 1969

Contracting entities in railway services
British Railway Board
Northern Ireland Railways

Contracting entities in urban railways, tramways, trolleybuses, or bus services
Entities providing bus services under the London Regional Transport Act 1984
Glasgow Underground
Greater Manchester Rapid Transit Company
Docklands Light Railway
London Underground Ltd
British Railways Board
Tyne and Wear Metro

Contracting entities in the field of airport facilities
British Airports Authority PLC
Airports managed by plcs under Airports Act 1986

Contracting entities for ports or terminal facilities
Harbour authorities under the Harbours Act 1964

Operation of telecommunications networks or provision of telecommunications services
British Telecommunications PLC
Mercury Communications PLC
City of Kingston upon Hull
Racal Vodafone
Telecoms Securicor Cellular Radio Ltd (Cellnet)

Source: Annexes I-X, Council Directive of 17 September 1990 on the procurement of entities operating in the water, energy, transport and telecommunications sectors, *Official Journal*, L 297, 29 October 1990

8.3.3.2 The use of European specifications is insisted upon where these exist. However, the Directive does not provide a hierarchy of other specifications. European specifications may be complemented by others, but these should be performance requirements rather than design or description characteristics. Similar derogations from the use of European specifications apply as in other public procurement directives (see Section 7.3.2). European specifications do not have to be used where they are 'inappropriate for the particular application' or do not take into account technical developments that have taken place since their adoption. This statement is surprising since the technical harmonization directives contain provisions that permit the approval of innovatory products either through European technical approvals, in the case of construction products, or else by EC type-examination. The presumptions against the use of trademarks or patents in specifications also apply. It should be noted that Article 6(1) of the Construction Products Directive requires Member States to ensure that private bodies acting as public undertakings or as public bodies by virtue of their monopoly position do not impede free trade in products that comply with that Directive through their rules or conditions. Thus, the question of whether specifications can be set other than by reference to harmonized European standards or seek quality levels other than those determined as the acceptable methods of attestation of conformity by the Commission would appear to apply to utilities (see Section 7.7.3). The argument has been advanced that a requirement in an individual contract is not 'rules and conditions' but it is a moot point as to how frequently this argument can be put forward before a series of individual requirements has become a condition[15].

8.3.4 Notices

8.3.4.1 The call for competition can take the form of a contract notice, a periodic indicative notice, or a notice of the existence of a qualification system. Contract notices for open, restricted, and negotiated procedures are similar to those found in other directives (see Section 7.4). *Periodic indicative notices* must be published at least once a year and identify the total supply contracts in each area for which it is expected that the total contracts awarded during a year will be at least equal to **750 000 ECU (£525 000)**. The essential characteristics of the works contracts must also be identified. The information in the notice includes the award procedure to be followed, the type of services or the sites for works, and dates for contracts. The *notice on the existence of a qualification system* identifies the purpose of the system, where the rules can be obtained, and the duration of the qualification system. The qualification system enables participants in restricted or negotiated procedures to be selected without there necessarily being a contract notice.

8.3.4.2 A contract award notice must be sent to the Commission within two months of the award. Part of this is to be published in the *Official Journal*, including information on the nature of the contract, award procedure, number of tenders, and date of award. There is also confidential information, which is not for publication except when aggregated with other data. This includes the value of the contract, country of origin of product or service, award criteria, and use of derogations from European specifications.

8.3.5 Selection of contractors

8.3.5.1 Contract award procedures are similar to those in the other public procurement directives. There are two main differences:

- Abnormally low tenders cannot be rejected if they are the result of state aid which has been notified to the Commission,
- Tenders for which at least 50% of the value comes from third-party countries, which do not have comparable access agreements with the EC, can be rejected. Where there are two or more equivalent tenders, with price differences not exceeding 3%, preference shall be given to those that come from countries which have a comparable access agreement with the EC, unless this would cause incompatibility with existing material or disproportionate costs.

8.3.5.2 Contracting entities can operate systems of qualification of suppliers but these must be based on objective rules. European standards are to be used where appropriate. Entities are not to impose conditions on some contractors without also applying them to others or require tests that duplicate objective evidence already available. Reasons must be given for any refusal to admit an applicant to an approved list and for bringing to an end a pre-qualification. Contracting entities can require contractors to obtain certification systems from third parties and can identify the third parties that meet their requirements. However, for the reasons discussed in Section 8.3.3.2, these provisions, when applied to construction products, appear to be in conflict with Article 6 (1) of the Construction Products Directive.

8.3.6 Services

8.3.6.1 The proposed Utilities Services Directive is intended to apply to the same entities as the Utilities Directive and to those of their activities that are regulated by this Directive. Thus, it does not apply to any purchase of services such an entity might make for other reasons. Therefore it will not apply, for example, to the development of surplus land by a utilities undertaking. It does not apply to the award of service contracts to affiliated undertakings or to joint ventures. The proposal is intended to come into effect from 1 January 1993.

8.3.6.2 The procedures to be followed are similar to those in the Utilities Directive, for example, which contracts are excluded, the use of technical specifications, when negotiated procedures may be used, when mineral exploitation and extraction can be excluded from the operation of the Directive, and when suppliers can be excluded from a contract. The thresholds for the advertisement of contracts are the same as those for supplies contracts. The proposal substantially follows the proposed Public Services Directive in matters such as which services the proposal is to apply to, the division of services into two groups (one of which is subject to less onerous requirements), which services are excluded from the scope of the proposed Directive, design contest rules, the notices advertising contracts, how contracts are to be valued, how to treat abnormally low tenders from public bodies, quality assurance certificates, and possible retaliation against third countries.

8.3.7 Enforcement

The Utilities Remedies Directive, which was adopted in February 1992, provides for a similar review of their works and supplies contracts to those of contracting authorities (see Section 7.6). The claimant must prove that he would have had a real chance of winning the contract had the infringement not taken place. Similar measures can also be expected for utilities service contracts once the proposed Utilities Services Directive has been adopted. The Utilities Remedies Directive grants the Commission similar powers to intervene in the event of a breach of Community law to those they enjoy under the Public Works and Supplies Directives. Member States are to offer to contracting entities the alternative procedure of having recourse to an attestation system. Under this the contracting entity is subject to periodic review of its purchasing procedures to attest that these are in accordance with Community law. Authorized persons to do this must be independent of the contracting entity and be objective. There is also a conciliation procedure open to aggrieved contractors. The Directive is to come into force by 1 January 1993.

8.4 CONCLUSIONS

8.4.1 The Public Supplies Directive has important implications for the construction products industry as construction products purchased by public bodies for their own use, for example, by direct labour organizations, come within the scope of this Directive. The suppliers of professional services in construction, such as architects, quantity surveyors, engineers, and town planners, and the suppliers of commercial services, such as property management and building maintenance, will be affected by the proposed Public Services Directive. The Utilities Directive, Utilities Remedies Directive, and proposed Utilities Services Directive will have the effect of extending the public procurement directives so as to encompass the purchases of construction products, construction works, and construction services by utilities entities in energy, transport, telecommunications, and water. It will not matter whether the utilities entities are in public or private ownership, both will be subject to these measures. However, the measures will not affect those activities of utilities entities which are not concerned with the supply of the specified products. Thus, a railway or water company that seeks to develop surplus land will not have to abide by the directives in the award of contracts for construction works or construction products or in assembling its design team. The proposed thresholds for advertising public services are likely to mean that the construction industry is more likely to be affected by the proposed Public Services Directive in areas like building maintenance than by the Public Works Directive for new building.

8.4.2 There is nothing in these measures that obliges a public body or a utility to put the supply of goods or services or construction works out to tender rather than to undertake them in-house. The measures only take effect once a decision has been taken to seek outside contracts. Thus, the measures are neutral with respect to compulsory competitive tendering but do affect how this is to take place.

8.4.3 The impact of these measures on quality management is similar to that of the Public Works Directive. The bodies covered by the measures are obliged to use European standards where possible and these may include quality control and quality assurance provisions. They set out the information that may be sought by way of technical references. The Public Supplies Directive is more explicit about the information that can be sought about quality management than is the case with the Public Works

Directive. The proposed Public Supplies Directive permits contracting authorities to seek the production of certificates drawn up by certification bodies conforming to the EN 45000 series of standards attesting to the conformity of a contractor's quality assurance system to the EN 29000 series. However, the potential problems that may stem from Article 6 (1) of the Construction Products Directive (in its requirement that public bodies shall not by their rules and procedures impede products that satisfy this Directive) also affect these measures. Whether this article prevents public bodies from specifying construction products other than by reference to harmonized European standards or setting levels of quality assurance in excess of the designated procedures for attestation of conformity remains an unanswered question.

References: 8 Public procurement of goods and services and by utilities

1. Council Directive of 22 March 1988 amending Directive 77/62/EEC relating to the coordination of procedures on the award of public supply contracts and repealing certain provisions of Directive 80/767/EEC (88/295/EEC), *Official Journal*, L 127, 20 May 1988.

2. Council Directive of 21 December 1976 coordinating procedures for the award of public supply contracts (77/62/EEC), *Official Journal*, L 13, 15 January 1977.

3. Council Directive of 22 July 1980 adapting and supplementing in respect of certain contracting authorities Directive 77/62/EEC coordinating procedures for the award of public supply contracts (80/767/EEC), *Official Journal*, L 215, 18 August 1980.

4. Council Directive of 21 December 1989 on the coordination of the laws, regulations and administrative provisions relating to the application of review procedures to the award of public supply and public works contracts (89/665/EEC), *Official Journal*, L 395, 30 December 1989.

5. HM Treasury (1988), *Guidance Notes on Public Sector Purchasing International Obligations: Supplies Contracts*, December.

6. Department of the Environment (1989), *European Economic Community Directive 88/295 Public Sector Supply Contracts*, Circular 6/89, 28 February.

7. The Public Supply Contracts Regulations 1991, SI 1991, No. 2679.

8. Institute of Purchasing and Supply (1989), *The European Community Supplies Directive: A Guide for Local Authorities*, Stamford.

9. Amended proposal for a Council Directive relating to the coordination of procedures on the award of public services contracts (91/C 250/05), *Official Journal*, C 250, 25 September 1991.

10. Council Directive of 17 September 1990 on the procurement procedures of entities operating in the water, energy, transport and telecommunications sectors (90/531/EEC), *Official Journal*, L 297, 29 October 1990.

11. Proposal for a Council Directive on the service procurement procedures of entities operating in the water, energy, transport and telecommunications sectors, *Official Journal*, C 337, 31 December 1991. The text of this and the Utilities Directive is combined in: Consolidated text integrating the provisions of the proposal for a Directive COM(91) 347 final (services contracts) into Directive 90/531/EEC (supply and works contracts) (92/C 34/04), *Official Journal*, C 34, 12 February 1992.

12. Council Directive 92/13/EEC of 25 February 1992 on the coordination of the laws, regulations and administrative provisions relating to the application of Community rules on the procurement procedures of entities operating in the water, energy, transport and telecommunications sectors, *Official Journal*, L 76, 23 March 1992.

13. Current values of the thresholds in pounds sterling have been taken from Commission of the European Communities, *Opening Up Public Procurement*, ISEC/B4/92, 20 February 1992.

14. Council Directive of 21 December 1988 on the approximation of laws, regulations and administrative provisions of the Member States relating to construction products (89/106/EEC), *Official Journal*, L 40, 11 February 1989.

15. Davies, A. (1992), *The Impact of EC Directives*, presentation to Water World 92, 13 May.

Part D Post-construction liability

9 Product liability

9.0 OVERVIEW

***9.0.1** The Construction Products Directive is an example of consumerist legislation aimed at affording a minimum level of protection to consumers. Its implementation in the UK, in common with other New Approach directives, draws heavily on the approach of parts of the Consumer Protection Act 1987. This Act was also the result of an EC Directive, namely the Product Liability Directive of 1985. It sought to ensure that there should be no distortion of competition within the EC as a result of different degrees of protection being given to consumers in different Member States.*

***9.0.2** The Consumer Protection Act does not impose liability for defects arising from the construction or assembly of a building or civil engineering works but is concerned with defects in component parts or materials. Enforcement of the Act is by weights and measures authorities to whom it grants various powers, including issuing prohibition, suspension, and warning notices, the ability to obtain information, and to seek the forfeiture of defective goods. The Act has been used as a model for the enforcement of New Approach directives but, to date, there have been two different approaches. The Gas Appliances Directive has been implemented by making safety regulations under Section 11 of the Act. By contrast, the Construction Products Directive has been brought into force by means of regulations which introduce similar offences and powers of enforcement to the Consumer Protection Act but which are not made under this Act.*

9.1 CONSTRUCTION PRODUCTS DIRECTIVE AND CONSUMER PROTECTION OBJECTIVES

9.1.1 The Construction Products Directive is an example of European legislation based upon a consumerist policy: namely, to afford a minimum level of protection to consumers using or potentially at risk from defective products. The preamble to the Directive refers to the opinion of the EC's Economic and Social Committee that:

> Member States are responsible for ensuring that building and civil engineering works on their territory are designed and executed in a way that does not endanger the safety of persons, domestic animals and property, while respecting other essential requirements in the interests of general well-being.[1]

The preamble to the Directive contains another significant passage, noting that:

> Member States have provisions including requirements, relating not only to building safety, but also to health, durability, energy economy, protection of the environment, aspects of economy, and other aspects important in the public interest . . . often the subject of national provisions laid down by law, regulation or administrative action . . . reflected in national product standards, technical approvals and other technical specifications and provisions which, by their disparity, hinder trade within the Community.[1]

9.1.2 The combination of these ideas gives the key to the purpose of the Directive. There is a perceived common need to ensure that building and engineering works do not endanger the safety of persons or property. The Member States have legislation and other mechanisms in place to secure this, but they are disparate. Their disparity is potentially inconsistent with the two principal aims of the EC as set out in the Treaty of Rome, namely:

- to promote competition and the conditions for a fair internal market,
- to give to consumers (i.e. clients, purchasers, tenants, users) a high level of protection.

The Construction Products Directive seeks to achieve uniform minima of consumer protection in respect of the essential requirements and to eliminate disparity which is inconsistent with fair internal competition.

9.1.3 The concept of EC legislation impinging upon UK law, so as not merely to cover new areas but to extend and change the existing substance, is not so long established as to be familiar. Nevertheless, there is a precedent for EC intervention by directive in UK consumer legislation. This is the Product Liability Directive of 1985.[(2)] Its conception and translation into UK legislation have certain analogous features which make it useful as a model both for comparison and contrast. The resultant UK legislation, the Consumer Protection Act 1987, is also intrinsically worthy of attention as it has potential impact upon construction liability and it is the legislative source for regulations made to implement certain New Approach directives, such as the Gas Appliances Directive (see Section 9.3.8). It should be made clear at this point that the Consumer Protection Act comprises quite different parts. Part 1 of the Act is concerned with civil liability for products. Parts II and IV deal with Consumer Safety and Enforcement and are virtually separate from Part I. It is Parts II and IV which provide a useful basis for understanding the Construction Products Regulations.

9.2 PRODUCT LIABILITY DIRECTIVE

9.2.1 The Consumer Protection Act 1987 was the result of the conjunction of two influences. First, there was a clear desire in the UK to reform the law relating to consumer protection. During the previous 15 years, this desire had prompted the enactment of such legislation as the Trade Descriptions Act 1972, the Unfair Contract Terms Act 1977, the Sale of Goods Act 1979, and the Supply of Goods and Services Act 1982. Both gaps in the coverage and the need for revision were evident. The second influence, an influence without which the Act would not have been passed either at that time or in that form, was European.

9.2.2 The history of consumer protection in the EC commences with a resolution of the European Council on 14 April 1975 concerning a preliminary programme for a protection and information policy for the consumer. In 1976 the Commission of the EEC pointed out that differing national laws on product liability could lead to a distortion of competition and also expressed concern that there should be equal protection for consumers within the Community. Examples of the different approaches in European states included:

France In relation to professional producers/sellers, liability was basically strict, i.e. it depended only on whether the requirements had or had not, been met in the end product. There was no state-of-the-art or development risks defence.

Germany The German system embodied the fault-based principle with the burden of proof on the plaintiff. This is similar to the system in Denmark, and also to non-member states such as Norway, Sweden and Austria.

UK Relied upon actions in contract, based on breach of implied terms as to merchantability of goods, with strict liability resting on the seller if the goods were defective, or upon an action in tort based on the fault/negligence principle. There is some concept of the state-of-the-art defence implicit in the ordinary competent practitioner standard.

Consumer lobbies within jurisdictions utilising the fault-based principle were exerting pressure for movement towards strict liability.

9.2.3 The draft of the Directive provoked much debate across the Community, especially from organizations such as the Confederation of British Industry which were concerned that too much liability was placed upon producers. The English and Scottish Law Commissions and the House of Lords Select Committee on the European Communities were of the opinion that the proposal was too wide, and concern was expressed about the sovereignty of national legislatures in that the Directive was required to be incorporated into the national law of Member States, albeit with discretion as to how this was to be done. Article 189(3) of the EEC Treaty states that 'A directive shall be binding as to the result to be achieved upon each member state to which it is addressed, but shall leave to national authorities the choice of form and methods.'

9.2.4 When the Product Liability Directive was issued on 25 July 1985, it had been amended to take account of the criticism by permitting derogation, i.e. allowing discretion as to the inclusion or exclusion of certain parts of the Directive according to the wishes of individual Member States. For example, the defence of development risk could be incorporated by those Member States wishing to do so. Table 20 summarises the main points in the Directive. Member States, including Britain, were required to act within three years from the date of the Directive to introduce legislation to comply with it.

Table 20 Summary of contents of the Product Liability Directive

Parties concerned (Articles 1 and 3)

Producer	A manufacturer of a finished product/component, a producer of raw material, a person fixing a trademark, etc.
Importer	One who imports into the EC a product for sale, hire, leasing or distribution in the course of a business.
Supplier	Where the producer or importer cannot be identified by the injured party.

All these are treated as producers for the purposes of the Directive and are liable for damage caused by defective products.

Product (Article 2)

All movables which have been industrially produced. This applies to movables used in the construction of or installed in immovables.

Defective (Article 6)

A product which does not provide the safety which a person is entitled to expect, taking into account circumstances of presentation, use to which it can reasonably be expected to be put, and the time that the product was put into circulation.

Damage (Article 9)

Death, personal injury, damage to property other than the defective product, provided that the item damaged is of a type ordinarily intended and mainly used for the injured party's private use.

Burden of proof (Article 4)

The injured party is required to prove damage, defect, and causal relationship.

Defences (Article 7)

a) That the defendant did not circulate the product.
b) That it is probable that the defect did not exist at the time of circulation.
c) That the product was not manufactured for sale/economic distribution.
d) That the defect was due to compliance with mandatory regulations of public authorities.
e) That the product was built at the state of the art.
f) That the defect was in the design of a product rather than the component fitted into it.

Limitation (Article 10 and 11)

An action must be brought within three years of the date on which the plaintiff became aware or should reasonably have become aware of the damage, defect and identity of producer.

All rights of action are extinguished after 10 years of the date of product circulation, unless proceedings have already been instituted.

Exclusion of liability (Article 12)

Producers may not rely on provisions limiting or excluding liability.

9.3 IMPLEMENTATION OF THE PRODUCT LIABILITY DIRECTIVE IN BRITAIN

9.3.1 The government acted swiftly following the Product Liability Directive of July 1985 to introduce the Consumer Protection Bill 1986. It adopted a somewhat ambivalent attitude to the need for response to a European directive with substantive changes to national law. When the Bill was introduced it incorporated wording which was quite different from that of the Directive. At the second reading of the Bill in the House of Commons, Mr Michael Howard, the then Parliamentary Under-Secretary of State for Trade and Industry, expressed the government's preference for market forces in ensuring quality: 'For most purposes, the best protection that consumers can have is that provided by fair competition in a free market. In general, that protection can best be achieved by letting business get on with the task of competing for customers', while accepting that 'fair competition can only be achieved in a suitable framework'.

Nevertheless, throughout Mr Howard's speech it was made clear that the whole purpose of Part 1 of the Bill was compliance with the Directive: 'Part 1 provides consumers who are injured by defective products with a new mechanism for seeking compensation. These provisions implement the European Community Directive on liability for defective products . . . the general purpose of the Directive is harmonization.'

9.3.2 The criticism that the government faced in debate in Parliament came from two sides: first from the 'ultra-consumerists' who argued that the Bill did not wholly implement the Directive and should have done and, on the opposite side, from those who believed that the Bill did implement the Directive and should not have done. The former lobby contended for more radical measures. Thus, Alan Williams (Labour) claimed that

> The Bill waters down the proposals that the EC has put forward. . . . The National Consumer Council believes that the government have deliberately created a loophole to appease the agricultural lobby and that the Ministry of Agriculture, Fisheries and Food has sabotaged consumer protection legislation. . . . The intentions of the Directive are much wider than those of the Bill.

9.3.3 In the Commons, particularly, there was disquiet about the effects of the Directive upon English law, notably relating to the repeal of the Trade Descriptions Act 1972, and concern was expressed at the government's apparent alacrity in acquiescence with the EC position that it contravened EC policy. This was seen as an acquiescence made without any significant attempt to protect British rights, or allowing British consumers the added protective measure of being able to make an informed choice in respect of goods purchased. The insidious effect of an EC directive on UK consumer law was highlighted in the House of Lords debate by Lord Morton of Shuna and by Lord Denning. Lord Denning felt that it was:

> time we all understood what these directives are. When they are issued by the Council of Ministers in Brussels they become part of our law. Not only that, but if we do anything or pass anything that is inconsistent or in conflict with it the directive governs . . . but where is it to be found? . . . These directives are very important, affecting all our law. Yet we have to search around and have copies made in the basement. . . . Those who have to consider the Bill, and the courts which have to consider the Act, when it is passed, ought to have before them the Directive on which it is based.

9.3.4 The Bill was enacted as the Consumer Protection Act 1987. Its key provision, from the point of view of technical harmonization measures, is the granting of power, under Section 11, to the Secretary of State to make safety regulations. These may contain provisions with respect to the content, design, construction, finish, or packing of goods, approvals, testing, and inspection of goods, any marks or instructions to be put on or accompany them, and any controls over the supply of goods. Thus safety regulations can encompass any regulations made to enact essential requirements, attestation of conformity provisions, or provisions concerning the use of the CE mark that are required by New Approach directives.

9.3.5 The Act created a number of offences. Section 10 makes it an offence to supply consumer goods which fail to comply with the general safety requirements, offering or agreeing to supply such goods, or exposing or possessing such goods for supply. Section 12 creates the offences of supplying goods where prohibited by safety regulations, contravening safety regulations that require a mark or particular kinds of information, failing to carry out tests or procedures required by safety regulations, and failing to give the information required by a safety regulation. Section 3 defines a defect in such a way as to take into account the use of any mark in relation to the product and any instructions and warning given with it. Thus, the Act would appear to provide a basis for implementing New Approach directives by creating offences that could be applied to their essential requirements and attestation of conformity provisions.

9.3.6 The Act creates various powers of enforcement including:

- Prohibition notices, which prevent the supply of unsafe goods,
- Notices to warn, which require a person to publish at his own expense a warning about unsafe goods,
- Suspension notices, which prevent a person from supplying specified goods for up to six months,
- The forfeiture of goods on the grounds that there has been a contravention of a safety provision,
- The obligation to provide information or to produce records on being served a notice by the Secretary of State.

The contravention of notices can result in a fine of up to level 5 on the standard scale and/or up to six months' imprisonment, with similar penalties for offences against safety regulations and similar fines for supplying, or recklessly furnishing, false information. Appeals can be made against suspension notices and against the detention of goods. Enforcing authorities are liable to pay compensation for the seizure and detention of goods where there has been no contravention of any safety provision. If a person is convicted of a contravention of any safety provision or a forfeiture order is made, the court may order the offender to reimburse the enforcing authority for any expenditure incurred in connection with the detention or forfeiture of the goods.

9.3.7 Enforcement is by the weights and measures authorities in Great Britain (district councils in Northern Ireland). They can make purchases and undertake tests of goods, enter premises, require the production of records, and seize goods or records. Customs officers can seize imported goods and detain them for two working days. The Act creates penalties for impersonating an officer of an enforcement authority and obstructing an authorized officer.

9.3.8 The Consumer Protection Act has supplied the model for enforcing regulations to implement New Approach directives in the UK. However, to date, two distinct approaches have been adopted.

- By making safety regulations under Section 11 of the Act to be enforced by the weights and measures authorities using the powers granted to them by the Act. This is the approach adopted in the Gas Appliances (Safety) Regulations 1992, which are proposed to implement the Gas Appliances Directive[(3)],
- Through the making of regulations under the European Communities Act 1972, which largely follow the provisions of Parts II and IV of the Consumer Protection Act, although enforcement is not under this Act. This is the approach adopted in the Construction Products Regulations 1991[(4)], which bring into force the Construction Products Directive.

9.4 LIABILITY IN CONSTRUCTION UNDER THE CONSUMER PROTECTION ACT

9.4.1 Section 9.3 has sought to show how the Consumer Protection Act creates concepts of regulation and enforcement which are analogous to the Construction Products Regulations. Part I of the Consumer Protection Act concerns civil liability and is not directly comparable to the Construction Products Directive. Its limited application to construction is considered in this section. The Act does not seek to impose civil liability for defects arising from the construction or assembly of a building. In the UK, civil liability is covered by a combination of the Defective Premises Act 1972 and the common law. The potential effect of Part I of the Consumer Protection Act is limited to liability for defects in component parts and materials incorporated into the construction of a building. Lord Morton had proposed an amendment in the definition of 'product' to include 'a product which has been incorporated into an immovable, or real, or heritable property'. He supported this as

> an attempt to include in the definition of 'a product' what the Directive says it must include. It appears to us that it has been excluded. It is clear that the Directive covers bricks, wood, cement and other things, even though they become part of a house. . . . In the Bill, 'product' as defined in the first few lines does not make that clear.'

The reply of Lord Lucas and the subsequent withdrawal of the proposed amendment supports the view that the legislation as enacted achieves this effect anyway. Lord Lucas said,

> There is a distinction to be drawn under the Directive between the components of a building and the building itself. While there is liability for defects in components, the Directive does not seek to impose liability for defects in the building itself; that is, a defect arising from the assembly or construction of the building, Clause 45(1) does not make that distinction. If we look at Clause 46(3) . . . this needs to be read with Clause 4(1)(b). This gives a defence to any producer that he did not at any time supply the product to another person. The result is to give a defence to the building contractor, for example, in respect of defects in buildings put on the market by him.'

The effect, then, is that liability for defective materials rests with the producer, manufacturer, or importer into the EC or, where these are not identifiable, the supplier, a subcontractor for example. The liability of the contractor or developer would be, *prima facie*, excluded by sections 46(3) and 46(4).

9.4.2 Section 46(3) provides that:

> the performance of any contract by the erection of any building or structure on any land or by the carrying out of any other building works shall be treated for the purposes of this Act as a supply of goods in so far as, but only in so far as, it involves the provision of any goods to any person by means of their incorporation into the building, structure or works.

9.4.3 Section 46(4) provides that (subject to exceptions under Part III on misleading price indicators):

> references in this Act to supplying goods shall not include references to supply of goods comprised in land where the supply is effected by the creation or disposal of an interest in the land.

9.4.4 Where liability such as that of a supplier does exist, damages are not recoverable by the injured party in respect of the defective product itself, but are recoverable for death, personal injury or loss or damage to any other property including land. There is a restriction in s.5(3) that liability for damage to property is limited to property which is:

> (*a*) of a description of property ordinarily intended for private use, occupation or consumption; and
>
> (*b*) intended by the person suffering the loss or damage mainly for his own private use, occupation or consumption.

Thus civil liability for damage to property under Part I is limited to domestic dwellings. However, civil liability for death or personal injury caused by defective products may extend to situations where those products are incorporated in other buildings or works.

9.5 CONCLUSIONS

9.5.1 Article 100a of the Single European Act provides that the Single Market must afford 'a high level of protection' with regard to health, safety, the environment and consumers. Protection of consumers and their health and safety underlay the issue of the Product Liability Directive. Notwithstanding the view of the government that 'for most purposes, the best protection that consumers can have is that provided by fair competition in a free market', the position of the European Parliament in general appears to be that intervention is necessary.

9.5.2 The Construction Products Directive derives from the same basic philosophy as the Product Liability Directive, namely that some intervention is necessary to protect consumers against injury or damage from defective products. The Construction Products Directive derives from the desire to ensure that products used in construction are fit for their intended use. Fitness is, however, defined for these purposes by reference to the essential requirements and it must be understood that the philosophy goes beyond mere physical safety. The second preamble to the Directive notes that Member States have 'provisions, including requirements, relating not only to building safety but also to health, durability, energy economy, protection of the environment, aspects of economy and other aspects important in the public interest', and it is to furtherance of consistency of protection for these interests that the Construction Products Directive is dedicated. Put simply, the interests to be protected are wider than safety. The preamble also notes that 'it is necessary to ensure the conformity of products', hence the Directive's requirements with respect to attestation of conformity.

9.5.3 The Product Liability Directive required legislation to implement it. It is a characteristic of directives that they do not take effect in the national law of Member States, but require the enactment, within a specified period, of measures which produce consistency between directive and national law. This was achieved by the Consumer Protection Act 1987. The Construction Products Directive also required UK legislation to implement it and this has been done by statutory instrument under s.2(2) of the European Communities Act 1972: the Construction Products Regulations 1991. The Construction Products Directive gave Member States 30 months from its notification to 'bring into force the laws, regulations and administrative provisions necessary to comply with the provisions of this Directive'. Notification was on the 27 December 1988 and the Construction Products Regulations would have had to have been produced by 27 June 1991 to have complied with the deadline. This was not achieved in the UK. Nothing is likely to turn upon this minor transgression of the time limit. The Regulations appeared on 15 July 1991 and came into force, by Regulation 1, on 27 December 1991, three years after the Directive. The UK's record on implementation is better than that of most other Member States. Theoretically, action could be taken against a transgressing government, but the time taken to mount such an action often means that implementation would have taken place well before the action came to trial before the European Court. One of the principal messages which this conclusions section seeks to impart is that directives change national law and affect the industries which are subject to them.

References: 9 Product liability

1. Council Directive of 21 December 1988 on the approximation of laws, regulations and administrative provisions of the Member States relating to construction products (89/106/EEC), *Official Journal*, L 40, 11 February 1989.

2. Council Directive of 25 July 1985 on the approximation of the laws of the Member States relating to product liability (85/375/EEC), *Official Journal*, L 210.

3. The Gas Appliances (Safety) Regulations 1992, SI 1992, No. 711.

4. Construction Products Regulations 1991, SI 1991, No. 1620.

10 The Construction Products Regulations and post-construction liability

10.0 OVERVIEW

10.0.1 The Construction Products Directive has been enacted by regulations that use as a comparative model the related area of product liability. Much the same comparative approach was taken by the Department of the Environment in its explanatory and consultative note published in August 1990, which sought to explain the proposed regulations by reference to Consumer Protection Act provisions as well as to the Toys (Safety) Regulations 1989. The latter comparison derives from the fact that, like the Construction Products Directive, the Toys Directive was produced under the New Approach to Technical Harmonization and Standards. The question is certain to arise in the mind of any participant in the construction process: how does this new departure affect my risk exposure and, specifically, what is the effect upon potential legal liability? Accordingly, this section is devoted to assessing what might be called the consequences of defective quality management.

10.0.2 The section examines the means by which the Construction Products Regulations 1991 are to be enforced, including the use of prohibition notices, notices to warn, and suspension notices and powers of forfeiture, obtaining information, making test purchases, searching, and detaining imports. It considers the implications of the Construction Products Directive for the potential legal liability of construction professionals. It is concluded that construction professionals, including designers, cannot be negligent just by specifying a non-CE-marked product but, also, that the specification of a CE-marked product does not release them from the obligation to the client of using reasonable care and skill. The presence of the CE mark does not say that the product meets the individual needs of a project or will perform in the way in which the client requires.

10.1 LEGAL LIABILITY AND THE CONSTRUCTION PRODUCTS REGULATIONS

10.1.1 John Barber[1] concludes that contracts and other forms of legal obligation are inadequate to assure quality. He gives a reminder of the truism that 'the courts will not ensure that a contract to construct a sewage treatment works actually results in the sewage treatment works being completed on time and in accordance with the specified requirements'.

It should be noted here that Barber's report is essential reading for those needing to understand the contractual implications of the operation of quality systems. It can be seen in some respects as complementary to this publication.

10.1.2 The Construction Products Directive[2] and the Construction Products Regulations[3] would be incapable of implementing the EC's policy if they were only enforcement mechanisms, or their chief purpose was to add to existing systems of enforcement. Key areas of the Directive and the Regulations are concerned with the concepts of product standards and the setting up of procedural systems to validate and approve those standards. This is all predicated upon the assumption that in developed, industrialized nations like the EC Member States, with construction industries which are in the main highly sophisticated, there will be both the capacity and the will to achieve a high degree of compliance with the standards produced by these procedures. So it is not the case that the EC, or the British Parliament, believes that legal weaponry could achieve its quality objectives or that legal remedies are capable of producing better buildings.

10.1.3 The fact that legal mechanisms are incapable of ensuring the achievement of quality does not mean that quality management and its failures are legally neutral. The Construction Products Regulations themselves do not expressly create civil liability nor mechanisms for recovery of compensation by injured parties, as Part I of the Consumer Protection Act did. They do create offences and enforcement mechanisms relating to the offering for sale of defective products. They may also indirectly have an effect on civil liability as a further factor to be considered by those specifying products. These variants of legal liability are dealt with below.

10.1.4 First, it is necessary to consider the scope of application of the requirements of fitness. The Directive itself in Article 2, paragraph 1, distinguishes clearly (as does Article 1) between construction products on the one hand and building and civil engineering works on the other. It says that fitness of the *products* means that provided the *works* are properly designed and built, the *works* will satisfy the essential requirements if the works are subject to regulations that contain such requirements. Reference can be made to Annex 1 of the Directive which deals with the essential requirements for further clarification (see Section 3.3). There it appears that the products 'must be suitable for construction works which (*as a whole and in their separate parts*) are fit for their intended use'. The relationship between products and works is not so clear from the Construction Products Regulations and there has been some debate as to their effect in this respect. It is assumed here that the purpose and the effect of the regulations is to implement the Directive in this as in other aspects.

10.1.5 The Construction Products Regulations create a number of offences, principally that of supplying a construction product that when incorporated into a building or construction works would result in them failing to meet the essential requirements, where the buildings or construction works are subject to regulations containing such requirements. The penalty is a fine of up to scale 5 on the standard scale and/or up to three months' imprisonment. It should be noted that Regulation 27 states that where a corporate body is guilty of an offence under the Regulations, which is shown to have been committed with the consent of or is attributable to one of its officers, proceedings can be taken against that officer. Until other Member States take action to bring the Construction Products Directive into force, it will not be apparent whether the penalties in the UK legislation are comparable with those in other Member States. Differences in penalties could distort trade in construction products, but the Directive contains no provisions for their harmonization.

10.1.6 The presence of the CE mark (described as an EC mark in the Regulations) is a claim by the manufacturer that the product has complied with the relevant directives (see Section 10.4.7. below on the significance of the CE mark in specification of a product and Section 2.3.2 for discussion of the CE mark). Member States are obliged to ensure that the CE mark is correctly used. Regulation 4 creates the offences of:

- Making an EC declaration of conformity for a product that has not met the requisite technical specifications or attestation of conformity provisions,
- Affixing the CE mark to a construction product that has not met the requisite technical specifications or attestation of conformity provisions,
- Affixing a mark to a construction product that is likely to be confused with the CE mark,
- Importing a construction product for supply within the EC to which has been affixed outside of the EC a mark that is likely to be confused with the CE mark or a CE mark when it has not met the requisite technical specifications or attestation of conformity provisions.

The penalties for these offences are a fine of up to level 5 on the standard scale and/or up to three months' imprisonment.

10.1.7 Under Regulation 26 a defence exists to the offences created by the Regulations – that the person took all reasonable steps and exercised all due diligence to avoid committing the offence. The offering of this defence, by alleging that the commission of an offence was due to an act or default by another, or by reliance on information from another, is permitted only if a notice is served on the person bringing the proceedings at least seven days before the hearing identifying the other person. Regulation 8 lists as acceptable defences:

- Reasonable belief that the product would not be used in the EC,
- The product was supplied in the course of carrying on a general retail business and there were no reasonable grounds for believing that the product failed to satisfy the regulations,

- The product was not supplied as a new product and provided for the acquisition of an interest in the product by the person supplied.

10.2 ENFORCEMENT OF THE CONSTRUCTION PRODUCTS REGULATIONS

10.2.1 The most significant parts of the Construction Product Regulations are concerned with the concept of fitness, according to the criteria set out by the essential requirements, and with the affixation and meaning of the CE mark. The enforcement provisions of the regulations are basically aimed at suppliers. This is far from meaning that others, such as construction professionals, need not be concerned about the effects of the regulations. The potential relevance of the regulations to their risk exposure is considered in Section 11 of this publication.

10.2.2 The whole coverage of the Regulations is based upon 'supply' of goods and the necessity to ensure that they are fit within the meaning of the essential requirements. Supply is defined in Regulation 2 as consisting of 'offering to supply, agreeing to supply, exposing for supply and possessing for supply, and cognate expressions'.

The Directive uses the more restrictive term, 'placed on the market', rather than supply, which would allow certain non-commercial ways of supplying construction products to escape regulation. A parallel with the Toys Regulations was drawn here in the Department of the Environment's Consultative Document[4], but there is some overlap with the Consumer Protection Act 1987 and its extension of the definition of producers who may be liable for products to:

> any person who, by putting his name on the product or using a trade mark or other distinguishing mark in relation to the product, has held himself out to be the producer of the product [and] any person who has imported the product into a Member State from a place outside the Member States in order, in the course of any business of his, to supply it to another.

10.2.3 Curiously, the Department of the Environment's consultative paper saw Regulations 9–31 as dealing with enforcement. Even more curiously, the Regulations describe Part II as concerning *Requirements relating to Construction Products* and Part III as *Enforcement of Part II*. By many standards, both Parts II and III would be regarded as related to enforcement. Regulation 7 enables the enforcement authority to require information about construction products not bearing the CE mark, i.e. to establish whether the technical performance of the product satisfies the essential requirements or that it has been produced in accordance with an acknowledged rule of technology, if a minor part product. Regulation 6 deals with information about products which do bear the CE mark. Regulation 8 enables the enforcement authority to prohibit the placing on the market of construction products not satisfying the essential requirements listed in Schedule 2. The only explanation which can be offered for this classification of Part II outside the enforcement provisions is the voluntary nature of the CE mark, but the substance of these sections means that they are enforcement related. It may be noted that the enforcement authorities for the Construction Products Regulations are to be the same as under the Consumer Protection Act 1987 (s.27), namely the local weights and measures authorities in Britain and the district councils in Northern Ireland. Circular 13/91 recommends that building control officers and approved inspectors who are of the opinion that a CE-marked product does not meet its specifications, or that the use of a CE mark is invalid, make available all relevant information to the enforcement authorities.[5]

10.3 POWERS OF ENFORCEMENT

The liabilities that can occur under the Regulations correspond to some extent to the enforcement powers given to the enforcement authorities and also with equivalent provisions in the Consumer Protection Act 1987. These enforcement powers fall into four categories.

10.3.1 Prohibition notices/notices to warn

10.3.1.1 Prohibition notices are a device found in similar form in the Consumer Protection Act 1987 (s.13), where they are defined as notices prohibiting persons (except with the consent of the Secretary of State) 'from supply, or from offering to supply, agreeing to supply, exposing for supply or possessing for supply' goods which contravene the legislation. Regulation 9 of the Construction Products Regulations defines them as prohibiting the person, except with the consent of the Secretary of State, 'from supplying any construction products which the Secretary of State considers do not satisfy the relevant requirement', i.e. any relevant essential requirements.

10.3.1.2 Notices to warn (also found in s.13 of the Consumer Protection Act) are described as 'a notice . . . requiring [a] person at his own expense to publish, in a form and manner and on occasions specified in the notice, a warning'. In the case of the Construction Products Regulations, they warn as to the inadequacy of the product with respect to one or more of the essential requirements.

10.3.1.3 These notices have to be issued in due form. The Construction Products Regulations (Schedule 4, Part I) requires that a prohibition notice contains a statement to the effect that the goods are considered to be in contravention of the Regulations, giving reasons, stating the date when the notice will come into force, and offering the recipient the opportunity to make written representations to the Secretary of State as to why the notice should be revoked. If he does so and the Secretary of State does not revoke the notice, a person must be appointed to hear further representations (orally or in writing).

10.3.1.4 Before a notice to warn can be served, a notification must be served, containing a draft of the proposed notice to warn, and giving reasons why the goods in the draft are considered unsafe. Again, there is an opportunity for the recipient of such a notification to make representations and a person will be appointed to hear them.

10.3.1.5 Contravention of either a prohibition notice or a notice to warn by a recipient is an offence punishable by up to three months in prison or a fine up to level 5 on the standard scale, or both. For example, if a supplier continued to offer to supply goods which were deficient in terms of one or more of the essential requirements, he would be in breach of a prohibition notice served on him, assuming any representations he might have made to have been unsuccessful. A recipient of a duty to warn notice who, say, failed to publish warnings as prescribed that a product supplied by him would give off toxic gas under certain circumstances, would be guilty of the offence of breach of the notice.

10.3.2 Suspension notices

10.3.2.1 An enforcement authority may, where a contravention of the Regulations has taken place, or where it has reasonable grounds for suspecting it, serve a suspension notice upon a supplier under Regulation 10. The effect of the notice is to ban a supplier from supplying the goods which breach the Regulations. The maximum duration of the effectiveness of the notice is six months. The notice should contain a description of the goods sufficient to identify them, the grounds on which the contravention is alleged, and details of the right of appeal. Note that no further suspension notice can be served at the end of the period it is in force unless proceedings are pending at that time in respect of contravention. As with the contravention of the prohibition notice or notice to warn, the penalty for the offence of breaching a suspension notice is imprisonment not exceeding three months or a fine not exceeding level 5 on the standard scale, or both. The Directive requires Member States to inform the Commission of any action taken to prevent the placing on the market of products that are declared not to be in conformity with it. The Secretary of State must be notified of suspension notices so that he can inform the Commission (see Section 10.3.6).

10.3.2.2 There is an aspect of suspension notices which may well inhibit their use. If there has been no contravention and there has been no default or neglect by the recipient of the notice, the enforcement authority is liable to pay compensation to any person having an interest in the goods. Any question of right or amount is to be referred to arbitration (in Scotland by an arbiter appointed by the sheriff), but it is simply defined as 'any loss or damage caused by reason of the service of the notice.' This is very wide-ranging and appears potentially to include consequential, i.e. economic, loss. Nor is it mere supposition to expect that this may act as an inhibition to action by enforcement authorities. An analogous power exists in planning law for the purposes of enforcement of development control. It is called a stop notice and can be served in conjunction with an enforcement notice to put an immediate stop to a breach of development control, whereas the activity could continue if no stop notice was served pending an appeal against the enforcement notice. If the enforcement notice appeal subsequently succeeds, so that the stop notice is shown, retrospectively, to have been unjustified, the planning authority (the exact equivalent of the enforcement authority) is liable to pay compensation for loss or damage caused by compliance with the stop notice. In the case of *Barnes* v. *Malvern Hills District Council* (1984), the local authority was held to be obliged to pay compensation including liability in liquidated damages under a building contract. A period of up to six months' prohibition from supplying a product could result in the supplier suffering very considerable economic loss, not least through contractual liability to customers for breach of a pre-existing supply agreement.

10.3.2.3 It is also worth pointing out the use of the wording in the Consumer Protection Act, 'any person having an interest in any goods in respect of which a suspension notice is for the time being in force', in defining both persons who may be able to claim compensation and persons who can apply to have a prohibition notice set aside. What constitutes 'an interest' in the goods may well become very significant. Could a main contractor or developer claim an interest for the purposes of compensation if he were unable to recover anything from an insolvent supplier? It is true that the 'retention of title' cases appear to hold that property in materials could not become the employer's before their placement on site for valuation (see *Archivent Sales and Developments Ltd* v. *Strathclyde Regional Council* (1984)[6] and *Dawber Williamson Roofing Ltd* v. *Humberside County Council* (1979)[7], which hold that a subcontractor is not bound by a main contract provision that property in materials passes on certification). But, if there is a contract for the supply of goods, the purchaser, the contractor, or, perhaps, the developer would have a right of action in respect of those goods if not supplied. That right of action could be argued to be a sufficient interest in the goods for the purposes of the Construction Products Regulations, considering that specific performance might be available to compel the supplier to deliver goods in his possession, so that the prohibition notice would be the only restraining factor. Again, a comparison may be drawn with planning, where the service of Planning Contravention Notices under the Planning and Compensation Act 1991 upon persons having 'an interest' in property is already destined to be the source of controversy and, potentially, of litigation, as it is not known how far 'an interest' is meant to extend, or if it would include a property manager having operational control. Similar problems may well attend the use of suspension notices and may act as a further inhibition of their use by enforcement authorities. It will not become clear until other Member States take action to bring the Construction Products Directive into force whether they will also provide for compensation for the wrongful seizure of goods and whether this compensation will be on the same scale as in the UK. If there are national variations in such provisions, these could distort trade in construction products.

10.3.3 Forfeiture

10.3.3.1 As with the Consumer Protection Act, the Construction Products Regulations contain provision in Regulations 12 and 13 for the forfeiture of construction products which contravene the regulations. This is to be done by application for an order to the Magistrates Court in England, Wales, or Northern Ireland by the enforcement authority (Regulation 12) or in Scotland by application by the procurator-fiscal to the sheriff (Regulation 13). The order may specify the destruction of the contravening products or their release to a specified person upon conditions. Conditions can include their release for scrap or for repairing or reconditioning. The enforcing authority can seek to recover the costs it has incurred in forfeiture from persons having an interest in the goods.

10.3.3.2 Mechanisms of appeal against an order of forfeiture are created for the benefit of 'any person aggrieved by an order' in England and Wales and Northern Ireland. In Scotland, the right of appearance at the sheriff's hearing and, thus, of appeal against his order is limited to 'any person upon whom a notice [of intended forfeiture] is served' and 'any other person claiming to be the owner of, or otherwise to have an interest in, the contravening products'. The same scope for dispute as to who has an interest in the products seems to be present here.

10.3.4 Other enforcement powers

The enforcement authorities (local weights and measures authorities or district councils in Northern Ireland) enjoy a number of other powers under the regulations. These are in many respects ancillary to the principal enforcement powers considered above, but are significant enough to warrant separate mention.

- *Obtaining information.* By Regulation 14, the Secretary of State can serve a notice upon any person requiring them to furnish necessary information within a reasonable time, including the production of records. Failure to do so within the specified time or giving misleading information would constitute an offence. One purpose of this weapon is to enable the government to respond directly to requests for action from the Commission or from other Member States. It should also be noted that there are no central registers of records generated by the attestation of conformity provisions of the Directive so that enforcement would be problematic without the right to gain access to appropriate records held in private hands. Regulation 6 requires those affixing the CE mark or importing CE-marked products into the EC to keep declarations and certificates of conformity for 10 years after affixing or supply respectively. The procedure is similar to that given to planning authorities by the planning contravention notice procedure instituted by the Planning and Compensation Act 1991, which empowers them to seek information from an owner suspected of a breach of planning control, where they are acting upon a report and need further evidence. There are also equivalent provisions in the Consumer Protection Act. Those supplying information are protected from its wrongful disclosure by making such disclosure an offence punishable by a fine of up to level 5 on the standard scale and/or two years' imprisonment,
- *Test purchases.* As under s.28 of the Consumer Protection Act, the Construction Products Regulations provide for enforcement authorities to purchase samples of products for testing to see whether they comply with the Regulations. Test purchases are governed by Regulation 16. Again, the identity of 'any person' may be crucial because they may also be entitled to have the products tested where the enforcement authority makes such a purchase,
- *Search.* Duly authorized officers of the enforcement authority may enter any premises, except a residence, at any reasonable hour, to inspect goods, examine production or testing procedures, or check records. This is governed by Regulation 17 and is based upon the Consumer Protection Act equivalent. This is an important power as without it enforcement authorities would lack the means to check that attestation of conformity procedures are being properly followed,
- *Detention by Customs.* Because of the need to control entry of suspect construction products into the UK, either from other Member States or from outside the EC, customs officers are empowered to seize imported construction products and detain them for two working days pending investigation. This is under Regulation 18 and, as the title of the Regulation indicates, these powers are supplemental to the provisions of Regulation 17 above.

10.3.5 Notifications to the Commission

10.3.5.1 Member States are required by the Directive to take all necessary measures to ensure that construction products are only placed upon the market if they are fit in the sense that they enable the works in which they are incorporated to satisfy the essential requirements. Article 21 permits Member States to take action against a product declared to be in conformity with the Directive where there is reason to believe it does not comply. However, Member States must notify the Commission of any measures taken against such products and, in particular, whether non-conformity is due to a failure to meet technical specifications, the incorrect application of technical specifications, or shortcomings in the technical specifications.

10.3.5.2 The need to inform the Commission means that the UK government has had to specify procedures to ensure that it is informed of actions taken by enforcing authorities. Regulation 30 imposes an obligation on enforcing authorities to 'give immediate notice' to the Secretary of State of suspension notices and applications for forfeiture. Speedy notification is essential as suspension notices only last for six months. Under Article 21 of the Directive, the Commission may need to seek the opinion of the Standing Committee for Construction on technical specifications and there is no time-limit in the Directive during which there must be a response.

10.3.5.3 Circular 13/91, Annex 4, sets out what information a notice to the Secretary of State should contain:

- Name and address of the enforcement body and the name of the enforcement officer, together with the name and address of the home authority, if different,
- A case reference,
- A description of the product, its manufacturer, any details appearing with the product, and any information accompanying the CE mark,
- Where the product was found,
- The nature of the offence, including the technical specifications used, and whether the offence was due to an incorrect application of the technical specifications or shortcomings in the technical specifications,
- A copy of the EC declaration or certificate of conformity, as appropriate,
- Details of the action taken.

10.3.5.4 It may be noted that by Regulation 26(1) it is a defence to show that 'all reasonable steps' have been taken and that 'all due diligence' has been exercised to avoid committing the offence. As with most statutory defences, the burden of proof would be upon the defendant. The presence in the provision for this defence of the words 'due diligence' and 'reasonable steps' should certainly be regarded as offering tenable arguments to those with quality systems in place – indeed, it may be increasingly difficult to claim due diligence or reasonable steps without them as such systems become usual.

10.4 LEGAL LIABILITY RELATED TO OBLIGATIONS RESULTING FROM THE CONSTRUCTION PRODUCTS REGULATIONS

10.4.1 This rather cumbersome subheading refers to the 'knock-on' effects in terms of potential legal liability of the Construction Products Regulations. It does not refer to the creation of statutory offences dealt with above, but to changes in the civil obligations of participants in the construction process other than suppliers. In particular, it focuses upon the duty of construction professionals in design. This is part of an area of law commonly known as post-construction liability, since, while the obligations are assumed with the design task, liability for non-performance or mis-performance only arises after construction, as a result of a defect or failure of some element of the building.

10.4.2 It must be made clear at the outset that this section is not about changes to construction contracts or associated documentation. There will undoubtedly be changes in forms of wording as a consequence of the introduction of the Construction Products Regulations and the advent of the CE mark. But it is not the function of this report to anticipate the responses of contract draughtsmen to this issue.

10.4.3 Nevertheless, there are important points which need to be made. Chief among these is the fact that the CE mark is not mandatory in the UK for construction products, although it is for gas appliances. This is significant in a number of ways which have implications for legal liability. If the CE mark were mandatory upon all construction products as the only way of satisfying the requirement of fitness, the construction of a house, for example, using unmarked products would have potential consequences for the producers. Thus, the builder could be said not to have complied with his duty under the Defective Premises Act 1972 to construct a dwelling fit for human habitation if its construction included materials not in conformity with the Directive. An architect could likewise be liable for such a failure. Failure to comply with a statute would be a breach of an implied term of a contract. In the case of *London Borough of Newham* v. *Taylor Woodrow–Anglian Ltd* (1981)[8] a contractual provision to the effect that the parties agreed that (building) regulations had been complied with, irrespective of whether they had or not, was declared to be meaningless and unlawful. Failure to comply with a statutory requirement can also be a tort – the tort of breach of statutory duty.

10.4.4 These are potential consequences in terms of liability, where the use of a particular practice or procedure is mandatory. Failure to use a CE-marked product could not automatically give rise to breach of an implied contractual duty (as opposed to an express one, which could well come to be imposed) nor to breach of a tortious duty. This is because it is non-mandatory.

10.4.5 However, it would be wrong to conclude that the Construction Products Regulations are neutral in terms of post-construction liability because use of CE-marked products is not mandatory. Designers in particular need to have regard to their obligations to their clients and, in the event of physical injury or damage occurring, to their liability in tort to third parties. When a designer is specifying components of the structure he is building, he has to have regard to their performance. Thus in *Richard Roberts Holdings* v. *Douglas Smith Stimson Partnership* (1989)[9], architects designing an effluent cooling tank were in breach of their duty of care to their clients in failing to research and explore the performance of the specified tank linings, which subsequently failed. Designers have to have regard to the fitness for purpose of the products which they are specifying as part of their design. This does not mean that they are themselves under a strict duty to achieve a guaranteed result. As was said in *George Hawkins* v. *Chrysler and Burne Associates* (1986)[10], a professional providing advice does not normally give an implied warranty beyond one of reasonable care and skill. The position is different where a party contracts for the design and supply of a product, where there is an implied duty to ensure fitness for purpose of the design, and this could lead to a designer acquiring a similar obligation, as in *Greaves and Co.* v. *Baynham Meikle* (1975)[11], where the designer knew of the precise design and build obligations of his client, the contractor, and was held to owe a similarly strict duty. The position is also different if the designer expressly warrants the achievement of a result, although his professional indemnity insurance may well be negated by the assumption of such a responsibility, certainly if he neglects to inform his insurers.

10.4.6 Chiefly, however, the designer is under a duty of reasonable care and skill to his client (and to third parties in tort). He must consider the fitness of the products specified to achieve their purpose as components of the design, but he does not guarantee the overall success of the design as in a warranty of fitness for purpose. What of the designer's duty to consider the suitability of a product? The Construction Products Regulations introduce criteria for fitness, the essential requirements. This creation of a set of criteria for fitness will make it harder than it now is to contend that a product deficient in terms of energy efficiency, for example, can be validly specified within the meaning of the designer's duty of reasonable care and skill. Put simply, while at present it could in theory be argued that any particular criterion was not crucial to fitness for purpose, the presence of a definitive set of criteria in statutory form will make harder to defend the specification of a deficient product. This is not a change in the law. The standard by which a designer will be judged remains that set out in *Nye Saunders* v. *Alan E. Bristow* (1987)[12]:

> The courts approach the matter upon the basis of considering whether there was evidence that at the time a responsible body of architects would have taken the view that the way in which the subject of inquiry had carried out his duties was an appropriate way of carrying out the duty, and would not hold him guilty of negligence merely because there was a competent body of competent professional opinion which held that he was at fault.

In *Kelly* v. *City of Edinburgh District Council* (1983)[13] it was held that departure from a code is not proof of negligence by a designer.

10.4.7 Thus, failure to specify a CE-marked product, even though that mark creates a presumption of fitness in the product's favour, is not necessarily evidence of negligence by the specifier. The specification of a non-CE-marked product would be tenable if its technical performance satisfied the essential requirements and was no less rigorous than equivalent CE-marked products. What would be harder to argue is that the inferiority or inadequacy of the specified products regarding one or more of the essential requirements is irrelevant to an assessment of the specifier's professional standards. This can be regarded as a consequence of the regulations, although not a departure in the law. In this respect regard should be had in specification to compliance with what the mark signifies, as set out in Article 4, paragraph 2, of the Directive (see Section 3.5):

(*a*) That [the products] comply with the relevant national standards transposing the harmonized European standards,

(*b*) That [the products] comply with a European technical approval with the essential requirements, *or*

(*c*) That [the products] comply with national technical specifications approved by the Commission as conforming with the essential requirements, where no harmonized specifications exist.

The mark also means that the product has been subjected to the requisite attestation of conformity provisions (see Section 3.8). Satisfaction of these requirements would certainly strengthen the position of the specifier in resisting any claim or allegation of failure in professional duty. The presence or absence of the CE mark can only be indicative rather than conclusive in this respect, as is discussed in this and the succeeding paragraph.

10.4.8 Another point which must be understood by designers is that the specification of CE-marked products is not definitive of their professional obligations. Just as specification of a non-CE-marked product is not necessarily negligence, so specification of a CE-marked product does not mean that professional obligations have been satisfied. Regulations, standards and codes are not co-extensive with the standards required of a designer by the law. It is axiomatic that any given design task might require standards well in excess of the general fitness as regards the essential requirements which is the meaning of the CE mark. The courts have often held that adherence to minimum standards required under statute does not automatically mean that a professional designer has not been negligent. In *McLaren Maycroft and Co.* v. *Fletcher Development Co. Ltd.* (1973)[(14)] in the New Zealand Court of Appeal, it was held that general compliance with current practice might fall short of what the situation demanded. In *Eames London Estates Ltd* v. *North Hertfordshire District Council* (1981)[(15)] the Official Referee had to assess the professional standards of an architect whose work had been accepted by the local authority as complying with the building regulations. When the building failed, the architect was adjudged negligent: 'An architect cannot shed his responsibility for foundations by ascertaining what will get by the local authority as this architect seems to have done.'

10.5 CONCLUSIONS

10.5.1 Just as a supplier cannot be guilty of an offence simply because he supplies a non-CE-marked product, so a designer cannot be liable in negligence simply because he specifies a non-CE-marked product. Nevertheless, a designer needs to consider the suitability of his product and is likely to find it hard to defend the specification of a product which has failed if it is deficient or significantly inferior to a CE-marked equivalent as regards the essential requirements.

10.5.2 However, the specification of CE-marked products does not release the designer from the primary professional obligation to the client of using reasonable care and skill and exercising judgement with those attributes. The presence of a CE mark does not necessarily indicate that the product meets the individual needs of the project or will perform as the client requires. It speaks only to general fitness within the meaning of the essential requirements, and should not be treated as some form of general excuse.

References: 10 The Construction Products Regulations and post-construction liability

1. Barber, J. (1992) *Quality Management in Construction: Contractual Aspects,* Construction Industry Research and Information Association Special Publication 84.

2. Council Directive of 21 December 1988 on the approximation of laws, regulations and administrative provisions of the Member States relating to construction products (89/106/EEC) *Official Journal*, L 40, 11 February 1989.

3. Construction Products Regulations 1991, SI 1991, No. 1620.

4. Department of the Environment (1990) *Implementation of the EC Directive on Construction Products: An explanatory and consultative note.*

5. Department of the Environment (1991), *European Economic Community: Directive 89/106/EEC Construction Products,* Circular 13/91.

6. (1984) 27 *Building Law Reports* 98.

7. (1979) 14 *Building Law Reports* 70.

8. (1981) 19 *Building Law Reports* 99.

9. (1989) 47 *Building Law Reports* 113.

10. (1986) 38 *Building Law Reports* 36.

11. (1975) 1 *Weekly Law Reports* 1095.

12. (1987) 37 *Building Law Reports* 93.

13. (1983) 5 *Scottish Law Times* 593.

14. (1973) *New Zealand Law Reports* 100.

15. (1981) 259 *Estates Gazette* 491.

11 The changing face of European post-construction liability

11.0 OVERVIEW

11.0.1 EC legislation has changed potential post-construction liability in the UK through the Consumer Protection Act 1987, which implemented the Product Liability Directive. Under this Act, compensation is available from a manufacturer or importer for defects, irrespective of the fact that they have been guilty of no fault or blameable conduct. This kind of liability is found in the English law of contract but not, on the whole, in the law of tort. The Act also introduced time-limits for liability, including a period after which rights of action are extinguished. This represents a departure from English law towards continental practice.

11.0.2 There are indications that the Commission may seek to change UK post-construction liability to bring it into line with that of other Member States. A proposal for a directive regulating the liability of providers of services if their service causes damage also proposed time-limits for action. A time-limit of 10 years is proposed for services relating to the design or construction of immovable property. In his report to the Commission in 1990, Claude Mathurin called for the harmonization of liabilities between developers and producers, the harmonization of financial protection for home owners, and uniformity in public works contract documents and building control documents. Progress of the Mathurin proposals has been stalled by conflicting views between Member States, although the draft Services Liability Directive contains proposals for fixed limitation periods that are in accordance with the Mathurin approach. In 1991 the First General Directive for the Mutual Recognition of Qualifications came into force in the UK, a sectoral directive of this nature on architects having been implemented in 1987. Mathurin expressed a preference for a system of required qualifications for producers, including both professionals and contractors, and this can be seen as a step in this direction through the mutual recognition of qualifications. The situation in the area of post-construction liability remains fluid and it can be expected that further developments that accord to some extent with the Mathurin proposals may appear in future EC legislation. These may not be concerned specifically with construction, but could take the form of more general directives that have implications for the industry.

11.1 EFFECT OF THE EC UPON UK POST-CONSTRUCTION LIABILITY

11.1.1 The starting-point of this section must be the recognition that European legislation has already changed the potential legal liability and hence the risk exposure of the participants in all manufacturing industries, including the construction products manufacturing industry. The Consumer Protection Act 1987, passed, at least in so far as Part I is concerned, as a direct and mandatory response to the Product Liability Directive, introduced major changes, both conceptual and practical, into the law of obligations of this country. Section 2 (1) of the Act states that 'where any damage is caused wholly or partly by a defect in a product, every person to whom Section (2) below applies, shall be liable for the damage'.

Section (2) includes the producer of the product, any person putting his name on it or using a trademark in relation to it, and any importer of the product into a Member State from a place outside the Member States in the course of a business. Although Section 4 creates defences based upon compliance with legislation or EC obligations, non-supply, private (non-business) supply, absence of defect, the state of scientific and technical knowledge, and the incorporation of the product into a subsequently defectively designed product, the burden of proof is upon the 'person proceeded against' to show the defence. This is a species of strict liability in that no negligence on the part of the defendant need be shown in order to establish liability. Compensation is available from a manufacturer or importer irrespective of the fact that they have been guilty of no fault or blameable conduct. This is the kind of liability found in the English law of contract but not, on the whole, in the law of tort, where there is no privity of contract between plaintiff and defendant, as between manufacturer and user of a product. Certainly it was alien to the law of product liability, which would deny a remedy in the absence of privity of contract or fault.

11.1.2 The Consumer Protection Act has also changed the law relating to the duration of liability. Schedule 1 of the Act contains two periods of time. The first follows existing provision in English law. The second represents a radical departure in favour of the time-limits of continental jurisprudence. The three-year period of limitation from whichever is the later of

- the date on which the cause of action accrued, and
- the date of knowledge of the loss or injury by the plaintiff,

is familiar in two ways. The three-year period existed under the Limitation Act 1980, which the Consumer Protection Act amends, in respect of personal injury actions. The provision is even closer to the alternative (to the basic six-year period) three-year period dating from actual or constructive knowledge introduced by the Latent Damage Act 1986, as a result of the well-known House of Lords decision in *Pirelli General Cable Works Ltd* v. *Oscar Faber and Partners* (1983)[(1)].

11.1.3 The second time-limit is, however, a complete departure from existing English law. The 'long-stop' period, meaning the provision which 'shall operate to extinguish a right of action . . . whether or not that right of action had accrued or time . . . had begun to run' is set at 15 years under the Latent Damage Act 1986. Under the Consumer Protection Act 1987, it is set at 10 years. This figure is of a far greater significance than a tacit acceptance that the 15-year period may be too long and, thus, unduly generous to the plaintiff. The significance is symbolic. Decennial liability is commonplace in civil law systems like the French. The responsibility of producers under the French Civil Code of Napoleon, which governs post-construction liability, includes the following provisions:

- Article 1792 *Si l'édifice construit a prix fait, périt en tout ou en partie par le vice de la construction, même par le vice du sol, les architectes et entrepreneurs en sont responsables pendant dix ans*

  being approximately translated:

  if a building constructed at fixed price, fails completely or in part as a result of defective construction, or through a defect in ground conditions, the designers and builders are responsible for a period of ten years,

- Article 2270 *Après dix ans, l'architecte et les entrepreneurs sont décharges de la garantie des gros ouvrages qu'ils ont faits ou diriges*

  being approximately translated:

  After ten years, the designer and builders are discharged from their liability in respect of serious defects which they have created or directed.

11.2 THE PROJECTED HARMONIZATION AND UNIFORMITY OF EC POST-CONSTRUCTION LIABILITY

11.2.1 It would be simplistic indeed to deduce from the choice of a ten-year limitation period in the Consumer Protection Act that the Commission proposes to change UK post-construction liability to bring it into line with that of France and other Member States. But there are other indications that this may well be the direction of the medium-term future. A 'straw in the wind' is perhaps to be found in Articles 9 and 10 of a proposal for a directive regulating the liability of providers of services if their service causes damage to individuals or private property, published on 20 December 1990 and circulated for consultation by the Department of Trade and Industry during January and February 1991. While the basic periods are three years from awareness of damage and five years (expiry of liability), separate note is made that 'periods of between 10 and 20 years are applied for services relating to the design and construction of buildings'. Article 10 in the draft makes no reference to 20 years or indeed anything between 10 and 20 years. It *does* provide that the basic limitation period of 3 years 'shall be extended to 10 years where the service relates to the design or construction of immovable property'.

11.2.2 The most profound indication of the intended direction of at least some of the Commission's strands of opinion was the Mathurin Report[2]. Claude Mathurin, a French engineer, was employed as special adviser to the EC, to advise on national post-construction liability systems and possibilities for harmonization at Community level. His final report, published in Brussels in February 1990, was a response to a resolution adopted by the European Parliament on 12 October 1988 calling for the standardization of contracts and controls in the construction industry, and the harmonization of responsibilities. M. Mathurin's brief, following his digest of national systems of Member States, *Controls, Contracts, Liability and Insurance in the Construction Industry*, was to investigate four issues defined by the Commission in the form of questions for investigation:

- Is there a need to harmonize/achieve uniformity?
- If so, is it achievable?
- If it is achievable, what should be the basic concepts?
- What proposals will achieve the desired result?

11.2.3 Mathurin began his report by outlining the complications caused by disparities between the contractual, building control, liability and insurance systems of the Member States. Table 21 illustrates this point.

Table 21 Some comparisons between EC construction law systems

Technical	Basic control by building control authority – approval of design	Basic duration of contractor's liability in contract*	Basic duration of designer's post-construction liability*	Post-construction liability insurance by architects
Belgium	No	10 years	10 years	Compulsory
Denmark	Yes	5 years (some variation)	5 years or less by contract	Voluntary – common
France	No	10 years	10 years	Compulsory
Germany	Yes	5 years	5 years to 2 under contract	Compulsory in some Länder; common elsewhere
Greece	Yes	15 months	Restricted liability	Rare and expensive
Ireland	Yes	6 or 12 years	No limit	Yes, but expensive
Italy	No	10 years	No liability	Rare and expensive
Luxembourg	No	10 years	10 years' work	For some
Netherlands	Yes	10 years	Restricted liability	Generally
Portugal	No	5 years	Restricted liability	Rare
Spain	No	10 years	No liability	Exists
** UK	Yes	6 or 12 years	15 years	Voluntary – common

* Note that these periods are intended to be indicative only. Before they can be used or in any way relied upon information would have to be obtained on the legal rules relating to commencement of the period (e.g. on accrual of the cause of action) in the jurisdiction in question.

** Note that there are differences in Scots limitation law from the rest of the UK.

Source: Utilising C Mathurin, *Controls, Contracts, Liability and Insurance in the Construction Industry.*

11.2.4 Mathurin's general recommendations to overcome the problems and their inhibition of the free market were as follows:

(i) Achieve uniformity of contractual documents in public sector works,

(ii) Achieve uniformity of building control documentation, e.g. building regulations applications, approvals, etc.,

(iii) Move towards harmonization of liabilities as between developers and producers,

(iv) Move towards harmonization of financial protection for home-owners.

11.2.5 It is in the specific proposals for (iii) above that evidence of a new regime of uniform post-construction liability can be found. Mathurin's proposal was the introduction of a 10-year liability for producers of buildings. This was to be backed by insurance attached to every new building or engineering works. Additionally, a mandatory latent defects insurance scheme should be introduced for housing, and mandatory project insurance for producers should also be introduced. Ten-year liability should be introduced for subcontractors and suppliers. The close similarity of Mathurin's system to the French system of compulsory property insurance set up under the Loi Spinetta (the Law of Spinetta) of 4 January 1978 is very obvious. It seeks to avoid the complex issues of liability of the Anglo-Saxon systems by making available to purchasers and subsequent purchasers of buildings the benefit of property insurance which will pay out for essential repairs rapidly and without proof of negligence. Consequential economic loss is not covered, but is available as an extra offered by insurers to 'bolt on' to the standard cover. The producers (the contractors and the designers) are required to be insured to cover their decennial liability and the property insurers can recover against that insurance. The UK development and construction sectors had been interested in insurance-based models for some time and it perhaps is no coincidence that the advent of the BUILD[3] scheme dates from the period of the preparation of the Mathurin report.

11.2.6 In the event, the progress of the Mathurin proposals was stalled by conflicting views of representatives of the Member States (see below). The Community split almost evenly between those who approved harmonization, Belgium, France, Spain, Portugal, Italy and Luxembourg, and those with reservations of varying degrees, namely Denmark, Germany, Ireland, the UK, Greece and the Netherlands. Those who opposed the introduction of civil law provisions through EC legislation into the UK's legal system saw the resistance to the Mathurin scheme as encouraging. This is a matter of opinion depending upon political philosophy and personal interest. The ten-year limitation period *beginning on the day on which the plaintiff became aware or should reasonably have become aware of the damage, service and identity of supplier*, contained in Article 10 of the draft Services Liability Directive, where the service relates to the design or construction of immovable property, post-dates the Mathurin Report and the resistance to it, but it was an important step towards the decennial liability of building producers advocated by Mathurin.

11.2.7 Another important step along the route to uniformity in this area was the passing of the European Communities (Recognition of Professional Qualifications) Regulations 1991[4], which came into force (in the main) on 17 April 1991. These arranged for the recognition of professional qualifications on a reciprocal basis in Member States, thus making transnational practice between the professionals of Member States genuinely viable. The Architects Directive which achieved the same purpose for that profession was implemented by statutory instrument in the UK in November 1987. This corresponds very closely with Mathurin's expressed preference for a system of required qualification for producers, including professionals, with reciprocal agreements for common recognition between Member States. Mathurin expressed a desire for that system to cover contractors as well.

11.2.8 Following Mathurin's completion of his report, published in February 1990, a number of attempts have been initiated in Brussels to move forward the process of harmonization. A meeting of the Group on Regulations, Information and Management on Liability, Guarantees and Insurance in the EC Construction Industry (GRIM) was held in Brussels in October 1990 to discuss a Commission Working Document (on possible action to be taken on harmonization of responsibilities, guarantees and insurance in the construction industry)[5]. It was at this meeting that the split was revealed fully between those who approved the principle of harmonization and those who (at least) required further proof of the need for it. Mathurin has also sought to advance his views by privately producing proposals for a directive for the construction sector.[6]

11.2.9 An initiative seeking to break the log-jam was the commissioning in 1991 of four Drafting Groups by the Division DG111/D in Brussels to produce a draft Construction Liability Directive. These groups were to receive contributions from the pan-EC interest groups but to produce their own reports. The tasks of the groups can be summarized as follows:

Group 1 Procedure for acceptance and determination of the commencement date for liability period,

Group 2 Responsibility and legal liability,

Group 3 Nature of insurance-backed warranty,

Group 4 Insurance backing.

It was intended that reports on the draft Directive should be available to DG 111/D by October 1991. This deadline was not achieved. Nevertheless, there are informal indications of progress towards overcoming the difficulties created by the wide disparity of existing domestic provision and by entrenched sectional interest[7]. During 1992 the reports have been produced forming the basis for consultation on the draft Directive.

11.3 CONCLUSIONS

11.3.1 Having described in Section 10 the potential effects of the Construction Products Regulations upon the legal position of suppliers and upon post-construction liability of producers more generally, it has been the purpose of Section 11 to adduce evidence that the position is not static, and that it is a misconception to see resistance to the comprehensive Mathurin scheme as resulting in a perpetuation of the status quo in the UK. Legislative changes have occurred in the Product Liability Directive and the Construction Products Directive and the UK implementations of these directives in the Consumer Protection Act and the Construction Products Regulations. They continue to be brought forward in other directives like the 1989 Directive on Recognition of Professional Qualifications and the consequent European Communities (Recognition of Professional Qualifications) Regulations 1991, and the proposed Directive on Services Liability which are of general application. The tendency of this legislation is to alter domestic UK law relating to the legal liability of suppliers and other parties to the construction process.

11.3.2 Evidence was adduced in this section of some of the difficulties relating to harmonization, particularly in such areas as scope of liability and commencement and duration of limitation periods. Nevertheless, the continuing initiatives in Brussels, specifically by DG 111/D, make progress probable in the medium term towards greater harmonization.

References: 11 The changing face of European post-construction liability

1. (1983) 1 *All England Law Reports* 65.

2. Commission of the European Communities, *Controls, Contracts, Liability and Insurance in the construction industry in the European Community,* 1990, III/3908/88-EN; *Study of Responsibilities, Guarantees and Insurance in the Construction Industry with a view to harmonization at Community Level,* 1990, III/8326/89–EN.

3. National Economic Development Office (1988), *Building Users' Insurance against Latent Defects.*

4. European Communities (Recognition of Professional Qualifications) Regulations 1991, SI 1991, No. 824.

5. Commission of the European Communities, *Commission Working Document on possible action to be taken on the study of responsibilities, guarantees and insurance in the construction industry with a view to harmonization at Community level,* 1990, 111/3750/90 – EN Rev 1.

6. Mathurin, C. (1991), *Elements for a Specific Directive on the Construction Sector.*

7. Bishop, D. (1991), Letter to *Building*, 30 December.

Current position of EC legislation

This publication covers documents published in the *Official Journal* up to 9 July 1992. For other documents the situations is less precise as they enter the public domain at varying intervals after their production and there is no reference list that can be checked. It must be emphasized that the situation described in the publication is continually evolving and that it is necessary for the reader to update that described here. This section describes the state of the major pieces of legislation when this publication went to press.

Technical harmonization

Construction Products Directive (Section 3): Implementation date 27 June 1991. The Construction Products Regulations 1991 brought it into force in the UK on 27 December 1991. Subsequent administrative action will be needed on harmonized standards and the designation of approved bodies. The Interpretative Documents have substantially been drafted and await approval by the Standing Committee and publication in the *Official Journal* in 1992. Once these have been published, the Commission can give formal mandates to CEN for the production of harmonized European standards and to the European Organization for Technical Approvals for the production of guidelines for European technical approvals. The list of 'minor part' products and the list setting out which products are to follow which route for the attestation of conformity are awaited. Consequential on these is the designation of approved bodies and the tasks that they may undertake. In the absence of harmonized standards and technical approvals, the Directive provides for the recognition of testing and certification undertaken in the country of origin to the specifications of the country of destination.

The Standing Committee on Construction has accepted the following guidance papers, though with Spanish reservations concerning all guidance papers:

5. Information to accompany the EC mark for construction products
6. Guidelines for the designation of approved bodies for construction products
7. Guidelines for the performance of the Factory Production Control for construction products
8. Choice of conformity attestation procedure
9. Guidelines for the assessment of construction products by an approved certification body
10. Guidelines for the assessment and certification of the factory production control by an approved body.

Guidance papers 1, 2, 3, 4, and 11 had still to be accepted. These concern:

1. Treatment of so-called 'Local Products'
2. Application of the CE mark
3. Criteria for appreciation of Grey Area Products
4. Transposition of Directive 89/106/EEC into national law
11. Guidance paper on the reference to levels or classes for the essential requirements on works or for the characteristics of products.

Copies of the interpretative documents and the guidance papers are available from the Department of the Environment.

Gas Appliances Directive (Section 4.1): Implementation date 1 January 1992, with a transition period to 31 December 1995 during which products manufactured to existing regulations can be supplied. The UK Regulations to bring the Directive into force were made on 11 March 1992 and came into effect on 6 April 1992. The first group of notified bodies and the conditions for the appointment of others are identified in a consultation paper published in July 1991. The Hot-water Boilers Directive was adopted in May 1992.

Electromagnetic Compatibility Directive (Section 4.2): Implementation date 1 January 1992, with a transition period to 31 December 1995, during which products can be manufactured to existing regulations. The Commission produced an explanatory document in October 1991 to clarify aspects of the Directive, but this has no legal status. The first harmonized standards were approved in April 1992 and draft UK Regulations were published in July 1992.

Machinery Directive (Sections 4.3 and 5.2): Implementation date 1 January 1992, with a transition period to 31 December 1994 during which products can be manufactured to existing regulations. A consultation paper containing the draft UK Regulations is expected from the UK government. Work has commenced on drafting Category C standards for specific classes of machinery. A second amendment that would extend the scope of the Directive to encompass lifting machinery for persons has been proposed and negotiations are expected to begin on this in 1992. Proposals for Used Machinery and Lifts directives have been put forward.

Personal Protective Equipment (Section 5.3.3): Implementation date 1 July 1992, with a transition period to 31 December 1992 during which products can be manufactured to existing regulations.

CE Mark (Section 2.3.2): A proposal for a Council Regulation concerning the affixing and use of the CE mark on industrial products was submitted to the Council in June 1991. Once adopted, the Regulation would amend all existing directives so that they conform to its requirements. It is under discussion by the Council.

Health and Safety of Workers at Work

Implementation date for the *Framework* (Section 5.1.1), *Workplace* (Section 3.16), *Work Equipment* (Section 5.1.3), and *Personal Protective Equipment* (Section 5.3.2) directives is 31 December 1992. Consultation documents, which include draft regulations, were issued by the Health and Safety Executive on the Framework Directive in October 1991, the Work Equipment Directive in November 1991, the Use of Personal Protective Equipment Directive in December 1991, and the Workplace Directive in January 1992. The Home Office issued draft Fire Precautions Regulations and an associated Guidance Document in 1992.

The *Temporary or Mobile Construction Sites Directive* (Section 5.1.2) has still to be adopted. A Common Position was reached in December 1991. Its proposed date of implementation is 31 December 1993.

Public Procurement

Public Works (Section 7) and *Public Supplies* (Section 8.1) directives: Brought into force in the UK by administrative action on 18 July 1990 and 1 January 1989 respectively. The Award of Public Works and Public Supplies Contracts Regulations, which provide legislative backing for the administrative action and bring into force the *Public Works and Public Supplies Remedies Directive* (Section 7.6), came into force on 21 December 1991.

Utilities Directive (Section 8.3): Implementation date 1 July 1992. *Utilities Remedies Directive* (Section 8.3.7) implementation date 1 January 1993.

Proposed Public Services directives: The modified proposals for a *Public Services* (Section 8.2) Directive reached a Common Position in February 1992. A *Utilities Services* (Section 8.3.6) Directive was formally proposed in December 1991.

Updating the information

Information can be obtained from:

- Department of the Environment's *Euronews Construction.*

- Department of Trade and Industry's *Europe Open for Business* series of booklets and 1992 Hotline (071-200 1992).

- The lead ministry for any area of legislation of interest. These are:

  - Construction Products Directive and the Construction Products Regulations 1991 – *Department of the Environment*

  - Gas Appliances, Electromagnetic Compatibility, Machinery, Personal Protective Equipment directives and general aspects of technical harmonization policy – *Department of Trade and Industry*

  - Public procurement, including the Public Supply Contracts Regulations 1991 and the Public Works Contracts Regulations 1991 – *Treasury*

  - Health and Safety of Workers at Work – *Health and Safety Commission.*

- European documentation centres. There are approximately 60 of these, mainly in university libraries. They are open to members of the public who wish to consult EC documents, such as the *Official Journal.*

- *Official Journal.* The L series records the legislation adopted and the C series proposals and other communications. There is no regular reprinting of proposals as they pass through the different legislative stages so that the situation can have changed since that published in the *Official Journal.*

- British Standards Institution for information about the activities of CEN and about European and harmonized European standards.

- British Board of Agrément for the activities of the European organization for Technical Approvals and European technical approvals.

- Trade associations for information concerning any specific products, such as the approach to be adopted for the attestation of conformity and technical specification.

Table of authorities

EC legislation, proposed legislation and policy documents

UK statutes, statutory instruments, draft regulations, and circulars

Cases

Standards

Index

12 Postscript

The Postscript discusses the main changes that took place between the completion of the final report in July 1992 and July 1993.

12.1 TECHNICAL HARMONIZATION

12.1.1 Single Internal Market

12.1.1.1 An advisory committee to the Commission on the Single Internal Market has been established[1]. Membership comprises two representatives from each Member State, with a representative of the Commission chairing it. It can be consulted on any practical problem concerning the functioning of the Internal Market. Its members can ask that the Committee is consulted by the Commission on any matter falling within its jurisdiction. Working groups can be established and experts may be invited to contribute to the discussion on specific items. At various points in the Report it was noted that there are problems with the interfaces between various Single Internal Market measures. An advisory committee of this nature could perform a useful function in coming to terms with these.

12.1.1.2 Many of the Single Internal Market measures adopted provide scope for Member States to determine exactly how they are to be brought into force within their jurisdictions. In consequence, there are likely to be differences in the solutions adopted by different Member States. It would be desirable for Member States to be aware of what others are doing and for good practice to become more widely known. A scheme has been set up with a budget of 17.3 million ECU for exchanges of officials engaged in Internal Market implementation[2]. This is intended to develop a convergent approach to the implementation of measures, to build mutual confidence between the Member States, and permit cross-fertilization.

12.1.1.3 In June 1992 the EC adopted the General Product Safety Directive with the aim of ensuring that products placed on the market are safe[3]. It will apply where there are no specific Community provisions governing the safety of products. Producers are obliged to place only safe products on the market and to provide consumers with relevant information to enable them to assess the risks inherent in a product. Products are deemed to be safe if they comply with national rules or, in their absence, European standards or technical specifications, national standards, or codes of good practice. Member States can still take action against products conforming to such specifications if there is evidence that they are a danger to the health and safety of consumers. They are to establish authorities to monitor compliance with the Directive. These are to have the power to take appropriate measures, including organizing checks on product safety, securing information, imposing prior conditions before a product may be marketed, ensuring that those at potential risk receive warnings, and prohibiting and securing the withdrawal of products from the market. The Directive incorporates provisions from earlier measures by which Member States notify the Commission when they take steps to restrict the placing of a product on the market and the Commission informs other Member states where it considers such action to be justified. The Directive does not seek to harmonize national rules on product safety and does not contain any explicit reference to attestation of conformity. However, it should help to identify instances where Member States take discriminatory action against products under the guise of action to secure consumer safety and where national safety rules have discriminatory effect. The Directive is to be brought into force by Member States by 29 June 1994 and the UK intends to issue a consultation paper concerning this during 1993.

12.1.1.4 The New Approach directives and the General Product Safety Directive ought to result in safe products being manufactured in EC for marketing therein. However, problems could still arise with products imported from third countries as the production facilities do not lie within the EC's jurisdiction. The EC has therefore taken steps to tighten controls over the importation of potentially dangerous products from third countries. In a Recommendation in November 1992 the Commission invited Member States to set up infrastructures needed to identify dangerous products at the external frontiers[4]. It was followed by a Council Regulation in February 1993[5]. This requires Member States to:

- inform the Commission of actions taken to prevent the release of dangerous products, with the Commission in turn notifying the other Member States;
- mark products that present a serious risk as being unauthorized for free circulation;
- take appropriate action against products that do not comply with Community or national rules on product safety, which may include prohibiting them from being placed on the market.

12.1.2 CE Mark

12.1.2.1 It was noted in section 2.1.3 that problems had arisen with the New Approach to Technical Harmonization and Standards as a result of differences between directives in the rules governing the use of the CE mark. The Commission proposed to tackle this through a regulation governing the use of the CE mark (section 2.3.2) and has now submitted proposals for a Directive and a Council Decision to modify each of the existing New Approach directives, the Low Voltage Directive, and the Council Decision on a Modular Approach to Conformity Assessment[6]. A common position was reached on 14 June 1993. These contain proposals for a number of detailed changes to each of the New Approach directives adopted to date, including the Construction Products, Gas Appliances, Electromagnetic Compatibility, Machinery, Personal Protective Equipment, and Hot Water Boilers Directives, as well as for six other directives not considered in detail in this Report. It also will bring the Low Voltage Directive within the scope of the CE marking procedures. The proposals are also designed to amend the Modular Approach Decision so that it contains standard procedures for the use of the CE mark to be incorporated into future directives and to bring the existing New Approach directives into line with these new arrangements. Departures from these proposals in future New Approach directives will have to be explicitly justified by special circumstances.

12.1.2.2 The principal proposals are:

- *To replace the term 'EC mark' by 'CE mark'.*
- *To introduce consistency in the treatment of transitional periods.* Directives such as the Construction Products, Machinery, Simple Pressure Vessels, Personal Protective Equipment, and Gas Appliances Directives contain the provision that the application of the CE mark requires the product also to conform to the requirements of other appropriate directives. However, a number of these directives contain transitional periods, during which manufacturers can choose either to comply with the directive or with a Member State's existing regulations. The measure proposes that the CE mark is affixed irrespective of which solution the manufacturer has adopted during the transitional period of other appropriate directives, even though this may mean that the provisions of these other directives are not fulfilled. The CE mark is to indicate that the requirements only of those directives applied by the manufacturer have been met. The documentation accompanying the product must give particulars of these directives.
- *Consistent treatment as to the size and shape of the CE mark, together with who is to affix it and when it is to be affixed.*
- *The identification of any body involved in the production control stage, for example in type-testing or certification.*
- *The allowing of other marks to be affixed alongside the CE mark, providing that they are not likely to be confused with it, render it illegible, or affect its visibility.* Trade marks similar to the CE mark, if they are used for the purpose of misleading, are to be outlawed.

- *Consistency in what the CE mark means so that all directives make it clear that the person affixing the mark has verified that the product conforms to all the requirements of a directive.* Some of the directives do not make it explicit that affixing the CE mark is to mean that all the provisions of a directive have been met, including attestation of conformity requirements as well as compliance with technical specifications.

- *Identification numbers to be assigned to approved or notified bodies involved in the production control phase and to European technical approvals bodies, with the Commission publishing lists of such bodies and their numbers.* Such bodies will have the same number irrespective of how many or which directives they are notified under. Member States are to notify each other of such bodies as well as the Commission.

- *Changes in the way that Member States are to respond to infringements of the CE mark.* These will permit Member States to set conditions to oblige manufacturers of non-conforming products to meet the requirements of appropriate directives. However, if the non-conformity continues Member States are to restrict or prohibit the product being placed on the market or ensure that it is withdrawn. The rewording implies that Member States can adopted a graduated and flexible response to infringements rather than just forbidding the use of the CE mark and requiring unsold products to be withdrawn. The proposals drop the requirements that Member States shall inform each other and the Commission of their actions. The Economic and Social Committee has however expressed concerned that the change may mean that Member States will not be sufficiently rigorous in rooting out infringements[7].

12.1.2.3 Once these proposals are adopted, the UK will need to amend the Construction Products, Gas Appliances, Machinery, Electromagnetic Compatibility, and Personal Protective Equipment Regulations. Member States are to adopt the provisions necessary to comply with the proposed Directive by 1 July 1994 and to apply them from 1 January 1995. Products produced under the New Approach directives that the proposals will amend can be placed on the market under their current marking provisions until 1 January 1997. The Commission is to produce by 1997 a report on any special problems raised by the incorporation of the Low Voltage directive into the CE marking procedures and any problems raised by overlapping Council directives[8].

12.1.2.4 The UK government has been involved in a dispute with the Commission as to whether the CE mark is mandatory for construction products. However, one of the proposed amendments to the Modular Approach Decision would appear to resolve any ambiguity concerning whether the CE mark will be mandatory for products covered by any future New Approach directive. It states that any industrial product covered by the technical harmonization directives must bear the CE mark. Specific directives may provide otherwise if appropriate grounds can be found, but as a derogation from 'cumbersome' conformity evaluation, though not from the marking provisions. However, this does not affect existing directives, such as the Construction Products Directive.

12.1.3 Interchange of Information on Technical Standards and Regulations

12.1.3.1 The Commission has proposed a number of amendments to the Directive on the Provision of Information in the Field of Technical Standards and Regulations (see Section 2.2.2). The Commission's proposals[9] are concerned with the following issues.

- *Defining more precisely the categories of technical specifications that fall within the jurisdiction of the Directive.* The proposals make it clear that the relevant technical specifications also include ones concerning the name under which a product is sold, conformity attestation procedures, production methods and processes, the protection of consumers and the environment, and those that affect the life cycle after a product has been placed on the market, such as conditions of use, maintenance, recycling, reuse and disposal. For example, problems have arisen with national regulations requiring the use of recyclable packaging and tax incentives for environmentally friendly vehicles, which Member States have not considered to be technical regulations within the scope of the Directive.

- *Defining de facto technical regulations.* De facto as well as de jure regulations were included within the scope of the 1983 Directive, but were not defined. The present proposals define them so as to include professional codes, codes of practice, technical specifications and requirements referred to in laws or regulations, voluntary agreements with which a public authority is associated, and technical specifications with which compliance is encouraged, particularly by fiscal or financial measures, even though compliance is not mandatory.

- *Introducing less cumbersome procedures to amend the official lists of European and national standardization bodies.* In July 1992 the list of European standardization bodies was amended so as to include the European Telecommunications Standards Institute (ETSI) alongside CEN and CENELEC[10].

- *Ensuring that proper communication of standardization work and technical regulations takes place.* There has been criticism that the requirements of the 1983 Directive have not been fully adhered to. It is proposed to abolish the current detailed procedural requirements that it contains and replace them by powers for the Commission to draw up rules for disclosure. The proposals would strengthen the obligations on Member States to require their standardization bodies to comply with the rules and not to prejudice European standardization, including requiring Member States not to recognise or use any national standard adopted in breach of the Directive. The proposals strengthen the obligations on Member States to communicate drafts of technical regulations to the Commission. The Commission has in the past stated that it regards technical regulations adopted without it being notified or respecting the standstill period as invalid and that national courts should refuse to enforce them[11], and this measure would give substantive support to this view.

- *Extending the period of time during which the Commission or another Member State can take action on a proposed technical regulation.* Member States will not be able to adopt technical regulations once the Council has adopted a common position on a proposal from the Commission and must postpone adoption for 18 months if the Commission finds that a proposed regulation concerns a matter for which a proposal has already been presented to the Council. These periods reflect the experience of the length of time needed for a measure to be adopted.

It is proposed that these amendments should take effect from 1 January 1994.

12.1.3.2 There is evidence that, in spite of problems encountered, European standardization has begun to make a significant impact. New European and national standardization activities increased from 3514 in 1988 to 10 210 in 1991, with the national shares of these activities falling from 75.8% in 1987 to 21.5% in 1991[12]. There are marked differences in the trends in national standardization activities between Member States, with approximately one-third of new national activities being French and declining activity in Britain and Germany. An idea of the scale of notification of technical regulations can be gained from the fact that the Commission received 365 draft technical regulations in 1990 and 435 in 1991, mainly from France, Germany, and the UK.

12.1.4 Mutual Recognition of Testing and Certification

The laboratory accreditation bodies in the EC and EFTA have established the Western European Calibration Cooperation (WECC) and the Western European Laboratory Accreditation Cooperation (WELAC) to coordinate their activities in the areas of calibration laboratory and testing laboratory accreditation respectively[13]. WECC was recognised as an agreement group by EOTC in September 1992 and similar status is being sought for WELAC. The members of both bodies accredit laboratories using the criteria in EN 45001 and ISO Guide 25, with the members operating to the requirements of EN 45002 and EN 45003. WECC has been signed by the accreditation bodies of Denmark, Finland, France, Germany, Italy, the Netherlands, Norway, Sweden, Switzerland, and the UK and WELAC by those of Denmark, France, the Netherlands, Spain, Sweden, and the UK.

12.1.5 Construction Products

Construction Products Directive

12.1.5.1 The essential requirements in the Construction Products Directive are to be given concrete form in a series of six Interpretative Documents (see Section 3.4). Until these have been adopted, formal mandates for harmonized standards cannot be finalised, European technical approvals granted, decisions made about which attestation of conformity route should be adopted for each product, or any construction product CE marked. It was intended that the Documents should have been adopted by June 1990 and, therefore, they are running more than three years behind schedule. The Standing Committee for Construction agreed the English language versions(14) in July 1993 and is expected to formally vote on them in the autumn of 1993. Each of the Interpretative Documents examines what is necessary for an essential requirement to be satisfied and the implications for construction products or parts of works. In a general introduction to the Documents, the Commission puts forward the view that they are evolving documents capable of further development(15). As the essential requirements are expressed in terms of objectives, the understanding given in the Interpretative Documents at a given moment could evolve due to technological development and the state of the art concerning construction products. Member States may request revisions in the Documents in order to accommodate proposed regulatory requirements for the performance of construction works within the scope of the essential requirements. The UK has taken the view that the Documents ought to anticipate the regulatory requirements of Member States. The six Documents have a common part dealing with their purpose and scope; levels or classes for essential requirements; definitions of terms, such as normal maintenance, intended use and economically reasonable working; life the basis for verification of the satisfaction of the essential requirement; technical specifications and guidelines for European technical approvals; and working life and durability(16). Once the Interpretative Documents have been adopted, many issues will still remain to be resolved. For example, the Department of the Environment has noted the potential difficulty where Member States have different requirements for attestation before products are permitted to be used in construction works(17).

12.1.5.2 Although in the absence of Interpretative Documents mandates for standards cannot be finalised, 33 end-use mandates covering the whole field of construction have been approved by the Standing Committee for Construction and the Advisory Committee of Standardization set up under Directive 83/189/EEC. Each identifies the specific products for which standards should be considered and 2000 to 2500 standards are likely to be proposed. The Commission has approved nearly 300 for funding, with work proceeding on 700 for which CEN was previously mandated(18).

12.1.5.3 The European Organization for Technical Approvals has been set up as a legal body under Belgian law and its statutes agreed (see section 3.7). The common procedural rules for granting European technical approvals have been endorsed by the Standing Committee for Construction(19). Applications are to be made by the manufacturer or his authorised agent in the EC. They may be made to just one ETA body and the manufacturer must confirm that this is the case. In the event of an ETA application not being accepted, the manufacturer can apply to another body. The applicant can receive an estimate of the time schedule for approval and its cost before making an application and must confirm that he will meet the cost. The application is to be accompanied by a description of the construction product, specifications, drawings and test reports, and a detailed explanation of the product and its intended use. The applicant must divulge the places of manufacture and ensure that these may be visited by the ETA body. Applicants have the duty to supply the ETA body with all necessary documentation for their task and to support the ETA body. The rules make it clear that the ETA is only concerned with the essential requirements and not with any wider fitness for purpose. Should these other aspects be taken into account, the assessment must clearly differentiate them from the essential requirements and such aspects of assessment are to be voluntary. The rules distinguish between ETAs granted with and without an ETA Guideline. Where there is a guideline, the ETA must correspond to it. There is a transitional period during which the comparability of the ETAs issued by approved bodies is investigated. Where an ETA is to be considered without a guideline, the approved body seeks the consent of the EOTA Technical Board to issue one, with the Commission giving the authority for one to be issued. There is consultation with other EOTA bodies involved in the subject area before testing and before the issuing of the ETA. Where procedures have been established for a product family, these are to be followed. ETAs have a life of up to five years but this can be extended, although the assessment should be as complete as the original one.

12.1.5.4 Article 16 of the Construction Products Directive sets out a procedure whereby, in the absence of European technical specifications, tests and certification can be carried out in the Member State of production in accordance with the specifications of the Member State of destination (see Section 3.15). The reports and attestations of conformity are to be accorded the same recognition by the latter as it would grant to its own corresponding national documents. The UK has successfully concluded the exchange of information necessary for the recognition by Spain of the certification of bond adherence of reinforcing steels by the UK Certification Authority for Reinforcing Steels[20].

Workplace Directive

12.1.5.5 There is an interface between the Construction Products Directive and the Workplace Directive, one of the health and safety at work directives (see section 3.16). The latter has requirements concerning the design and maintenance of workplaces, which have implications for the construction products used and the assembly of construction works. These dovetail with the essential requirements in the Construction Products Directive. The Workplace Directive was brought into force in the UK on 1 January 1993 by means of the Workplace (Health, Safety and Welfare) Regulations 1992 and its associated Approved Code of Practice (ACOP)[21]. The ACOP was made under the Health and Safety at Work Act 1974. Whilst failure to comply with its provisions is not in itself an offence, this could indicate a breach of the Regulations unless an employer has adopted an alternative means of complying with them. The Regulations came into force with respect to new, modified, extended, or converted workplaces from 1 January 1993 and will come into effect for existing workplaces from 1 January 1996. Until then existing legislation remains in force for the latter. Generally, and in contrast to the Directive, there are no substantive differences with respect to the requirements for new and existing workplaces other than the date of implementation. Modifications include any alteration but not a simple replacement. Conversions include large buildings converted into smaller industrial units, conversions of houses into workplaces, and changes of use involving structural alterations to workplaces. Workplaces are defined as being premises made available as a place of work, including access to them. They therefore include not only factories, shops, and offices but also hospitals, schools, hotels, nursing homes, places of entertainment, hostel kitchens, private roads and paths on industrial estates, and temporary work sites, though not construction sites which are the subject of a separate measure (see Section 12.1.10.3). Domestic and military premises are excluded from the Regulations.

12.1.5.6 The Regulations oblige employers to ensure that workplaces under their control comply with their requirements. The Health and Safety at Work Act 1974 places the obligations on employers to ensure the health, safety and welfare of their employees at work and on persons in control of non-domestic premises towards non-employees who use them. Landlords should ensure that common parts and facilities and access comply with the Regulations. Responsibility does not extend to areas which are not within an individual's control, for example, parts of premises let to a tenant. There are a number of specific requirements in the Regulations.

- Workplaces shall be maintained in an efficient state (from the viewpoint of health and safety) and in good repair and efficient working order. This also applies to any equipment necessary to ensure that the workplace is properly maintained, with proper systems of maintenance being installed as appropriate.

- Enclosed workplaces shall be ventilated by sufficient quantity of fresh or purified air.

- Temperatures inside buildings during working hours shall be reasonable.

- Every workplace shall have suitable and sufficient lighting.

- The workplace, furnishings and fittings shall be kept sufficiently clean. This includes that the surfaces of floors, walls and ceilings shall be capable of being kept sufficiently clean and may influence the choice of construction materials.

- Every room where people work shall have sufficient space for their health, safety and welfare.

- Every workstation shall be arranged so that it is suitable both for the person at work and for the work to be undertaken.

- Floors and surfaces of traffic routes shall be suitable for the purpose for which they are used, including not being uneven or slippery, having drainage where necessary, and not exposing persons to risk of falling.

- Effective measures are to be taken to protect persons from being injured by falling or being struck by a falling object.

- Windows, doors and walls containing translucent or transparent material shall be protected against breakage and marked so as to make them apparent.

- Windows, skylights and ventilators capable of being opened shall not expose persons to risk during opening or whilst being open.

- Windows and skylights shall be designed and constructed so that they may be cleaned safely, if necessary with the aid of equipment or devices.

- Workplaces shall be organised so that pedestrians and vehicles can circulate safely and traffic routes shall be sufficient in number, in suitable positions, and of sufficient size.

- Doors and gates shall be suitably constructed, with safety devices as necessary.

- Escalators and moving walkways shall function safely, be equipped with necessary safety devices, and accessible emergency stop controls.

- Suitable and sufficient sanitary conveniences shall be provided at accessible places and these must be adequately ventilated, lit, and be kept clean.

- Suitable and sufficient washing facilities shall be provided at accessible places, including in the immediate vicinity of sanitary conveniences and changing facilities, and shall include hot and cold water, soap, and means of drying.

- An adequate supply of wholesome drinking water shall be provided at readily accessible places.

- Suitable and sufficient accommodation shall be provided for clothing not worn during working hours and for special clothing worn just at work. There is an interface here with the Personal Protective Equipment at Work Regulations (see Section 12.1.9.4), which require employers to provide accommodation for personal protective equipment.

- Suitable and sufficient facilities shall be provided for persons to change clothing where special clothing has to be worn for work.

- Suitable and sufficient rest facilities shall be provided at readily accessible places. These shall include suitable facilities to eat meals and for pregnant women and nursing mothers, and shall protect non-smokers from discomfort caused by tobacco smoke.

12.1.6 Gas Appliances

The proposals for a Council Regulation on the CE mark (see Section 12.1.2) seek to bring about changes in certain of the attestation of conformity requirements in the Gas Appliances Directive[6]. These would amend the procedures for EC Verification and EC Unit Verification so that they are more closely aligned with modules F and G of the modular approach to conformity assessment (Sections 4.1.5.5 and 2.3.1.4).

12.1.7 Electromagnetic Compatibility

12.1.7.1 The UK brought the Electromagnetic Compatibility Directive (see Section 4.2.5) into force through the Electromagnetic Compatibility Regulations 1992[22]. These came into effect on 28 October 1992 and so do not apply to electrical apparatus supplied or taken into service before that date. The Regulations apply to electrical apparatus with an intrinsic function for the end user and supplied as a single commercial unit, which is an electrical or electronic appliance or a system. This includes apparatus supplied in kit form. The Regulations do not apply to components, spare parts, or installations of two or more items of apparatus not designed as a single functional unit by a manufacturer. Also excluded from the scope of the Regulations are second-hand apparatus, electromagnetically benign apparatus, apparatus for use in a sealed electromagnetic environment, military equipment, amateur radio equipment not available commercially, and apparatus wholly or partly covered by other directives, such as active implantable medical devices. Add-in printed circuit boards however are regarded as having an intrinsic function and so fall within the scope of the Regulations[23].

12.1.7.2 The Regulations require that apparatus shall not be supplied unless it

- conforms with the protection requirements;
- has met the conformity assessment requirements;
- has a correctly affixed CE mark;
- is accompanied by an EC declaration of conformity.

No person shall take apparatus into service unless it conforms to the protection requirements. However, such a person, unlike a manufacturer placing apparatus on the market, does not have to satisfy the Directive's conformity assessment or CE marking provisions. The protection requirements are that apparatus shall not generate electromagnetic disturbance that exceeds a level allowing other apparatus to operate as intended and has a level of intrinsic immunity which is adequate to enable it to operate as intended. Whether the level of intrinsic immunity is adequate depends on what level of performance is reasonably expected of the apparatus, the acceptable level of degradation of performance provided by the manufacturer, and the consequences of degradation of performance. Schedule 2 of the Regulations expands on the Directive by listing specific phenomena and effects that may be regarded as electromagnetic disturbance, though it should be noted that the list is not exclusive of other phenomena.

12.1.7.3 The Regulations create a number of offences including supplying or taking into service apparatus in a manner that does not comply with the Regulations, misuse of the CE mark, failure to retain documentation, contravention of prohibition or suspension notices, obstruction, and supplying false or misleading information. Penalties are comparable to those for similar offences created by the regulations bringing other New Approach directives into force, namely fines of up to level 5 and, in certain cases, liability to up to three months imprisonment. Enforcement, other than for wireless telegraphy and electricity meters, is by weights and measures authorities, which are granted similar powers to those given by the Consumer Protection Act 1987 (see Section 9.3). The DTI has noted that fines and costs likely to be awarded against companies may be small in comparison with the financial benefits to be gained from selling a product. However, it considers that the penalties are adequate since the product may also be forfeit and the manufacturer risks the loss of reputation.

12.1.7.4 The Regulations follow the Directive in providing for two main routes to attestation of conformity according to whether there is compliance or non- or partial compliance with harmonized European standards. In the latter case, the manufacturer is required to produce a technical construction file with a technical report or certification from a competent body. The Regulations define in general terms what technical construction files should contain. They include the requirement that those submitted to a UK competent body must be in English. The DTI has produced non-legally binding guidance on technical construction files for use by firms and competent bodies[24]. This includes suggestions as to what the technical construction file might contain in different circumstances, for example, where there are no applicable harmonized standards as opposed to where harmonized standards exist but cannot be tested due to the physical properties of the installation. The appointment and operations of competent bodies are determined in a similar fashion to the approved or notified bodies designated under other New Approach directives. The Regulations explicitly permit a competent body to refuse to consider an application on the grounds that its heavy workload would not enable this to be done within three months. They also set out how a competent body might use subcontractors to perform tests and undertake assessments. By May 1993 27 competent bodies had been appointed with the aim of avoiding any shortage of resources for certification. They include some manufacturing organizations. A condition of their appointment is that they must be willing to accept assessments of technical construction files from other manufacturers. This route to attestation of conformity may be forced upon suppliers of building services, who may assemble for their clients installations made up of separate items of apparatus designed to undertake a defined operation. There are problems in finding standards for large systems and, clearly, the interconnections between the parts need to be tested for electromagnetic compatibility.

12.1.7.5 CENELEC has produced guidance documents to assist in the use of standards to demonstrate compliance with the Directive(25). Three types of standard will be produced, generic, product-family, and product. Product-family and product standards will take precedence, with generic standards being used where these do not exist. It is likely that manufacturers will have to comply with several standards for a product, covering its electromagnetic immunity and different aspect of emission, such as harmonics, voltage fluctuations, and radio interference. There may be problems in selecting appropriate product or product-family standards for a given application, particularly for multi-function equipment. Generic standards contain a set of requirements and test procedures, which are applicable to all products or systems intended for use in an environment. Two environments have been chosen, residential, commercial and light industrial and industrial. The requirements are based on approved CENELEC and IEC standards. There are restrictions on the applicability of generic standards. Manufacturers using them are obliged to express performance criteria in a specific way which relates to the performance of their product, and this must be made available to users on request. Where certain tests are not carried out, the rationale for this is to be recorded in the test report. CENELEC has suggested that the test report should contain the identity of the manufacturer, descriptions of the apparatus, the standards applied, the tests carried out and their results, emission levels, any decisions not to carry out tests, and the signature of the responsible person. These suggestions raise some important implications that also arise with respect to the EC declaration of conformity, which also requires some of this information. The model description implies that judgement must be exercised by a manufacturer as to when a change in model has sufficient changes in electromagnetic emissions or immunity as to require retesting. The signature of a responsible person implies that there is a management system in place with clearly defined levels of responsibility, reporting, and control(26). A quality management system could assist in the achievement of both of these. There are likely to be limitations on manufacturers producing to generic standards. For example, the Directive permits Member States to apply special measures with regard to the taking into service of apparatus, to overcome problems with specific sites, and to protect public telecommunications and safety services. It is possible that equipment that legitimately bears the CE mark through compliance with generic standards could still be subject to such restrictions.

12.1.8 Machinery

Machinery Directive

12.1.8.1 The UK has brought both the Machinery Directive and its first amendment into force by means of the Supply of Machinery (Safety) Regulations 1992(27). These took effect on 1 January 1993 and apply to machinery supplied for the first time from that date. They implement the Directive's provisions concerning essential requirements, attestation of conformity, the appointment of approved bodies, and the transitional periods discussed in Sections 4.3 and 5.2. The Regulations use the term Schedule 4 machinery for that machinery described earlier in the Report as Annex IV machinery.

12.1.8.2 The Regulations make it an offence to supply machinery that is unsafe, fails to satisfy the essential safety requirements, has not satisfied the appropriate attestation of conformity procedures, does not have an EC declaration of conformity (unless it is for incorporation in another machine), or have a properly affixed CE mark. It is also an offence to affix a CE mark in contravention of the Regulations. These offences can carry penalties of up to three months imprisonment and/or a fine of level 5 on the standard scale. In addition, offences of affixing a mark that is capable of being confused with a CE mark, the failure to retain the technical file, or failure to supply information about a CE mark carry a penalty of a fine of up to level 5. Penalties can be applied to the officers of a body corporate that commits an offence. Enforcement of the Regulations is in the hands of two bodies. The Health & Safety Executive is responsible for enforcement where the machinery is used at work, using powers granted by the Health & Safety at Work Act 1974. The weights and measures authorities are to enforce the Regulations where machinery is supplied for private use or consumption, using powers granted by the Consumer Protection Act 1987 (see Section 9.3). An enforcement authority that takes action against any machinery is to notify the Secretary of State so that the Commission can be informed.

12.1.8.3 The Regulations contain a definition of supply that has important implications for the construction and property industries. Where persons manufacture or import machinery which they put into service for their own use, they are deemed to be supplying that machinery to themselves. Thus, they are defined as being suppliers of machinery and are subject to the same requirements as those placed on other suppliers. They may find themselves regarded as being manufacturers who must ensure that the machinery is safe and satisfies the Directive's essential requirements, attestation of conformity procedures, and CE marking requirements. This could apply to construction companies assembling or importing machinery for their own use or to landlords or tenants who install machinery in buildings.

12.1.8.4 As with the Gas Appliances (Safety) Regulations, the government has the power to appoint approved bodies, determine what services they can perform, and regulate their fees. The Regulations also provide for judicial review of their decisions provided that leave to apply to the Court is made promptly and within three months of the date when grounds for application first arose. CEN has produced a number of harmonized European standards and pre-standards, for example concerning safety distances between parts of human bodies and protection devices.

Machinery Directive Second Amendment

12.1.8.5 The second amendment to the Machinery Directive was adopted in June 1993[28] (see Section 5.2.5). This extends the scope of the Directive so as to include:

- cableways and lifts for carrying persons and goods, including construction site hoists;
- safety components.

The latter are defined as being components, that are not interchangeable equipment, that fulfil a safety function when in use and whose failure or malfunction endangers the safety or health of exposed persons. The revision makes it clear that the essential requirements for machinery also apply to safety components. Additional essential requirements are added for all types of machinery, including those relating to the risks of being trapped in a machine and the risk of slipping, tripping or falling. There are also changes made to the essential requirements that deal with the language of instructions so that, for example, maintenance instructions for specialised personnel employed by the manufacturer can be drawn up in a Community language they understand, which may not necessarily be the language of the country where the machinery is installed. There is a new class of essential requirements for the hazards of lifting or moving persons. These include requirements with respect to controls, for example so that excessive speeds do not cause hazards, risks of persons falling from the carrier, and risks of the carriers falling or overturning. Additions have been made to the list of Annex IV machinery ie the class of machinery with special attestation of conformity requirements. The list now includes devices for the lifting of persons involving a risk of falling from a vertical height of more than three metres and certain safety components, including roll-over protective structures (ROPS), falling-object protective structures (FOPS), and electro-sensitive devices designed to detect persons. Safety components require an EC declaration of conformity before they can be placed on the market but are not CE marked. The declaration includes the name and address of the manufacturer or his representative in the Community, a description of the component and the functions it fulfils, the standards and specifications used, and any notified body that has taken part in attestation of conformity. Member States are to adopt the amendment by 1 July 1994 with effect from 1 January 1995. There is a transitional period to 31 December 1996, during which period safety components and machinery for lifting or moving persons can comply with national provisions.

Proposed Lifts Directive

12.1.8.6 The Commission has put forward a number of amendments to the proposed Lifts Directive[29] (see Section 5.2.6). The amendments modify the coverage of the proposed Directive so that it is concerned with lifts in constructions as well as permanent buildings. The lifts covered must operate between rigid guides and can be used to carry goods instead of persons, provided that there is a cab with accessible operating controls that persons can get into. The changes here are due to the need not to overlap with the second amendment to the Machinery Directive. A new attestation of conformity procedure is introduced that gives the manufacturer the choice of combining the placing on the market and putting into service rather than having separate design and acceptance phase procedures. This is achieved by a notified body carrying out unit verification (module G) and by the manufacturer introducing a full quality assurance system (module H).

Use of Work Equipment Directive

12.1.8.7 The Machinery Directive is concerned with the manufacture and taking into service of machinery. There is an interface with the health and safety at work directives, which are concerned with the use of machinery in work. The principal interface is with the Work Equipment Directive (see Section 5.1.3), which was brought into force in the UK on 1 January 1993 by the Provision and Use of Work Equipment Regulations 1992. The Health and Safety Executive has produced guidance on these Regulations[30]. There are also interfaces with other health and safety directives. For example, the Workplace Directive (see Section 12.1.5.6) contains provisions concerning mechanically operated doors and windows and escalators and moving walkways and the Provision and Use of Work Equipment Regulations have requirements for lighting which may have implications for the design of the workplace. In due course, there will be an interface with the Construction Sites Directive (see Section 12.1.10.3), for example, on safety coordination between different employers on a site, particularly where work equipment is jointly used.

12.1.8.8 Work equipment is defined extremely broadly by the Provision and Use of Equipment Regulations as 'any machinery, appliance, apparatus or tool and any assembly of components which, in order to achieve a common end, are arranged and controlled so that they function as a whole.' Their use includes transporting, repairing, modifying, maintaining, and cleaning as well as use that is directly productive. The HSE Guidance suggests that structural items, such as walls, stairs and roofs are not work equipment, nor are substances such as cement. The obligations in the Regulations fall on all employers, the self-employed in respect of themselves, and on any person who has control of non-domestic premises made available as a place of work. Persons in control of non-domestic premises have a duty towards those who are not their employees but use their premises. This could apply to a landlord, for example, with respect to lifts or to a main contractor with respect to scaffolding. The Regulations apply to all industrial sectors except shipping and the military. The obligations fall into two principal sections. The first is concerned with the duties of employers and have been applicable since 1 January 1993. The second deals with characteristics that work equipment is to attain, with the date of implementation depending upon the date when the work equipment was made available for use.

12.1.8.9 There are a number of obligations on employers.

- Work equipment must be suitable for the purpose for which it is used or provided. This includes addressing the risks that are inherent in the equipment itself, where it is located, and the purpose for which it is used.

- Work equipment is to be maintained in an efficient state (from the viewpoint of health and safety), in efficient working order, and in good repair. Where there is a maintenance log, this is to be kept up to date.

- Where the use of work equipment involves a specific risk to health and safety, it is to be used only by those given responsibility to use it. Repairs, modifications and maintenance are to be restricted to those designated and trained for the purpose.

- All persons using work equipment, and their supervisors and managers, shall receive adequate health and safety information and instructions.

- All persons using work equipment, and their supervisors and managers, shall receive adequate training for health and safety purposes. This is to include training in the use of the equipment, the risks this entails, and the precautions to be taken.

12.1.8.10 The date for implementing the sections concerning the characteristics of work equipment varies according to whether the equipment is new or already in existence when the Regulations came into force. For new equipment the implementation date was from 1 January 1993. New equipment includes second-hand equipment, so that when a company purchases equipment from another, it must ensure that it satisfies the Regulations. Hired and leased equipment is treated in the same way as second-hand equipment. For equipment first provided for use before 1 January 1993, there is until 1 January 1997 to comply. Thus, employers have a four year transition period during which they can either replace their work equipment or to make such modifications as are necessary to ensure that it meets the Regulation's requirements. These are set out in Regulations 11 to 24 and are:

- that measures are taken to safeguard against risks to workers from dangerous parts of machinery by preventing contact with it;

- that there is adequate prevention of exposure to risk from specified hazards, namely falling or ejected items, rupture or disintegration of work equipment, equipment catching fire or overheating, unintended or premature discharges, and unintended or premature explosion of the equipment or items within it;

- that there is prevention of injury resulting from high or low temperatures;

- that there are adequate controls, where appropriate, for starting or changing operations, stopping, and emergency stops, and that the controls are visible and identifiable and do not place workers at risk;

- that there is a means to isolate work equipment from sources of energy;

- that work equipment is stabilised, by clamping or otherwise where necessary;

- that there is suitable and sufficient lighting for the operations to be carried out;

- that maintenance operations, which carry risks for health and safety, are carried out when equipment is shut down or without risk;

- that the equipment is marked with clearly visible and appropriate markings for health and safety reasons e.g. hazardous contents of storage vessels;

- that the equipment incorporates unambiguous, easily perceived, and easily understood warnings or warning devices, which are appropriate for the risks to health and safety.

12.1.8.11 There is a general obligation in Regulation 10 that employers shall ensure that any item of work equipment complies with enactments in Great Britain of any relevant EC directive. This obligation applies to new equipment as the directives referred to are not retrospective. Second-hand equipment will have to comply with Regulations 11 to 24 from the appropriate implementation date rather than one of these directives. The directives referred to include all the New Approach directives as well as older technical harmonization directives, for example the Low Voltage Directive and the Roll-Over Protective Structures and Falling-Object Protective Structures Directives. The Regulation also provides that, where an item of work equipment complies with one of these enactments, the requirements of Regulations 11 to 24 are not applicable to that item to the extent that compliance with them corresponds to the Regulations. The most important of the directives is the Machinery Directive, whose essential requirements substantially dovetail with Regulations 11 to 24. Thus, a situation can be expected to develop in which the normal means of satisfying the Regulations for new work equipment will be to obtain equipment which bears the CE mark.

12.1.9 Personal Protective Equipment

Personal Protective Equipment Directive

12.1.9.1 The Commission has proposed changes in the implementation dates for the Personal Protective Equipment Directive (see Section 5.3.3). The Directive contains a transitional period during which manufacturers can continue to produce in accordance with national regulations where harmonized standards are not available, with manufacturers having to comply with national measures in force on 30 June 1992. The Commission proposes to extend this period by two years to 31 December 1994[31]. The Economic and Social Committee, whilst accepting that there is no alternative to extending the transitional period, has been highly critical of the Commission and, to a lesser extent, of CEN and the Member States[32]. It has argued that

> the period in the Directive should have been adequate had the vital sense of priority been given to the implementation of the safety and health measures which affect so many citizens. Notwithstanding a number of operating difficulties encountered by the Commission and others, the Committee believes that the Commission should have given greater attention to implementation.

It has claimed that the resulting situation has created confusion for manufacturers and has argued that the transitional period ought to be extended by only one year. The proposals extend the list of Annex I equipment (that lying outside the scope of the Directive) to include helmets and visors intended for users of two- or three-wheeled motor vehicles.

12.1.9.2 Harmonized European standards for the Directive are being drafted by CEN. These will deal with respiratory, eye, face, head, hearing, foot and leg, body, and hand and arm protection, protection against falling from height, and protection against drowning. A CEN task force is looking at personal protective equipment that incorporates several functions[33].

12.1.9.3 The UK brought the Personal Protective Equipment Directive into force through the Personal Protective Equipment (EC Directive) Regulations 1992[34], which took effect from 1 January 1993. These apply to personal protective equipment supplied in the EC for the first time after 31 December 1992. Thus, the Regulations do not apply either to personal protective equipment for export outside the EC or to second-hand equipment. There is a transitional period until 1 January 1994 during which the enforcement provisions are deferred so as to allow manufacturers time to meet the attestation of conformity requirements and run down existing stocks. The Regulations closely follow the Directive with respect to the personal protective equipment covered, the definitions of equipment of simple design and of complex design intended to protect against mortal danger, the basic requirements, and attestation of conformity requirements. Their enforcement is by trading standards officers under powers granted by the Consumer Protection Act (see Sections 9.3.6 and 10.3).

Use of Personal Protective Equipment Directive

12.1.9.4 The Directive on the Use by Workers of Personal Protective Equipment at the Workplace (see Section 5.3.2) has been brought into force in the UK by the Personal Protective Equipment at Work Regulations 1992. The Health & Safety Executive has published guidance both on the Regulations and the selection of personal protective equipment[35]. Certain equipment has been excluded from the Regulations because there are already specific regulations in force which meet the Directive's requirements. These include the Construction (Head Protection) Regulations 1989, Noise at Work Regulations 1989, and the Control of Asbestos at Work Regulations 1987. This means that certain types of equipment, such as ear protectors and respiratory equipment, are not covered by the Regulations produced under this Directive but by other regulations. In general, the Regulations do not apply where there are comprehensive regulations already in existence and complement existing regulations where these are not comprehensive. The Regulations largely follow the Directive and the proposed UK Regulations discussed in Section 5.3.2. They provide for personal protective equipment to comply with enactments on design and manufacturing so that, where appropriate, they must comply with the Personal Protective Equipment Directive and be CE marked. Thus, there is an interface between the directive dealing with the supply of personal protective equipment and that dealing with its use at work. Employers must assess what personal protective equipment is required and this assessment follows on from, but does not duplicate, the assessment of hazards to be undertaken under the Management of Health and Safety at Work Regulations (see Section 12.1.10). They are to provide training for employees on the equipment. This is to include theoretical training, for example as to why personal protective equipment is needed and the factors that influence the protection given, as well as practical training. There are obligations imposed upon employees, including using the equipment in accordance with instructions, to return it after use, and to report losses or defects. There are some aspects of the Regulations that have particular implications for construction. Employers must provide accommodation where personal protective equipment can be stored when not in use, which has implications for the design of workplaces. Site operators can provide the equipment rather than the employer. This has implications, for example, for subcontractors coming on to site and for peripatetic maintenance operatives as it permits their employees to use equipment provided, for example, by a main contractor or a client rather than obliging their employer to supply it. However, the employer in such situations remains responsible for ensuring that the equipment is provided and that the Regulations are complied with, even though another party has actually provided the equipment. In summary, the Regulations imply that employers are to have effective management systems in place so that they are able, for example, to undertake risk assessment, choose and supply appropriate equipment, provide accommodation for that equipment, and quarantine equipment awaiting repairs or maintenance. Such a system could be provided by having a quality management system.

12.1.10 Health and Safety of Workers at Work

Framework Directive

12.1.10.1 The UK brought the Framework Directive on Health and Safety of Workers at Work (see Section 5.1.1) into force on 1 January 1993 through the Management of Health and Safety at Work Regulations and an Approved Code of Practice (ACOP)[36]. At the same time, the UK brought into force the other directives adopted with the Framework Directive and concerned with individual sources of risk to workers. These are the directives concerned with the workplace (see Section 12.1.5.6), work equipment (see Section 12.1.8.7), personal protective equipment (see Section 12.1.9.4), display screen equipment, and manual handling operations[37]. The ACOP has been made under the Health and Safety at Work Act 1974. Although failure to comply with the ACOP could be taken as evidence of a contravention of the Regulations, there is no obligation on employers to adopt it as they can comply with the Regulations by some other means.

12.1.10.2 The Regulations do not apply to ships or to the military. Employers must make assessments of the risks to health and safety to which their employees are exposed when at work and also to persons not in their employment arising from the conduct of their undertakings. The self-employed must also carry out such assessments for themselves. Where five or more persons are employed, the significant findings and employees especially at risk must be recorded. The assessment should be systematic and should ensure that all relevant risks or hazards are addressed. Preventative and protective measures should stem from the risk assessment. These should aim to avoid risks altogether, to combat risks at source, and to create an active health and safety culture. Employers shall undertake effective planning, organization, control, monitoring, and review of preventative and protective measures, and these are to be recorded where there are five or more employees. Health surveillance is to be provided as appropriate according to the risks identified by the assessment. Competent persons are to be appointed to enable employers to comply with the

Regulations. Procedures must be established in the event of serious and imminent danger and competent persons nominated to implement evacuation of premises. Employers are to provide their employees with information on risks, protective and preventative measures, and procedures in the event of serious and imminent danger. Where two or more employers share a workplace, they are to cooperate, coordinate the measures taken, and inform other employers of any risks to their employees. Multi-occupied buildings or sites, where each unit is under the control of an individual tenant, are regarded as separate workplaces. Employers also have responsibility where their employees work in host employers' premises, for example, undertaking repairs or maintenance. All employees are to be provided with adequate health and safety training, particularly on recruitment and on being exposed to new or increased risks. This should include refresher training. Employees have the duty to use equipment in accordance with training and instructions and to inform employers of risks to health and safety and shortcomings in the employer's protection arrangements. Regulation 13 brings into force the directive concerned with the safety of temporary workers[(38)]. This provides for temporary workers to be afforded the same protection as other workers. The Regulation requires employers to provide all workers, explicitly including those on fixed-term contracts, with comprehensible information on any special qualifications or skills needed to carry out the work safely and any health surveillance to be provided to employees.

Temporary or Mobile Construction Sites Directive

12.1.10.3 The Temporary or Mobile Construction Sites Directive was adopted in June 1992, with some corrections in August 1992[(39)]. It applies to sites where building and civil engineering work is carried out, including excavation, earthworks, assembly and disassembly of prefabricated components, conversion and fitting out, alterations, renovation, repairs, dismantling, demolition, upkeep, maintenance, and drainage work. Thus, a site may temporarily be a construction site although it is permanently used as a workplace for some other purpose. The Directive excludes drilling and extraction for the extractive industries, which are the subject of a separate health and safety directive[(40)]. The Directive sets out more specific industrial requirements within the scope set by the Framework Directive. The client or project supervisor appoints coordinators for health and safety matters at both the project preparations and project execution stages. Their appointment does not, however, diminish the liabilities of either the client or employers for the health and safety of the workers. The client or project supervisor has the responsibility of ensuring that a safety and health plan is drawn up prior to the setting up of a construction site. Member States, after consultation with management and the workforce, are allowed derogation from the requirement that coordinators are to be appointed. However, derogation is not permitted in two situations.

- Where the work involves particular risks. These situations are listed in Annex II of the Directive and include where workers are at risk of burial or engulfment, from chemical or biological substances, or from drowning, or working with radiation, on wells, in underground earthworks or tunnels, in compressed air or a system of air supply, or where using explosives, or assembling or dismantling heavy prefabricated components.

- Where prior notice has to be given to the authorities because work is scheduled to last longer than 30 days and on which more than 20 workers are simultaneously occupied or on which the volume of work is scheduled to exceed 500 person days. Annex III sets out a format for the prior notice, which includes the address of the site, the client, type of project, project supervisor, safety and health coordinators, planned start date and duration, estimated maximum number of workers on the site, planned number of contractors and self-employed persons, and details of contractors already chosen.

12.1.10.4 Clients and project supervisors are to take account of the principles for the prevention of risks to health and safety set out in the Framework Directive during the designing and preparing of the project, particularly when deciding on architectural, technical and organization aspects of the project and in estimating the time for completing each stage of the work. The coordinator at the project preparation stage implements the taking into account of the health and safety principles, draws up a health and safety plan, and prepares a file containing the relevant safety and health information for construction work. The coordinator at the project preparation stage applies the principles of prevention and safety when technical and organizational aspects are being decided and when estimating the time required for work stages, and coordinates their implementation. He adjusts the safety and health plan as required, organizes cooperation between employers and self-employed persons, checks that working procedures are being implemented correctly, and ensures that only authorised persons enter the site.

12.1.10.5 Article 8 applies to construction sites the general obligations on employers by setting down in specific terms what these mean in the construction industry. They include:

- keeping the construction site in good order and a satisfactory state of cleanliness;
- the choice of workstations in relation to access to them and the movement of equipment;
- the handling, storing and use of materials;
- maintenance and checks on installations and equipment;
- the storage and disposal of waste;
- adaptation of time periods for work;
- cooperation between employers and the self-employed;
- interaction with industrial activities at or in the vicinity of the site.

Annex IV sets out minimum health and safety requirements for construction site as workplaces and for on-site workstations, both indoor and outdoor. The former are concerned with issues such as stability, emergency routes, fire detection and fire fighting, ventilation, lighting, temperature, exposure to particular risks, traffic routes, first aid, sanitary equipment, rest rooms, and accommodation areas. The requirements for indoor workstations are concerned with matters such as stability, emergency doors, ventilation, temperature, lighting, traffic routes, windows, doors, room dimensions, and escalators. For outdoor workstations, the concerns are matters such as energy distribution installations, atmospheric influences, falling objects, falls, equipment and machinery, and the risks in particular types of work, such as excavations and demolition work. The Directive provides for the consultation of workers and for them to be provided with information. Member States are to bring the Directive into force by 31 December 1993.

12.1.10.6 The Health & Safety Commission's approach to bringing the Temporary or Mobile Construction Sites Directive into force has been to treat it as having two distinct elements. One part is seen as being an extension of the requirements of the Framework Directive to meet the specific conditions encountered in the construction industry. For this the HSC has published proposals for Construction (Design and Management) Regulations and an associated Approved Code of Practice[(41)]. This is a radical document that seeks to bring into the achievement of health and safety in the construction process all those with any potential contribution to make, including those not directly concerned with site work, such as quantity surveyors. It seeks to lay important responsibilities on to clients and designers and, in so doing, challenges the traditional division in construction between design and assembly. It also has implications for post-construction liability. The second aspect of the Directive, as seen by the HSC, is an extension of the Workplace Directive to construction sites, setting out the minimum conditions for them to be acceptable as workplaces. The HSC proposes to issue a consultative paper dealing with this, which in effect means Annex IV of the Directive and its supporting articles. The proposed Regulations do not include provision for the appointment of a project supervisor but the planning supervisor and principal contractor undertake his responsibilities at the preparation and execution stages respectively, as well as carrying out the tasks of the preparation and execution stages coordinators. Coordinators are to be appointed for all sites, even where there is only one contractor. Health and safety plans are to be prepared for all work and not merely for the high risk activities listed in Annex II of the Directive. Thus, the UK does not intend to take advantage of the derogations permitted by the Directive.

12.1.10.7 The proposed Regulations seek to replace the definitions of building operation and work of engineering construction found in the Factories Act 1961 by a broader definition that embraces all aspects of construction work. This is defined as being the carrying out of any building, civil engineering, or engineering construction work. It includes the construction, alteration, conversion, fitting out, renovation, maintenance, or demolition of a structure; the preparation and laying out of foundations; the assembly or disassembly of prefabricated elements of a structure; the removal of a structure or any product or waste resulting from demolition; installation, maintenance or removal of services that are an integral part of a structure; the commissioning of any fixed manufacturing plant, where such work involves a risk of falling more than two metres; and the cleaning of glass walls, windows, ceilings, or roofs, where this involves a risk of falling more than two metres. Structures are also defined very broadly so as to include, amongst other items, formwork, scaffolding, drainage works, railway lines, pipelines, and earth-retaining structures. The proposed Regulations seek to impose duties at all stages in a construction project and not just design and building work. These include responsibilities at stages such as project formulation, the preparation of specifications and bills of quantity, the assessment of tenders, and maintenance of the completed structure.

12.1.10.8 The Regulations impose a number of responsibilities on clients including:

- the appointment of a planning supervisor;
- the appointment of a principal contractor;
- the notification of the Health & Safety Executive of projects expected to last more than 30 days or involve more than 500 person days;
- to ensure that adequate financial provision is made and adequate time is allowed to enable statutory duties to be complied with by all involved in the construction process;
- to specify that contractors comply with health and safety plans and to ensure that appropriate pricing for this has been included in the tenders accepted;
- to ensure that the planning supervisor is provided with information about the premises or land so as to be able to develop the health and safety plan;
- to ensure that the information in the health and safety file is available for any person who may need it to meet his responsibilities, including leaseholders, renters, and subsequent purchasers.

The responsibilities imposed on clients only apply where the client carries out the project in connection with trade, business or other profit-making or non-profit-making undertaking. Thus, they do not apply, for example, to house occupiers carrying out work on their residences or having a house built for them. Where there is no client to whom the proposed Regulations apply, designers are to cooperate with each other in appointing a planning supervisor and contractors in the appointment of a principal contractor. Housebuilders are treated as clients by the proposed Regulations.

12.1.10.9 The planning supervisor is responsible for coordinating the work of the design team. Specifically, he is responsible for ensuring that :

- the design will not expose persons at work in building, maintaining or repairing the structure to risks to their safety or health;
- a health and safety plan is prepared before the construction phase commences, that sets out arrangements for the project that protects the health and safety of those at work on it and that can be used by contractors in tendering;
- adequate financial provision is made and adequate time is allowed to enable every person to comply with his duties and this includes ensuring that health and safety plans form part of the tender documents and that tenders are assessed on their adequacy with respect to health and safety;

- a health and safety file is prepared containing the information about the design or materials needed for the health and safety of those working on the construction phase, and that the file is delivered to the client.

Designers are obliged to ensure that designs do not expose those who work in building, maintaining or repairing structures to risks to their health and safety. They are to ensure that adequate information on any aspect of design or materials that might affect health and safety of construction workers is incorporated into the designs. They are obliged to cooperate with the planning supervisor. Design is defined very broadly and includes the drawing up specifications, bills of quantity, and design of temporary works.

12.1.10.10 The principal contractor is responsible for:

- ensuring that all the contractors meet their statutory obligations to coordinate and cooperate on safety matters and share information;

- coordinating cooperation between contractors, including both those at work on the site at the same time and those at work at different times;

- ensuring that the health and safety plan is developed so that it continues to satisfy requirements and that contractors and their employees comply with it;

- ensuring that only authorised persons are allowed into any area;

- ensuring that the notice of work given to the Health & Safety Executive is displayed on the site and, if the client is not one to whom the Regulations apply, accepting responsibility for giving the HSE notice;

- providing other contractors with comprehensible information on risks to health and safety and ensuring that they provide their employees with requisite information;

- discussing health and safety matters with employees and self-employed persons, receiving advice, and coordinating the views of employees.

The principal contractor can give reasonable directions to other contractors, but only in so far as they relate to health and safety matters and not to other aspects of a contract. There are interfaces between these duties and those under other health and safety at work directives. For example, the Provision and Use of Work Equipment Regulations requires that, where work equipment is shared, there shall be coordination in its provision and use. This is likely to fall upon the principal contractor. Contractors are obliged to cooperate with the principal contractor, provide him with information, and comply with his directions. Contractors shall not commence work until they have been provided with the names of the planning supervisor and principal contractor and the relevant parts of the health and safety plan.

12.2 PUBLIC PROCUREMENT

12.2.1 Public Works and Public Supplies

12.2.1.1 The public procurement directives are subject to regular amendment in two respects.

- *The list of bodies subject to public law.* This must be revised periodically to reflect the closure of some bodies and the creation of others. In the UK, it has been necessary to ensure that, as the government creates agencies responsible for their own budgets, the list makes it clear that they remain public bodies. The latest list was produced in July 1992[42]. There are few changes for the UK to the list in Table 11 other than to make it clear that universities, polytechnics, maintained schools, colleges, and national museums and galleries are public bodies.

- *The conversion of thresholds expressed in ECU into national currencies.* The national currencies do not have a fixed exchange rate against the ECU so that periodic readjustment of the thresholds in, for example, sterling terms, is necessary. For 1993[43] the thresholds are:

Supplies	400 000 ECU	£282 862
	750 000 ECU	£530 366
Works	5 000 000 ECU	£3 535 775.

12.2.1.2 The Public Works and Public Supplies Directives have been through a series of amendments since they were first adopted in 1971 and 1977 respectively. It is desirable that the various amendments should be consolidated into a single document in each case. In addition, there are certain inconsistencies between the various public procurement directives which ought to be resolved. The Council adopted a consolidated Public Works Directive and a consolidated Public Supplies Directive in June 1993, though neither had been published in the *Official Journal* by the end of July. It is believed that the new Public Works Directive is just a technical consolidation and had immediate effect. The new Public Supplies Directive is due to come into force on 14 June 1994 and is believed to contain some minor but substantive changes. The proposals for this Directive, for example, would have removed the limitations on the use of restricted procedures so as to bring supplies into line with the Public Works and Public Services Directives[44].

12.2.2 Public Services

12.2.2.1 The EC adopted the Public Services Directive in June 1992[45]. It substantially follows the draft discussed in Section 8.2, though there have been certain changes. These include:

- the threshold at which the Directive applies is 200 000 ECU net of VAT;
- at least one-third of the members of design contest juries are to have the same qualification, or its equivalent, as the contestants;
- all financial services, with the exception of central banking and the sale or issuing of securities, have been placed in 1A and are therefore subject to the full requirements of the Directive;
- reference to public service concessionaires has been dropped so that there are no requirements in the Directive as to the contracts they offer;
- reference to retaliatory action against third party countries, which restrict access by EC firms to their public service contracts, has been dropped.

The Directive also amends the Public Works and Public Supplies Compliance Directive so as to bring services contracts within its scope (see Section 7.6). This provides remedies for contractors who have wrongfully been discriminated against.

12.2.2.2 Although the Directive largely follows the procedures set out in the Public Supplies Directive, there are also some differences from this notably:

- explicit reference to the EN 29000 series with respect to quality assurance and the EN 45000 series with respect to certification;
- the ability to use negotiated procedures, with a call for competition, where services cannot be specified with sufficient precision to allow the use of open or restricted procedures, for example, where services require conceptual thought;
- not having to apply the Directive's provisions to lots of less than 80 000 ECU, providing that these are less than 20% of the contract value.

There can be problems in deciding what a service contract is. The Commission has stated that a contract for the lease or hire of goods is a supplies contract but, if an operator is also supplied, it is a services contract. The Directive does not oblige contracting authorities to seek services from external suppliers. It is not a directive for compulsory competitive tendering. If a contracting authority seeks outside offers, it must evaluate any in-house offer on the same basis as the outside ones. However, the Directive does not oblige an authority to accept a superior external offer in preference to an internal one.

12.2.2.3 The Directive should have come into force on 1 July 1993. The UK has yet to make any regulations concerning the Directive but it is expected that these will be presented to Parliament during the autumn of 1993. A consultative note and draft regulations have been published by the Treasury[46] and these substantially follow the text of the Directive. The Treasury takes the view that the Directive came into force on 1 July through administrative action and that the bodies affected by it should have been following its provisions since then.

12.2.3 Utilities

12.2.3.1 The UK has brought the Utilities and Utilities Remedies Directives (see Section 8.3) into force with the Utility Supply and Works Contracts Regulations 1992[47]. These came into effect from 13 January 1993. They do not apply to service contracts entered into by a utility, which are likely to be the subject of future regulations. The Utilities Services Directive was adopted by the Council in June 1993 and this is due to come into effect on 1 July 1994. However, it had not been published in the *Official Journal* by the end of July. The Regulations amend those concerned with public works and public supplies contracts so that only one set of these regulations apply to any individual contract and to eliminate any overlap between the regulations.

12.2.3.2 The utility contracts affected by the Regulations are defined in terms of the type of utility and activity and these are set out in Schedule 1 of the Regulations. They are concerned with the supply of drinking water, sewage disposal, electricity supply, gas supply, district heating, exploring for or extracting gas, oil, coal, or other solid fuel, and the provision of airports, ports, railways, tramways, trolley buses, buses (where others are excluded from providing a service), and telecommunications networks. Other activities carried out by utilities do not fall within the scope of the Regulations. Neither do:

- activities carried on outside of the EC;
- the acquisition of goods or construction works for resale, unless the utilities have special or exclusive rights to sell or hire them;
- contracts the government classifies as secret;
- contracts resulting from international agreements;
- purchases of fuel or energy for the production of energy;
- purchases of water for the supply of drinking water;
- contracts for telecommunications services for the transmission and routing of signals;
- contracts where an entity exploiting oil, natural gas, coal, or solid fuel is not considered as operating under special or exclusive rights.

Only contracts that meet the requisite thresholds fall within the scope of the Regulations. For construction works this is 5 million ECU; for telecommunications supply contracts it is 600 000 ECU, and for other supply contracts it is 400 000 ECU. The rules for calculating the value of a contract follow those in the Public Works and Public Supplies Directives.

12.2.3.3 If a utility wishes to lay down technical specifications for works or goods, it must do so in the contract documents. Usually, this is to be done by reference to European specifications.

However, there are certain permissible exceptions to this, for example, if it is impossible to establish that goods or works conform to European specifications, or if it would result in incompatible goods or works, or if the specifications are inappropriate. If European specifications are no used, then other standards in common use in the Community should be used instead. Specifications shall not favour or eliminate particular suppliers or contractors. This means that trade marks and the like cannot be used, although if this is unavoidable, they are to be qualified by the phrase 'or equivalent'.

12.2.3.4 Contractors can be sought by open, restricted , or negotiated procedures (see Section 7.2). Periodic indicative notices are to be published in the *Official Journal* for the supply of goods, where purchases in excess of 750 000 ECU are expected and for construction works. Usually, a utility must make a call for competition when seeking offers in relation to a proposed contract. The Regulations permit certain exceptions to this, such as when there is an absence of suitable tenders, for technical or artistic reasons, in the case of extreme urgency caused by unforeseen events, purchases in a commodity market, or to take advantage of bargains or insolvency. Utilities may operate qualification systems for suppliers, providing that they are based on objective rules and criteria and use European standards as a reference where appropriate. Objective criteria and rules must also be followed when restricted or negotiated procedures are used. Potential suppliers can be rejected, as with the other public procurement directives, on grounds of insolvency, a criminal offence or grave misconduct relating to the business or profession, non-payment of taxes or social security, or misrepresentation. Contracts can be awarded on the basis of the lowest price or most economically advantageous offer. The criteria for the latter are to be included in the contract documents in order of importance. Statistical reports are to be sent to the relevant government minister, who can seek other information as appropriate.

12.2.3.5 Utilities owe a duty to suppliers and contractors to comply with the Regulations. A breach is not a criminal offence but is actionable in the High Court (or Court of Sessions in Scotland). Proceedings may not be brought unless the utility has been informed of the breach and the action is brought promptly and, in any event, within three months. The Court can order a suspension of the award of a contract, set aside a decision, order a utility to amend a document, or award damages. Once a contract has been entered into, the Court can only award damages and not set the contract aside. Thus, successful contractors are not put at risk by actions by the unsuccessful. Although other redress may be sought, the Court can award damages of the cost of preparing the tender and participating in the contract award procedures. Aggrieved contractors can also apply to the Commission through the Treasury to use the conciliation procedure.

12.2.3.6 To date, the most contentious aspect of the Utilities Directive has been the way in which it favours EC suppliers over those from third countries. This applies where more than 50% of the value of goods originates in countries which do not have agreements with the EC for comparable access to their markets for EC undertakings. A utility need not accept an offer from such a third country. Where the bid from such a third country is equivalent to another bid, the latter is to be accepted. Bids are to be regarded as being equivalent if they are not more than 3% greater than the third country bid. The EC has been concerned about lack of access for its firms to US public and utilities contracts. The EC and US negotiated a memorandum of understanding on 10 May under which the EC would grant US contractors equivalent access to EC ones for public supplies contracts of at least 125 576 ECU, public service contracts of at least 200 000 ECU, and public works contracts of at least 5 000 000 ECU in return for the US waiving the application of the Buy America Act. They also agreed to open up contracts for each other's electricity utilities and supply contracts for utilities. They undertook to sponsor a study of procurement opportunities with a view to reaching a comprehensive agreement on procurement[(48)]. However, at the end of May the USA introduced sanctions to restrict EC firms from tendering for public contracts. On 8 June the EC responded by requiring public bodies to reject tenders from US contractors for supply contracts below 125 576 ECU, services contracts below 200 000 ECU and for higher values for certain designated services (principally those in Annex 1B of the Public Services Directive - see Table 17), and works contracts below 5 000 000 ECU[(49)]. Certain derogations are permitted, for example, to avoid disproportionate costs or to avoid limiting competition to a single supplier. However, Germany has refused to apply the sanctions citing the 1954 German-US Friendship Treaty. It should be noted that the EC and US sanctions are in the areas not covered by the Memorandum of Understanding. Whilst much political capital has been made about the value of the contracts affected, each individual contract is so small as to be unlikely to attract much interest from outside the Member State. Thus, the effectiveness of the sanctions is open to doubt.

12.3 POST-CONSTRUCTION LIABILITY[50]

12.3.1 In Section 11.2.9, it was noted that efforts had been made by Division DG III/D to break the log-jam caused by disagreement over the Mathurin proposals for uniformity in post-construction liability amongst EC member states. These consisted principally of the commissioning of the GAIPEC (Groupes des Associations Industrielles et Professionelles) from the 14 Pan-EC associations representing all sides of the construction industry. The groups did not meet the October 1991 deadline, but did report in February 1992.

12.3.2 The overall recommendations were:

- that the Directive should be concerned only with post-construction liability and should not be concerned with pre-construction contractual obligations;
- that the Directive should be concerned both with public and private sector work;
- that the Directive should cover all building and ancillary engineering work, except that civil engineering works should not be covered by the proposed warranties (see Section 12.3.3 below);
- that the Directive should chiefly be concerned with suppliers of construction services and their relationship with consumers, although this would not exclude supply of services and products.

12.3.3 A summary of the recommendations of each group is set out below.

- *Group 1: Procedure for acceptance*
  The time for acceptance is fixed as the moment of signing a certificate, the equivalent of practical completion. A single date for accrual of causes of action will be agreed.
- *Group 2: Liability*
  Despite much controversy in this group, it was agreed that the Directive should govern a general contractual duty on the part of designers and contractors. Joint liability should be abolished. Designers should be liable for specifying the wrong product, but not for sub-standard performance by suitable products. Owners acquiring the freehold or a full repairing lease would inherit the developers' post-construction rights against producers. Defences admissible should include inadequate maintenance, the 'state of the art' defence, and the occurrence of improbable events. The limitation period was particularly controversial. The recommendations say 5 years, but France and other Member States are likely to insist upon a 10 year liability.
- *Group 3: The warranty*
  The warranty is proposed to be a non-cancellable assignable mandatory insurance for all dwellings. Equivalent cover would be available but not mandatory on other types of building. The concept of damage will reflect the influence of the Construction Products Directive, with reference to the six essential requirements. The duration will depend upon the eventual limitation period (see Group 2 above).
- *Group 4: Financial backing for warranties*
  The hoped for diversity of financial arrangements did not materialise and the warranty will be insurance-backed.

After the reports were submitted, the discussion document was re-written by Renato Caronna of DG III and forwarded to Martin Bangemann, to be followed by translation and preparation for publication.

12.3.4 There is evidence of continuing movement in construction liability and that a published draft Directive will be based upon the GAIPEC conclusions. There are two real reservations about its progress. First, there is doubt about whether construction will be included in the horizontal Services Directive, which concerns only physical injury to persons or damage to private property, with no compensation for pure economic loss. Construction is very likely to be excluded if the industry specific Construction Liability Directive proceeds. If, however, there is further delay on that front, DG XI might well leave construction in the Services Directive, which accordingly should not yet be discounted. Second, the Maastricht agreement requires the issue of subsidiarity to be considered for application to all draft and proposed Directives, to see whether they are more properly dealt with at EC or at national level. While the expected result is that post-construction liability will not be regarded as appropriate for subsidiarity for reasons discussed in the Mathurin report (see Section 11.2), the requirement of consideration may cause significant delay.

References 12: Postscript

1. Commission Decision of 23 December 1992 on the setting up of an Advisory Committee for the coordination of the Internal Market field (93/72/EEC), *Official Journal*, L 26, 3 February 1993.

2. Council Decision of 22 September 1992 on the adoption of an action plan for the exchange between Member States administrations of national officials who are engaged in the implementation of Community legislation required to achieve the internal market (92/481/EEC), *Official Journal*, L 286, 1 October 1992.

3. Council Directive 92/59/EEC of 29 June 1992 on general product safety, *Official Journal*, L 228, 11 August 1992.

4. Commission Recommendation of 27 November 1992 calling upon Member States to set up the infrastructures needed to identify dangerous products at the external frontiers (92/579/EEC), *Official Journal*, L 374, 22 December 1992.

5. Council Regulation (EEC) No 339/93 of 8 February 1993 on checks for conformity with the rules on product safety in the case of products imported from third countries, *Official Journal*, L 40, 17 February 1993.

6. Modification of the proposal for a Council Regulation (EEC) concerning the affixing and use of the CE mark of conformity on industrial products in a proposal for a Council Directive and a proposal for a Council Decision (93/C 28/02 & 93/C 28/03), *Official Journal*, C 28, 2 February 1993; Department of Trade & Industry (1993) *CE Marking : Proposed Council Directive and Proposed Council Decision – An Informative Document*, June.

7. Economic and Social Committee, Opinion on the modification of the proposal for a Council Regulation concerning the affixing and use of the CE mark on industrial products, *Official Journal*, C 129, 10 May 1993.

8. Amended proposal for a Council Decision amending Decision 90/683/EEC concerning the modules for various phases of the conformity assessment procedures, supplementing it with provisions relating to the arrangements for affixing and using the CE conformance marking (93/C 113/12), *Official Journal*, C 113, 23 April 1993.

9. Proposal for a Council Directive amending for the second time Directive 83/189/EEC laying down a procedure for the provision of information in the field of technical standards and regulations (92/C 340/10), *Official Journal*, C 340, 23 December 1992.

10. Commission Decision of 15 July 1992 amending the lists of standards institutions annexed to Council Directive 89/189/EEC (92/400/EEC), *Official Journal*, L 221, 6 August 1992.

11. Commission communication concerning the non-respect of certain provisions of Council Directive 83/189/EEC of 28 March 1983 laying down a procedure for the provision of information in the field of technical standards and regulations (86/C245/05) *Official Journal*, C245, 1 October 1986.

12. Economic and Social Committee, Opinion on the report from the Commission on the operation of Directive 83/189/EEC in 1990 and 1991 (93/C 201/07), *Official Journal*, C 201, 26 July 1993.

13. 'European laboratory accreditation' *NAMAS Newsletter*, Spring 1993.

14. Commission of the European Communities (1993) *Interpretative Document for the Essential Requirement No 1 : Mechanical Resistance and Stability*, Document TC 1/019 rev 4, June; Commission of the European Communities (1993) *Interpretative Document Essential Requirement No 2 : Safety in Case of Fire*, Document TC 2/023 rev 2, June; Commission of the European Communities (1993) *Interpretative Document Essential Requirement No 3 : Hygiene, Health and the Environment*, Document TC 3/024 rev 4, 21 June; Commission of the European Communities (1993) *Interpretative Document Essential Requirement No 4 : Safety in Use*, Document TC 4-014-rev 5, 21 June; Commission of the European Communities (1993) *Draft of the Interpretative Document for the Essential Requirement Nr 5 : Protection Against Noise*, Document TC 5/019 rev 1, 18 June; Commission of the European Communities (1993) *Interpretative Document for the Essential Requirement Nr 6 : Energy Economy and Heat Retention*, Document TC 6/016.

15. Commission of the European Communities (1993), *General Introduction to the 6 Interpretative Documents*, CONSTRUCT 93/106 Rev 4, Brussels, 17 June.

16. Commission of the European Communities (1993), *Common Parts of Interpretative Documents*, CONSTRUCT 93/110 rev 1, Brussels, June.

17. Department of the Environment (1993) *Draft Discussion Document : Classes of Attestation – A Reflection Note*, JAC(TS)(93)P43, 7 June.

18. Department of the Environment, *Euronews Construction*, No 20 October 1992, No 21 February 1993.

19. European Organization for Technical Approvals (1993) *Common Procedural Rules for requesting, preparing and the granting of European technical approvals*, 9 February.

20. Department of the Environment, *Euronews Construction*, No 22 May 1993.

21. Health and Safety Commission (1992) *Workplace Health, Safety and Welfare – Approved Code of Practice : Workplace (Health, Safety and Welfare) Regulations 1992*, L 24.

22. The Electromagnetic Compatibility Regulations, SI 1992 No 2372.

23. Department of Trade and Industry (1993) *Product Standards: Electromagnetic Compatibility (EMC) – Guidance Document on the UK Regulations (the Electromagnetic Compatibility Regulations SI 1992/2372 implementing EC Directive 89/336/EEC)*, May.

24. Department of Trade and Industry (1992) *Electromagnetic Compatibility (EMC) : Guidance Document on the preparation of a technical construction file as required by EC Directive 89/336*, October.

25. CENELEC (1992) *Guidance on how to use standards for the implementation of the EMC Directive*, Brussels, Standing CENELEC Document CLC (PERM) 009; CENELEC (1993) *Guide to Generic Standards*, Brussels, R110-002; CENELEC (1992) *Low frequency emission limits for equipment connected to public power supply systems : Relation between standardization and the EMC Directive*, Brussels, Standing CENELEC Document CLC (PERM) 010.

26. Williams T (1992) *EMC for Product Designers : Meeting the European EMC Directive*, Newnes.

27. The Supply of Machinery (Safety) Regulations 1992, SI 1992 No 3073.

28. Council Directive 93/44/EEC of 14 June 1993 amending Directive 89/392/EEC on the approximation of the laws of the Member States relating to machinery, *Official Journal*, L 175, 19 July 1993.

29. Amended proposal for a Council Directive on the approximation of laws of the Member States relating to lifts (93/C 180/07), *Official Journal*, C 180, 2 July 1993.

30. Health & Safety Executive (1992) *Work Equipment – Guidance on Regulations : Provision and Use of Work Equipment Regulations 1992*, L 22.

31. Proposal for a Council Directive amending Directive 89/686/EEC on the approximation of the laws of the Member States relating to personal protective equipment (93/C 36/08), *Official Journal*, C 36, 10 February 1993; Amended proposal for a Council Decision amending Directive 89/686/EEC on the approximation of the laws of the Member States relating to personal protective equipment (PPE) (93/C 199/13), *Official Journal*, C 199, 23 June 1993.

32. Economic and Social Committee, Opinion on the proposal for a Council Directive amending Directive 89/686/EEC on the approximation of the laws of the Member States relating to personal protective equipment (93/C 129/01), *Official Journal*, C 129, 10 May 1993.

33. Department of Trade and Industry (1993) *Product Standards : Personal Protective Equipment*, DTI Business in Europe.

34. The Personal Protective Equipment (EC Directive) Regulations 1992, SI 1992 No 3139.

35. Health & Safety Executive (1992) *Personal Protective Equipment at Work : Guidance on Regulations – Personal Protective Equipment at Work Regulations 1992*, L 25.

36. Health & Safety Commission (1992) *Management of Health and Safety at Work – Approved Code of Practice : Management of Health and Safety at Work Regulations 1992*, L 21.

37. The Manual Handling Operations Regulations 1992, SI 1992 No 2793; The Health and Safety (Display Screen Equipment) Regulations 1992, SI 1992 No 2792. There is a summary of the six sets of regulations bringing the health and safety at work directives into force in Tyler M (1993) New European and UK health and safety requirements, *Property Management*, vol 11, no 1, pp 53-66 and of their ergonomic implications in McKeown C (1992) Meeting the EC Directives in the Workplace, *Property Management*, vol 10, no 2, pp 125-131.

38. Council Directive of 25 June 1991 supplementing the measures to encourage improvements in the safety and health at work of workers with a fixed-duration employment relationship or a temporary employment relationship (91/383/EEC), *Official Journal*, L 206, 29 July 1991.

39. Council Directive 92/57/EEC of 24 June 1992 on the implementation of minimum safety and health requirements at temporary or mobile construction sites (eighth individual Directive within the meaning of Article 16(1) of Directive 89/391/EEC), *Official Journal*, L 245, 26 August 1992; Corrigendum to Directive 92/57/EEC (Construction Sites), *Official Journal*, L 245, 26 August 1992.

40. Council Directive 92/91/EEC of 3 November 1992 concerning the minimum requirements for improving the safety and health protection of workers in the mineral-extracting industries through drilling (eleventh individual Directive within the meaning of Article 16(1) of Directive 89/391/EEC), *Official Journal*, L 348, 28 November 1992.

41. Health & Safety Commission (1992) *Proposals for Construction (Design and Management) Regulations and Approved Code of Practice*.

42. Commission Decision of 31 July 1992 concerning the up-dating of Annex I to the Directive 71/305/EEC (92/456/EEC), *Official Journal*, 3 September 1992.

43. Exchange value for the ECU : Threshold values in the field of public procurement (Council Directive 90/531/EEC) applicable as of 1 January 1993/ 31 December 1993 (92/C 301/09) *Official Journal*, C 301, 18 November 1992.

44. Proposal for a Council Directive coordinating procedures for the award of public supply contracts (92/C 277/01), *Official Journal*, 26 October 1992.

45. Council Directive 92/50/EEC of 18 June 1992 relating to the coordination of procedures for the award of public service contracts, *Official Journal*, L 209, 24 July 1992.

46. H M Treasury (1993) *Public Procurement : The UK Regulations on the Award of Public Service Contracts – Note by the Treasury*, 24 May.

47. The Utilities Supply and Works Contracts Regulations 1992, SI No 3279.

48. Council Decision of 10 May 1993 concerning the conclusion of an Agreement in the form of a Memorandum of Understanding between the European Economic Community and the United States of America on government procurement (93/323/EEC) and Council Decision of 10 May 1993 concerning the extension of the benefit of the provisions of the Directive 90/531/EEC in respect of the United States of America (93/324/EEC), *Official Journal*, L 125, 20 May 1993.

49. Council Regulation (EEC) No 1461/93 of 8 June 1993 concerning access to public contracts for tenderers from the United States of America, *Official Journal*, L 146, 17 June 1993.

50. Reference has been made in preparing this section to papers by Prof Donald Bishop to the Commission on Post-Construction Liability (W-87) of the International Council for Building Research, London, November 1992 and Joseph Huse, Freshfields, to the Society for Construction Law, London, January 1993.

CIRIA Special Publication 89 1993

THE IMPACT OF EUROPEAN COMMUNITIES' POLICY ON QUALITY MANAGEMENT IN CONSTRUCTION

Richard Grover BA MPhil CDipAF
Anthony Lavers LL.B M. Phil PhD ACIArb

CONSTRUCTION INDUSTRY RESEARCH
AND INFORMATION ASSOCIATION
6 Storey's Gate
Westminster
London SW1P 3AU
Tel 071-222 8891
Fax 071-222 1708

Summary

Membership of the EC means that the UK has given up its absolute sovereignty over quality management policies. Until recently this fact was of little significance as the EC did not have policies that affected quality management. However, the situation changed with the adoption of the aim of completing the Single Internal Market by the end of 1992. This is concerned with removing legal and administrative barriers to trade, and a number of the measures adopted or proposed have implications for quality management.

Principal among the measures are the directives adopted under the New Approach to Technical Harmonization and Standards. They include the Construction Products Directive and directives concerned with gas appliances, machinery, and electromagnetic compatibility. They set minimum standards that products must achieve before they may be placed upon the market. Products that achieve these will enjoy freedom of mobility throughout the EC without impediment from the Member States. The standards include technical specifications derived from essential requirements and minimum levels of quality assurance set out in procedures known as the attestation of conformity. The latter can vary from a manufacturer's declaration through to third-party certification of the product and its production system. It is necessary to adapt the UK's quality infrastructure so that it can fulfil its functions under these directives.

There are interfaces between the New Approach directives and other EC measures. The family of directives that lays down minimum health and safety standards for workers at work deal with the use of products whose production is determined by the New Approach directives. The public procurement directives also have an influence on quality management. They are concerned with the purchase of goods, services, and construction works by public bodies and utility undertakings, and seek to ensure that there is no discrimination in procurement against firms from other Member States. They require the use of European standards where possible and define the technical references that may be sought from firms, including information about their quality management systems. The New Approach directives have implications for post-construction liability. As liabilities vary between Member States and this could impede free trade, the EC has been examining the possibility of harmonising liabilities, warranties, and guarantees in construction.